GI Joe

GI Joe

THE LIFE AND CAREER OF
Dr. Joseph B. Kirsner

by James L. Franklin, M.D.

The University of Chicago
Department of Medicine/Section of Gastroenterology, Hepatology and Nutrition
DISTRIBUTED BY THE UNIVERSITY OF CHICAGO PRESS, CHICAGO DISTRIBUTION CENTER

JAMES L. FRANKLIN, M.D., received his training in gastroenterology at
the University of Chicago and practiced gastroenterology as a faculty
member of Rush University Medical School in Chicago

The University of Chicago
Department of Medicine/Section of Gastroenterology,
Hepatology and Nutrition
© 2009 by The University of Chicago, Department of Medicine / Section of
Gastroenterology
Printed in the United States of America

13 12 11 10 09   5 4 3 2 1

ISBN-13: 978-0-615-22605-7 (cloth)
ISBN-10: 0-615-22605-1 (cloth)

CIP applied for.

Publishing services provided by Mendoza Publishing Group, L.L.C.

This book is printed on acid-free paper.

Contents

Foreword

This biography of Dr. Joseph B. Kirsner meets the definition of this style of text, a biography, but it is also considerably more. Given Dr. Kirsner's guiding impact on the development of the field of gastroenterology as a medical specialty, and his longevity and stature as a faculty member of the University of Chicago, this book also serves the additional functions of being a first-person report of the histories of both.

Dr. Kirsner's work in the field of digestive diseases helped to pioneer the study of inflammatory bowel disease as a distinctive clinical and academic problem in the field of medicine. Indeed, from 1975 through 2004 he published six editions of the definitive textbook dealing with this important group of diseases. He not only served as president of the American Gastroenterological Association but was critical to the founding of the Gastro-Intestinal Research Group of that organization in the mid-1950s and also played a central role in the development of the use of endoscopy for GI diseases around this same period. His interest in approaching this new discipline of gastroenterology from a research direction led him to obtain formalized training in research, for which he was awarded a Ph.D. in 1942, thus aiding in the identification of a new training pathway for those who wished to push the research boundaries of their subdisciplines in various fields of medicine.

Dr. Kirsner's contributions to our understanding of the history of biology and medicine at the University of Chicago simply relates to the fact of his being here. He joined the faculty of the University of Chicago in the Department of Medicine in 1935 and to this day dutifully comes to work and participates in the life of the university every day. At his 95th birthday celebration, I recall quipping that when one has a faculty member like Joe Kirsner, one simply wishes there were two. But in fact there were two long Joe Kirsner careers on our faculty—it's just that they occurred in sequence, rather than in parallel! An insight into his immersion in the history here is brought home by a specific story. Shortly after arriving at the university in 2002, I was about to oversee the investiture of a faculty member as the next occupant of the Leon O. Jacobson endowed chair. Jacobson was a legendary figure at Chicago: a young investigator who recognized the potential of the spleen as a source of new blood components, a pioneer of chemotherapy, and a critical force on the medical side of the Manhattan Project during World War II. He also served as dean of the Division of Biological Sciences and Medical School from 1966 to 1975—in short, he was a hero of biomedicine from the somewhat distant past. I had prepared remarks relating to Jacobson's career at Chicago but had trouble finding anyone who had actually known him in these previous capacities. On entering the reception area, I spotted Joe Kirsner and asked if he had known Jacobson, this giant from the past. His response, "Of course, I taught Leon when he was a student here!"

It is his firsthand exposure to medicine, gastroenterology, and Chicago over more than half a century that makes any biography of Joe Kirsner so worthwhile.

James L. Madara, M.D.
CEO, University of Chicago Medical Center
Dean, Pritzker School of Medicine and the Division of Biological Sciences
Sara and Harold Lincoln Thompson Distinguished Service Professor
CHICAGO, DECEMBER 2007

Preface

This book tells the story of the life and career of one of the great physicians of the 20th century. It is a story that spans most of the last century and now extends well into the first decade of the current century. The career of Dr. Joseph B. Kirsner has been distinguished by his humanism and accomplishments in the field of patient care, medical education, medical research, and philanthropy. The 20th century has been characterized by an exponential growth in scientific and technological progress, which was translated into the "scientification" of medicine.[1] Dr. Kirsner remained on the crest of these advances; and while he never lost his sensitivity to the needs of the patient, he made outstanding contributions to his chosen field of gastroenterology in the clinical care of patients and in basic medical research. He played a major role as one of the leaders responsible for establishing gastroenterology as an important subspecialty of internal medicine, and he also participated in the development of the national and international societies that today represent the field of digestive diseases. Readers of this book will see that he has had a major impact on medical education in the fields of gastroenterology and internal medicine, both by furthering our knowledge of disease and by advocating for the highest standards of excellence and compassion in the care of the patient.

Dr. Kirsner began his professional career with the strong desire to care for the individual patient. Over the years, the doctor-patient relationship became the cornerstone of his career. Through fortuitous and felicitous circumstances, he found his way to a great university, the University of Chicago. There his vision was expanded to encompass the many possibilities of medical research and the importance of continuing medical education. Shortly after arriving at Billings Hospital in 1935, he recognized, in the person of Walter Lincoln Palmer, M.D., Ph.D., the attributes he wanted to develop in himself as a physician. In 1927 Dr. Palmer had been appointed to head the first academic section of gastroenterology of the newly formed medical school, patterned after the Flexner-Rockefeller model for medical education, which was blossoming at the recently constructed Billings Hospital on the Midway.[2] Dr. Palmer introduced Dr. Kirsner to the relatively new and not fully recognized field of gastroenterology and became his model for excellence in patient care, for being an academic physician, and for academic achievement. Dr. Palmer and the exciting environment of the new medical school provided the stimulus for him to become involved in medical research. The requirements needed to accomplish credible laboratory-based research led Dr. Kirsner to pursue his doctorate degree in the Department of Biological Sciences at the University of Chicago. This background would lead him to make his own contribution to our understanding of the immune mechanisms of inflammatory bowel disease, ulcerative colitis, and Crohn's disease. Through his exposure to Dr. Palmer and the intellectual environment of the university, his horizons were expanded, and he sought a role in national and eventually international medical societies. He would come to found five important national societies in the field of gastroenterology and would play a leadership role in already-existing societies of gastroenterology and internal medicine.

His accomplishments in the field of medical education are manifest through the innumerable physicians whose lives and careers he has influenced. These include students, interns, and residents at the University of Chicago who were exposed to his teaching, irrespective of the field of medicine they eventually entered. His impact on physicians in training was also felt at the numerous universities where over his long career he has been invited to speak as an honored lecturer or visiting professor. As the leading member of the nationally recognized Section of Gastroenterology at the University of Chicago, he has attracted more than 200 physicians from all parts of the United States and from other countries throughout the world who have come to Chicago to receive their training in gastroenterology under his guidance. These gastroenterologists, who are his most direct medical progeny, have made distinguished contributions in communities throughout the United States and abroad. Among them are many whom he inspired and guided to pursue the three goals of the academic physician: excellence in patient care, medical research, and medical education.

As a true medical scholar, he has made a distinguished and impressive contribution to the medical literature through the hundreds of articles he has authored or coauthored, and through the many chapters that he has written for major medical textbooks on the care of the patient. He has been the author and editor of major textbooks in the field of gastroenterology, in particular his *Inflammatory Bowel Diseases*. During his long and extraordinary career, he has participated, organized, and contributed to literally hundreds of national and international meetings and symposia promoting and disseminating knowledge in the area of clinical care and research in gastroenterology.

In the 1950s his commitment to medical research led him into a leadership role in the National Institutes of Health, where he would serve over a period of two decades in guiding the funding of research in the area of digestive diseases. His belief in the importance of medical research as critical to the advancement of patient care led him to found the Gastro-Intestinal Research Foundation of Chicago (GIRF), to play a major role in the Crohn's and Colitis Foundation of America, and to serve for approximately fifty years as a medical consultant to the Cancer Research Foundation of the University of Chicago. His loyalty to the University of Chicago, to the care of the patient, and to the importance of medical research has made him an inspirational spokesman for major philanthropic ventures at the university.

This is the story of a man who began life as the son of immigrant parents in a working-class neighborhood in the East End of Boston, and of how he made the most of every opportunity that life offered him. Thanks to his desire to be the very best and to his own extraordinary hard work, he accomplished the goals he set for himself and still kept his compassion for his patients and an enduring dedication to helping the sick. Throughout his celebrated career, he has always retained his personal warmth and openness with his colleagues and is beloved by the institution he has served for over seven decades. At the age of 99, he remains active and involved in the activities of the Section of Gastroenterology at the University of Chicago, the affairs of the university, and the progress being made in the field of gastroenterology. He remains committed to the welfare of his family and a wide circle of friends. As a physician, he served his country during World War II in both the European and Pacific theaters of war. He has served his country as an ad hoc ambassador for America and the medical profession through his friendship and care over a 20-year period of the late king of Morocco, Hassan II, members of his family, and many other patients from that country who sought his help.

The physician in the 21st century is the guardian of unprecedented scientific and technological knowledge in his quest to fight disease and promote the well-being of his patients. At a time when the physician is under ever-increasing public scrutiny, these very tools threaten to destabilize and diminish the doctor-patient relationship. The challenge for the physician is to remain abreast of all these advances while at the same time retaining the confidence of patients and responsiveness to their needs. The life and career of Dr. Joseph B. Kirsner serves as an inspiration to all physicians in the field of medicine, those who would aspire to the calling of a career in academic medicine, and those involved in the field of medical education. This is the story of how all this was accomplished, in the words of one of his close colleagues, "with eloquence, grace and persuasion."[3]

Notes

1. This term was used by JBK in the title of his October 7, 1994, George Brohee Lecture at the 10th World Congress of Gastroenterology in Los Angeles: "The Scientification of Gastroenterology during the 20th Century."

2. For an overview of the Flexner report on medical education published by the Carnegie Foundation in 1910, see Coke M et al., American medical education 100 years after the Flexner report, *New England J of Med* 355:1339-44, 2006.

3. Personal communication from Dr. Morton F. Arnsdorf, professor of medicine, University of Chicago, to JBK, December 5, 2006.

Acknowledgments

First and foremost I wish to thank Dr. Joseph B. Kirsner for honoring me by requesting that I write his biography. Throughout this project, Dr. Kirsner enthusiastically gave of his time and resources, providing many interviews and access to his files and personal papers, and placing me in contact with individuals who could provide important information related to his life history. It has been an inspiring experience to work with and observe Dr. Kirsner, who, while advancing in age, maintains his well-known qualities of kindness, dignity, and intellectual focus. Without his efforts, this biography could never have been written. I am happy to note that Dr. Kirsner's complete papers will be deposited with the Special Collections Research Center in the University of Chicago's Regenstein Library.

A special word of thanks to James L. Madara, M.D., Dean of the Division of Biological Sciences and the Pritzker School of Medicine and Sara and Harold Lincoln Thompson Distinguished Service Professor, for writing his elegant foreword.

I wish to express my appreciation to Dale C. Smith, Ph.D., Professor of Medical History of the Uniformed Services University of the Health Science, Bethesda, Maryland, for conducting key interviews with Dr. Kirsner's son, Robert, and his brother, Morris, and for locating articles written by Dr. Kirsner while a medical student at Tufts and during World War II.

I am grateful to the many individuals who generously gave of their time and allowed me to record interviews conducted both in person and over the telephone. Their individual contributions have been cited in the notes. Many of these individuals have also supplied documents or written recollections of their interactions with Dr. Kirsner that have aided in the creation of this biography, for which I am further grateful. A special mention of appreciation is due to members of Dr. Kirsner's immediate family who have helped in this project, including his son, Robert Kirsner; his granddaughter, Rachel Schneider; his grandson, Daniel Kirsner; his nephew Burton Resnic; his sister Gertrude London; and Paul and Nancy Weiss (his wife's niece). Colleagues and former fellows who have similarly contributed include Stephen B. Hanauer, M.D., the Joseph B. Kirsner Professor of Medicine and Director of the Section of Gastroenterology; Eugene Chang, M.D., the Martin Boyer Professor of Medicine; Terrance Barrett, M.D., Director of the Section of Gastroenterology, Northwestern University Medical School; Charles Winans, M.D., the Sara and Harold Lincoln Thompson Professor; Richard Breuer, M.D.; Murray Dworetzky, M.D.; John Fennessy, M.D.; Anderson Hedberg, M.D.; Erwin Levin, M.D., and his wife, Ruth Levin; Michael H. Levine, Chief Development Officer, Division of Biological Sciences, the Pritzker School of Medicine; Sumner Kraft, M.D.; David A. Morowitz, M.D.; Eugene A. Gelzayd, M.D.; Joel D. Levinson, M.D.; Alan Oestreich, M.D.; João Carlos Prolla, M.D.; B. H. Gerald Rodgers, M.D.; Odile Voinchet, M.D.; Howard Schachter, M.D.; and Marshall Sparberg, M.D. Useful information on the early history of the Gastro-Intestinal Research Foundation of Chicago (GIRF) was provided by Martin Sandler and the late Joseph Valenti. Marge Dowling, the Executive Director of GIRF, kindly made available invaluable material from the GIRF archives. Special thanks to Seymour Taxman, CEO of the Taxman Corporation, for providing the text of the citations presented to Dr. Kirsner on the occasion of his 99th birthday celebration. Denise R. Halverson provided very helpful material on the history of the Cloisters. Andrew Herskee and Mr. and Mrs. Burton Herskee provided a very helpful perspective on the patient's experience at Billings Hospital. Secretarial and administrative assistance was provided by Amanda Serrano, Betsy Hunt, and Cindy Cheers of the Section of Gastroenterology. I appreciate the receipt of archived material from the Boston Public Schools, the English High School of Boston, the Archives of the Chicago Medical Society, Tufts University, the American Gastroenterological Association, the Archives and Special Collections Department of the Regenstein Library of the University of Chicago, the Lincoln Academy of Illinois, and Elizabeth Sidney, editor of *Chicago Medicine*.

I wish to acknowledge the helpful advice I received throughout various phases of this project from my friend and colleague Malachi J. Flanagan, M.D. The author wishes to thank Mr. Harry Rosenberg for a very informative interview.

I also wish to express my appreciation to Ruth Melville, for her careful editing and advice on textual aspects of this biography; Jill Shimabukuro, Design Manager of the University of Chicago Press, for her contribution to the art and design of this book; and especially to Sylvia Mendoza, Design and Production Manager of the University of Chicago Press and President of Mendoza Publishing Group, for overseeing all the details necessary to bring this volume to fruition.

The conception and creation of this biography have been made possible by the friendship of a number of loyal supporters of Dr. Kirsner, of the Section of Gastroenterology at the University of Chicago, and of GIRF. They include Martin and Mary Boyer, Mrs. Barbara Crain, Miles and Shirley Fiterman, Bernard and Marjorie Mitchell, Martin and Lucie Sandler, Mrs. Hortense Singer, Joseph and Marci Valenti, and Mrs. Jane Woldenberg.

GI Joe

1 ✳ Boston, 1909–1933

In his encyclopedic volume *World of Our Fathers,* Irving Howe identi-
fies 1881 as a turning point in the history of the Jewish people. It was
on March 1, 1881, that Alexander II, the czar of Russia, was assassi-
nated by a terrorist who flung a bomb under his carriage. The liberal-
ism of his regime came to an end, and a wave of pogroms followed
the accession of his successor, Alexander III. The new czar pursued a
relentless anti-Jewish policy that forced the five million Jews living in
the Pale of Settlement to question whether they'd ever achieve peace
as permanent residents of the Russian Empire. Jewish immigration
to the United States between 1820 and 1870 approximated 7,500, and
in the 1870s rose to 40,000.[1] The numbers would skyrocket in the decades after 1881 until the Reed-Johnson Act of 1921 put a stringent
quota on foreign immigration and drastically reduced immigration
from Eastern Europe.[2] By 1890 immigration had brought the Jewish
population of New York to 165,000, of Philadelphia to 26,000, and
of Boston, Baltimore, Cleveland, and Chicago to 20,000 each. In the
next 30 years, by 1910, these figures would increase by a factor of five
in each of these cities.

It was against this background that the parents of Joseph Barnett
Kirsner immigrated to the United States. His father, Harris Kirsner
(his first name had been changed from Hershel), was born in 1882 in
the town of Rivne (pronounced Rovno), a city in Ukraine, west of
Kiev, that had been annexed to Russia in 1783 and was the regional
town of Volyn-Gubernyu. (On June 28, 1941, Rivne would be captured by the Nazis, and in November of that year 23,000 of the Jewish
inhabitants of the town would be taken to a pine grove and killed—

an event that would play a part in Joseph Kirsner's decision to enlist in World War II.)

In the 1890s Harris and his older brother, Aaron, possibly fleeing conscription in the czar's army, found their way to the United States, entered the country through Ellis Island, and settled in Boston, Massachusetts. The family remembers that Harris Kirsner retained his membership in the Volyn Burial Society in Boston. They had another brother who immigrated about the same time to South America and was never heard from again, while their parents and several sisters remained in Rivne. Both brothers entered the clothing industry and both worked as clothing pressers. Harris worked for a prominent men's clothing store, Hyman Brothers, located on Washington Street in downtown Boston. He worked five and a half days a week at the store and would continue to work for this company for the remainder of his life. Dr. Kirsner's long-held view was that his father simply worked himself to death.

Dr. Kirsner's mother, Ida (Waiser), was born in 1890 in the same area of Ukraine. She told her family she was born in a small village called Lexandria. Ida came to the United States in 1904 or 1905, when she was 15 years of age. The details of how she came to this country, whether she came alone or with friends or family members, have been lost to family memory. Similarly, we do not know why she decided to come to the United States. Like Harris, she entered the country through Ellis Island and came to settle in Boston. In Boston she was introduced to Harris Kirsner through Aaron's wife, Cecelia. Cecelia was a first cousin on Ida's mother's side of the family. Ida and Harris were married in 1907 and took up residence in the East End of Boston. We know that her parents and siblings remained in Eastern Europe and that she communicated with them through the 1930s. She sent clothing and small amounts of money to them until all communication ceased during the chaos of World War II. Although it is not known with certainty, they were probably victims of the Nazi invaders. Thus Dr. Kirsner grew up never knowing any of his grandparents. The only uncle or aunt he knew was his uncle Aaron and his family. Aaron and Harris remained close and lived within walking distance of each other. They and their growing families frequently visited each other and celebrated holidays together.[3]

On September 21, 1909, the couple's first child, Joseph, was born. The Record of Birth of the Commonwealth of Massachusetts (certificate #21597), issued by Edward J. Cronin, Secretary of the Commonwealth, lists Harris as the father and Ida (maiden name Waiser) as the mother. For both, the place of birth is listed as Russia, and the birth of Joseph Barnett Kirsner was recorded on October 9, 1909. We do not know what dreams and hopes the Kirsners had for their first-born son, but surely it was a joyous event. It is inconceivable that they could have envisioned that their newborn son would become an internationally renowned physician and medical educator who would play a major role in shaping the field of gastroenterology.

Coincidentally, 1909 was an auspicious year in the medical world. In 1890 Harvard University, in conjunction with the Brigham Trustees, initiated discussions that would lead to the purchase of 25 acres of land in Roxbury as the site of the new Harvard Medical School. Peter Bent Brigham was a self-made merchant who had amassed millions in real estate which he bequeathed to Suffolk County, Massachusetts, to establish a hospital for the poor. He stipulated that the funds first be allowed to accumulate for 25 years following his death, in 1877. In 1902 these monies became available, and plans were underway for the construction of the Peter Bent Brigham Hospital (The Brigham), which would open its doors in 1909 as the major teaching hospital of Harvard Medical School.[4] This added to the list of important hospitals in the Boston area at the time of Joseph's birth: Massachusetts General Hospital, Boston City Hospital, and Boston Children's Hospital. Also in 1909, Abraham Flexner was preparing to publish his influential report on medical education in the United States for the Carnegie Foundation. This report, which measured all other U.S. medical schools against the standard set at Johns Hopkins University School of Medicine, would later be the model upon which the University of Chicago School of Medicine would be planned. By a similar twist of fate, an ocean away in London, 1909 was the year of the first symposium devoted to a little-known disease, "sporadic" ulcerative colitis. This would mark the first systematic attempt to categorize and study the disease to which Dr. Kirsner would devote much of his medical career.[5]

Harris Kirsner completed the process of naturalization in 1911. At that time, an alien had to have resided in the country for five years; by law, his wife automatically became a citizen at the same time. The naturalization certificate, dated April 3, 1911, listed their children as Joseph, age one year, and Ethel, age one month. Their place of residence was 9 Parkman, Boston. Mrs. Kirsner was not content with automatic citizenship under her husband's name, however, and went of her own accord to night school to learn civics and English. The family would continue to grow, and Joseph's siblings would eventually include Ethel (born 1911), Morris (born 1915), Lena, called Lee (born 1917), and Gertrude (born 1923).

Life in the home revolved around the practices of Orthodox Judaism. Dr. Kirsner remembers that his father observed his morning prayers by donning a tallis (prayer shawl) and tefillin (phylacteries). Joseph and Morris accompanied their father and mother to the synagogue on the Sabbath. It was an Orthodox shul, and they remember that the women sat in a separate area above the male congregation.

Harris Kirsner felt a strong sense of patriotism for his new country. When the United States entered World War I, he volunteered to work in a munitions factory. Dr. Kirsner saw him as a man "dogged by financial worry." He recalls that his father would walk from their apartment in Roxbury to downtown Boston to save the cost of car fare, 10 cents at the time. But all was not drudgery. Besides being dedicated to his family, his father found time to involve himself in local politics, Democratic in particular. On a national level, Franklin D. Roosevelt was his hero. There was also time for sports, and he avidly followed the Boston Braves. The right fielder for the Braves, Walley Berger, was one of his favorite players. Harris's love of baseball rubbed off on his Joseph, who, peering through a knothole in the fence to watch the game for free, quickly became a member of the Braves "knothole club."

Ida and Harris Kirsner dedicated themselves, as was characteristic of their generation, to giving their children the opportunity to succeed in America. As a homemaker, Ida devoted her life to the comfort of her family. Dr. Kirsner remembers, and marvels, at the wonderful meals she was able to prepare given the family's modest resources. All the Kirsner children grew to adulthood in spite of an array of typical childhood illnesses. But in 1940 their eldest daughter, Ethel, who was already married and had a young son, Burton, developed Hodgkin's disease. After a two-year illness she passed away, leaving her parents grief-stricken. They took both Burton and Ethel's husband into their home, but after a short time, Ethel's husband abruptly left the family and never returned. Burton remained with his grandparents, who raised him as their own son. He recalls that in the summer his grandmother would take him to the beach by public transportation. His grandparents saw to it that he went to Hebrew school and was bar mitzvahed when he was 13 years old. Burton's description of his bar mitzvah and the reception at a local restaurant indicates that it was a far more splendid affair than had been possible when his uncles Joseph and Morris celebrated their bar mitzvahs.

Both parents were very patriotic, and during the years of World War II they proudly displayed in the living-room window of their apartment two striped flags with a silver star, which indicated that the family had two sons in active duty, Joe and Gertrude's husband, Eli. Gertrude, who had recently married, moved back into the family home for the war. The family's spirit of generosity was evident when Ida, having made contact with David Gorach, a cousin who had survived the war, helped him successfully immigrate to this country, found him a job, and welcomed him into their home for several years until he could support himself.

Roxbury was one of the town's first residential districts. Originally known as Roxbury Flats, in the 1830s it was a desolate fens and marshland that was gradually filled with gravel. The nation's first railroad tracks ran over this area from Boston to Worcester, a 45-mile trip, in 1835. Initially, Roxbury was home to the increasing number of Irish immigrants who were settling in the Boston area. By the 1860s it was connected to Boston by horse-drawn streetcars, and in 1867 it was incorporated into the city. Neighboring Dorchester was incorporated in 1869, and Charlestown, Brighton, and West Roxbury followed suit in 1873. Annexation of these "streetcar" suburbs transformed Boston into a metropolitan area comparable in size to New York, Philadelphia, and Chicago.[6]

As far back as the 18th century, Portuguese and Spanish Jews were living in Boston, but the immigration of new families ceased after 1800, and by 1840 few remained. From 1840 to 1890 there was a slow influx of German and then Polish Jews, whose numbers rose to some 200 families. In 1816 Abraham Touro had registered a Portuguese Jewish synagogue in Boston, and German and Polish synagogues would follow in 1843 and 1849, respectively. Roxbury's Eastern European Jewish population and neighborhoods grew dramatically after 1890.[7]

Boston itself was undergoing dramatic political changes in the first decade of the 20th century. In 1906 John Francis "Honey Fitz" Fitzgerald became the first Irish-Catholic Boston-born mayor. His daughter Rose was destined to be the mother of the first Irish-Catholic American president, John Fitzgerald Kennedy. The patronage abuses of Fitzgerald's first term in office led to major reforms in the Boston City Charter, establishing civil service commissions and a system of civil service examinations. The new charter of 1909, drawn up by the Financial Committee (known as the "Fin Com"), provided for two-year terms for council members and aldermen and expanded the mayor's term to four years. By 1910 "Honey Fitz" was back in office for a four-year term. The Democratic Irish ward bosses, recognizing their new political base in the flood of Eastern European immigrants, met the ships in Boston Harbor with placards signaling "The Democratic Party welcomes you to America."[8]

The Kirsners lived on the top floor of a three-flat apartment building that was adjacent to a popular grocery store. Joseph's first introduction to school came with his enrollment in the local public school, the Phillips Brooks Grammar School. Here he had his first exposure to reading, grammar, and arithmetic. His parents also saw to it that he was enrolled in a traditional Hebrew school, where he studied Hebrew until his bar mitzvah. Both Joseph and Morris remember a neighbor, Joe Pearlstein, who lived in the apartment below the Kirsners and drove a delivery truck for the *Boston Globe*. Mr. Pearlstein impressed both brothers with his love of books and classical literature. Dr. Kirsner can still reflect back over some 85 years and remember that neighbor, who set an example of how a person could rise above modest circumstances and become so well informed.

Street baseball was a favorite game played nonstop by children in this immigrant neighborhood during the summer months. The rough-and-tumble games, giving rise to various minor athletic injuries that required medical attention, gave young Joseph his introduction to the medical profession. The caring and kindness of the family doctor during his visits to the home made a lasting impression on Joseph. He also remembered visits to the emergency rooms of the local hospitals, including the emergency room at Boston City Hospital, and various clinics, including those at Massachusetts General and Beth Israel. His family seemed to contract every infectious disease imaginable. As a child he was impressed with the doctors and nurses in their white uniforms. They all seemed so knowledgeable, efficient, and caring. By the age of nine, Joseph knew he wanted to be a doctor. Looking back, he felt that the atmosphere of caring and professionalism he was exposed to as a boy was important in strengthening his decision to pursue a medical career. His decision was encouraged by his mother and father, who were dedicated to the idea that their two sons should receive a college education regardless of financial limitations.

The years that Joseph spent in Phillips Brooks Grammar School, 1913 through 1923, included those of World War I. In 1918 thousands of Bostonians died in the Great Influenza Pandemic; on October 1 of that year 202 citizens died in a single day. Despite his impression that his family was subject to every infectious disease circulating through the community, Dr. Kirsner could not remember any member of his family being stricken with influenza that year.

When he was ten years old he began his first job, selling newspapers at the corner of Massachusetts and Huntington Avenues near Boston Symphony Hall. These were tough times on the streets of Boston, and selling papers on the streets meant facing hostile Irish gangs of youths determined to protect their "turf." This is how Theodore H. White characterized the climate he faced growing up in Boston in his memoir *In Search of History*.

> Within the boundaries of our community we were entirely safe and sheltered. But boundaries were real. We were an enclave surrounded by Irish. To the south of us, across the railway tracks, lived the very tough Irish-working-class Irish. The local library lay in such an Irish district, and my fights happened en route to the library to get books. Pure hellishness divided us, but after one last bloody-nose battle, I was given safe passage by the Irish boys whenever I went to the library.[9]

Both Joseph and his brother, Morris, could remember that the dangers of the neighborhood were such that their father would come to pick him up after selling papers so as to ensure his safe return home.

A family photograph from 1921, taken when Joe was 11 years old, shows four Kirsner children together behind the building where they lived on Lawrence in Roxbury. It is a typical photograph from this era when few families had their own Kodak cameras and peddlers would travel the neighborhoods with a pony and a camera and induce mothers to have their families photographed. In the photograph Joe is standing quite straight and staring attentively back at the camera. He's dressed, probably for school, with a short beaked cap, a jacket over a sweater, and knee-high knickers. In front of him stands his oldest sister, Ethel, about 10 or 11 years old, smiling back at the camera and gently clasping the reins of a very stoical pony. It must be somewhat cold, since she too is wearing a cap, gloves, and boots. Mounted on the pony and also bundled up with winter coats and caps are Morris, age 5, holding on to the pommel, and behind him Lee, then age 7. Their youngest sister, Gertrude, was not yet born. Commenting on this photograph, Morris Kirsner observed that he could see in Joe's bearing that he was already showing his position as leader of the family.

Joseph entered Boston English High School in September 1923. He would somewhat wistfully reflect in later years that perhaps, since he was already displaying talented scholastic ability, he should have been guided to seek admission to the prestigious Boston Latin School. This venerable institution was the first public school in the nation and had opened its doors in 1635. It was a Latin grammar school open to all boys regardless of social class. It boasted such distinguished graduates as Charles William Elliot, the philosopher George Santayana, and Leonard Bernstein. But Boston English High School served Joseph well, as it had many in the immigrant community.

Boston English High School opened in 1821 and was the oldest public high school in the nation. The school had provided leaders for the scientific, business, and cultural institutions of the nation, including General Matthew B. Ridgeway, Henry Kidder, Charles Hayden, Leonard Nimroy, J. P. Morgan, and Samuel Langley. Reading the school's *Fifty-Sixth Annual Catalog of 1926-1927,* one senses a certain quaintness in the language. The catalog lists its "Head Masters" dating back to 1821, including Mr. Walter F. Downey, the headmaster during Joseph's high school years. The teachers are called "Masters." The courses of study also reflect those of a bygone era, such as hygiene, phonography, public speaking, commercial law, commercial geography, and merchandizing. The catalog outlines the academic goals for each of the four years of study, and it is evident that high school seniors in this era were challenged academically. In the senior year of English the students were expected to read Milton's minor poems, Shakespeare's *Macbeth,* and Macaulay's *Life of Johnson.* In mathematics, the senior year required trigonometry, logarithms, and the application of trigonometry to surveying and navigation. Examination of Dr. Kirsner's transcripts reveals that over his four years of high school his studies included four years of English, mathematics, and science (one year each of general science, biology, chemistry, and physics), four years of physical training, and household arts. He took three years of Latin and French (he won a citywide competition in each language) and history, two years of hygiene, and a smattering of military drill, choral practice, manual arts, penmanship, and phonography. It is noteworthy that over the four years his grades significantly improved, to almost exclusively As and Bs in his last two years. The transcript mentions that he received the school's Lawrence Prize for Excellence in Latin and a prize in 1927 for Fidelity and Deportment. On being shown these transcripts at the age of 96, Dr. Kirsner dryly commented, "Not a very promising student."

Joseph did well in school, and he would graduate as one of the valedictorians of a very large class in 1927.[10] He remembers winning a prize for an outstanding essay on a subject that he had developed a great delight in studying, classical history. (This early awakening to scholarship is reflected in his later taste for citing Latin epigraphs at the top of his papers of a more philosophical nature on medical practice.) His essay earned him the honor of being selected as one of three students to read their essays to the entire class during an assembly in his second year of high school. He carried away from this experience a lesson on public speaking that he would remember for the rest of his life. He recalled overhearing two of his classmates speaking in the boys' washroom after the event, and one of them said to the other,

"The first guy talked so fast, I hardly could understand a word he said."

His education did not come without personal sacrifice. He worked at a number of odd jobs, including in a shoe store. Eventually, he was able to get a regular and better-paying job at the local Upsham Corner Branch of the Boston Public Library, taking out trash and straightening books on the shelves. This allowed Morris to take over his paper route and added another $10 a week to the family income. Several years later, Morris took the same job at the library and would remember that the librarian, Beatrice C. McGuire, remembered and loved his brother Joe. The Boston Public Library, founded in 1849, had the distinction of establishing the country's first branch library system in 1869.

Despite his reservations about his small and "puny" physique, Joe had the temerity to try out for the junior varsity football team. Naturally, he sought a position as the team's quarterback. The coach put him on the line against the heftiest players, and a broken nose quickly convinced him that his talents lay elsewhere. In general, though, this was a childhood with no vacations or trips, an absence of money, and little time for sports. He would remember that he and his brother did find time to play handball at the local YMCA, and that Morris, who was quite athletic, was truly outstanding at this difficult and demanding game. Morris, however, remembers that at least for some period of time Joe was given an opportunity to study the violin, and that his mother kept the instrument in a closet for many years after he had left home, "in case Joe might need it."[11]

As the four years of high school drew to a close, Joseph was drawn to Tufts because most of the doctors he had met were Tufts graduates. His decision to consider Tufts was strengthened by the fact that the school offered a six-year program leading to a medical degree. This program had been developed through the Bigelow Fund, which had been established by Dr. Sturgis Bigelow in an effort to educate more physicians for the growing population of Massachusetts and the New England area.

Tufts College had established its medical school in 1893. The college's original charter, which dated from 1852, had forbidden conferring medical degrees, a concession made in deference to Harvard

Medical School. In 1867 the trustees of the college considered establishing a medical school and even convinced the Massachusetts state legislature, over Harvard's objections, to lift the restriction. The plan went no further, however; it was considered a second time in 1883, but again no further action was taken.[12]

Two years later, in 1885, a group of faculty at the Boston College of Physicians approached the trustees of Tufts about establishing a medical school. The initial proposal was rejected, but in 1893 the concerned group of faculty resigned from the Boston College of Physicians and pressured the trustees of Tufts College to reconsider. This time the trustees agreed, and the new medical school was established on a probationary basis requiring that the school prove itself academically and fiscally. The original seven founders of Tufts School of Medicine each contributed a sum of $50 to allow the school to open in October of 1893. The initial site of the school was 188 Boylston Street "in the city of Boston, directly opposite the Public Gardens, and within a few steps of Park Square, one of the great street-car centers of the city, making it convenient to all the hospitals, dispensaries and public buildings and the railway stations."[13] (The site is occupied today by the Four Seasons Hotel.) The advertisements for the new school made it clear that this was a coeducational institution and offered full credit to former students under their instruction. In October 1903 the school opened with a complement of 80 students, 57 men and 23 women. From 1893 to 1914 admission to the medical school required that the student had graduated from an approved high school. In 1913 the American Medical Association denied a "Class A" rating to schools that did not require one year of work in chemistry, physics, English, and French or German. The school itself provided the year of premedical work, increased to two years in 1918, but finally discontinued its premedical education program in 1927, the year that Joseph Kirsner entered medical school. His class was the last to begin their undergraduate career at Tufts Medical College.

In 1925 the Association of American Medical Colleges required that all college work that was to be part of the premedical requirement be given only at institutions qualified to award bachelor's degrees. The dean of Tufts College prepared a seven-year program that would include three years of undergraduate work and a bachelor's degree to be awarded after the first year of medical school. The plan was considered in 1927 but was not adopted until after Dean Stephen Rushmore resigned later that year. The new dean, A. Warren Stearns, would serve through the years that Dr. Kirsner was a medical student.

By 1927 the class size at Tufts Medical College stood at approximately 125, and the percentage of women had fallen to about 5 percent. Ninety percent of his classmates were from the New England area, and 70 percent from the state of Massachusetts.

The tuition in 1927 was $400 a year, with additional laboratory fees. The cash value on a life insurance policy that his father owned provided $200 toward his first year's tuition, and Joseph would have to earn the remainder. He needed to find work. Harris Kirsner had an interest in local politics and had done some work to support a local politician. The summer before he entered medical school, these connections made it possible for Joseph to hold two jobs in the post office system. The first job was as a janitor at the Upsham Corner Branch near his home. He would start at six in the morning and work until two thirty in the afternoon. He would walk home and rest for a few hours and then head downtown to the Atlantic Avenue post office, where he would sort railway mail from six until ten in the evening. He lived at home throughout his medical school education, traveling by streetcar daily from Roxbury to school, which was located on Huntington Avenue near the corner of Huntington and Massachusetts Avenue.

The building on 416 Huntington Avenue was built in 1900 at a cost of $110,000 on land that had been purchased for $57,000. This was technically the fourth location of the medical school. At the original site, 186 Boylston, the school had been crowded into two floors. By 1896 additional space was needed, and a former Baptist Church was purchased at Shawmut Avenue and Rutland Street. The building had to be gutted and reconstructed. Temporary space was rented in the former Chauncey Hall School building, which was opposite the original Boston Museum of Fine Arts in Copley Square.

The Huntington Avenue facility opened on October 3, 1901. It would be the site of the Tufts School of Medicine throughout the years that Dr. Kirsner attended the school. An old photograph of the 416 Huntington Avenue building, with two 1920-vintage automobiles parked in front, shows a brick four-story structure with an imposing marble entranceway in the center of the building. The most unusual feature of the building is that the left and right sides expand out at 45-degree angles along two diagonal streets. Plans of the building show the front of the building on Courtland Street, and the left wing along Rogers Avenue; the left side, the medical school side, is on Huntington Avenue. The building consisted of a dental school on the left side of the building and the medical school on the right. The basement of the medical school had a locker room, a lecture hall, and a dispensary. The bursar's office, a faculty room, library, and laboratories were located on the first floor. The second floor contained a women's study, the bacteriological laboratories, and faculty offices. There was a large amphitheater extending from the first to the third floors of the building.

In 1910 an additional floor was added to the building to increase laboratory facilities. The school bought additional property on Mechanic Street for the same purpose, and in 1917 property behind the school was purchased for the anatomy department and for premedical school classes. In 1920 the Council on Medical Education criticized the school for not having an adequate number of science instructors to teach its student body. The distance of the school from its clinical facilities and its lack of a teaching hospital led the trustees in 1925 to consider moving the campus of the medical school to the Medford campus or to Boston City Hospital. Tufts president John Cousens considered a plan with Abraham Flexner to move the medical school to the Medford campus. This plan was dropped after a change in the administration of the General Medical Council. In October 1929 the president reported that Arthur Rotch, a member of the board of trustees of the Boston Dispensary, had approached him with the proposal that the Boston Dispensary and the Boston Floating Hospital for Infants and Children join forces to establish a new medical center in the city. It was against this backdrop of change that Joseph Kirsner began his medical career. It would not be until after the war, in 1948, that the campus of the medical school would move to the Harvard Building at 136-140 Harrison Street.

The first two years of premedical education included general biology and chemistry with laboratory-based work. Classes were also held in French, English, and American history. Joseph spent the summer of 1928 working at the two post office jobs. The second year of school was an extension of the first, with more biology, organic chemistry, and mathematics, including logarithms and trigonometry. There were three lectures each week in literature with an emphasis on the scientific thought of the 19th century. Joseph completed his two years of premedical school with good grades and was one of 135 admitted to medical school in 1929.

Dr. Kirsner remembers that in the summer before starting medical school he realized that he was so physically run-down by the schedule of school and work that he had to take the summer off. He remembers also that his father was somewhat displeased at this, since he would have liked him to continue to work. Joseph spent part of his time frequenting the L Street beach, which was on the Atlantic Ocean and not far from his home. He used the time for exercising, swimming, and generally building up his stamina. His intuition in this matter seems to have been correct, and he doesn't remember ever being ill during his years in medical school.

October 29, 1929 was historic "Black Friday," the day of the great Wall Street crash. Joseph had just begun the medical school portion of his career at Tufts School of Medicine. Perhaps he would again have agreed with Theodore H. White, who observed that "for those of us of the underclass, the Depression had begun long before then."[14]

Henry H. Banks, in his book *A Century of Excellence: The History of Tufts University School of Medicine, 1893-1993*, provides tables showing the curricula of the medical school at various time during the century, including 1893, 1900, and 1929. In the years that Dr. Kirsner attended medical school, the first year was entirely class work in gross anatomy, histology, physiology, and biochemistry. It was not until the second year that the student began to get a sense of medicine and the career to which he aspired. The greater part of the curriculum in the second year of medical school was centered on the study of pathology, bacteriology, and pharmacology. For the physician, pathology is the most important pillar in his or her understanding of disease. Here he learns the true face of disease and its disruption of the normal state. It is with this picture in mind that he begins to approach the patient. There was also chemical pathology and toxicology, hematology, and neuropathology. Physical diagnosis was taught in the second year, and this gives the young physician his first tools in approaching the patient. He or she begins to learn how to correlate an inventory of symptoms with the most readily observable manifestations of disease that can be found in the physical examination of the patient. The habits acquired in this crucial period of learning will serve the physician the rest of his life. The orderly and systematic steps of inspection, percussion, palpation, and auscultation are important throughout an entire career. Pharmacology occupied a major part of the second semester of the second year. This year also saw the student's first exposure to patients in medical and surgical clinics.

Morris, who shared a room at home with his older brother, remembers Joe's study habits. Morris, who was six years younger than Joe, would often be awakened in the early morning hours by the tap-tap-tap of a pencil and see his brother in the light of the desk lamp studying until one or two o'clock in the morning.

The third and fourth years were entirely clinically oriented. Medicine, surgery, and obstetrics and gynecology predominated the week's class lectures and corresponding clinics. Students were also exposed to pediatrics, otolaryngology, ophthalmology, urology, orthopedics, and psychiatry, in classes and parallel clinics. There was also an introduction to "roentgenology," as the specialty of radiology was then called.

A footnote in the catalog told the fourth-year student that this year would be entirely clinical. Students assigned as junior interns lived in the hospital, and all classes met daily, except Sunday. The year was devoted to medicine, surgery, obstetrics, and specialties.

The goal of the school was the training of general practitioners for the New England area; courses in therapeutics reflected the medical practice of the day and included massage, electrical stimulation, and hydrotherapy. There was little talk of research, and the degree of patient contact seems to have been limited primarily to observation. Dr. Kirsner was a diligent note taker and prepared his class notes so carefully that he was part of a group that sold their notes to other classmates. In his second year he gave his first presentation, at a scientific forum on an unusual case of diphtheria.

The *Tufts Medical News* of January 1932 carried the first contribution to the medical literature by the future Joseph B. Kirsner, M.D., Ph.D.[15] At this time he was simply Joseph B. Kirsner, '33. His book review of *Fads, Frauds and Physicians,* by T. Swann Harding, dealt with issues that still concern us today. In his book Harding deplores the lack of expertise in diagnosis on the part of "dormant physicians" cloaked by guild organization, excessive fees charged by specialists, and fee splitting. He proposes that the solution to these problems is "State Medicine," with doctors serving as civil employees at salaries ranging from $3,000 to $7,000 a year, and he points to the success of this type of medical regulation in Sweden. The reviewer seems to be neutral in his final paragraph, noting, "The reaction of the profession to this vigorous attack should prove quite interesting." How interesting it is to read this review by a medical student then only 23 years of age and already concerned with questions of quality care, the public image of his chosen profession, and the socioeconomic issues that revolve around our national approach to health care. Clearly he had already begun to seek the larger view of medical practice that would occupy his thoughts, writing, and career for many decades to come.

The humane side of this young medical student comes through in Dr. Kirsner's reminiscences. For example, he remembers a man he saw in the hospital who was alone and dying and no one came to see him. Joe would go back after hours to sit with this man, to hold his hand and comfort him. In later years he often reflected on this patient, commenting that one of the worst things that could happen to a patient was "to die alone without anyone coming to see you and without any emotional support."

Joseph Kirsner's clinical experience was scattered throughout the city. He spent time at Boston City Hospital and Beth Israel Hospital, and also at Carney Hospital and Roxbury Veterans Administration Hospital, among others. During his training, he met outstanding teachers and clinicians he would long remember. Benjamin Spector was an exceptional teacher and a favorite with the students. He was a professor of anatomy and osteology and made the subjects come alive for the students. He had received training in Germany and at the Mayo Clinic and started teaching anatomy at New York University in 1915. He had graduated from Bellevue Hospital Medical College in 1922, the year he began his career at Tufts. In 1933 he became the chairmen of the Department of Anatomy.

H. Edward MacMahon was another new faculty member who would make a lasting impression on the medical student Joseph Kirsner. He had taken graduate training in pathology at Boston City Hospital with Dr. Frank E. Malloy and developed his interest in diseases of the liver. By 1929 he was professor and chair of the Tufts Department of Pathology. Generations of Tufts alumni remembered him as an outstanding teacher.

Although little was said about research during his medical school years, Dr. Kirsner remembers that Dr. William Dameshek, born in Russia and a 1923 graduate of Harvard Medical School, was an outstanding physician-scientist. He was one of the founders of hematology and on the staff of Beth Israel Hospital. Dr. Kirsner remembers Dr. Lois E. Phaneuf as an outstanding teacher. He was a gynecologist and obstetrician and in 1927 was gynecologist and obstetrician-in-chief at the Carney Hospital and professor on the Tufts faculty. Other memorable figures included John Pratt, M.D., a distinguished internist with an interest in the pancreas, and Hyman Morrison, who was a superb bedside clinician.

Joseph spent one of the summers during medical school working at North Grafton State Hospital, near Worcester, Massachusetts. He lived in the facility and along with other students performed admission histories and physical examinations as well as admitting laboratory work. It was a pleasant experience and took him away from the central city.

At the time when he began his fourth year, internship was not a requirement for the practice of medicine in the State of Massachusetts. But even then Joseph Kirsner knew that he needed more experience. While the education he had received to that point was satisfactory, he needed to know more and so began the process of applying for an internship. By 1933 the internship was a well-accepted part of medical education, although only 17 states required an internship before medical school graduates could practice medicine. Virtually all of Joseph's classmates at Tufts would seek one. Although he had had a slow start academically, with initial Bs under the strain of working while going to school, by graduation he was elected to the honorary William Osler Society and would graduate with honors in spring of 1933. His excellent record in medical school would lead to his retroactive appointment to the Alpha Omega Alpha Society some years later, after the society came into existence and sought members among recent graduates of American medical schools.

He studied the *Journal of the American Medical Association* for internship opportunities. His first round of applications to hospitals in Pennsylvania and New York State were rejected. Other members in his class were successful in getting internship positions, and in view of his high academic standing in the class, he could not explain his rejections. A second round of applications led to an offer from Woodlawn Hospital in Chicago, which he accepted. He made a decision to move to a city he had never visited; he knew nothing of the neighborhood where the hospital was located and did not even know about its proximity to the University of Chicago. If one looks at the listing of internship programs in Illinois posted in *JAMA* in 1932, there is little about Woodlawn Hospital to distinguish it from the two dozen other programs in the state of Illinois.[16]

Joseph would be leaving his home and traveling to a distant city where he had no friends or relatives. His thought at the time was that he would remain in Chicago for perhaps one or two years and then return to the Boston area, where he would take up practice as a general practitioner. It was a time of drama and high excitement for a young man who could not even begin to imagine the adventures that lay ahead of him. He would often reflect that although he had no advice or guidance during his career, there always seemed to be a providence looking after him that he could not explain.

Notes

1. Irving Howe, *World of Our Fathers* (New York: Harcourt, Brace, Jovanovich, 1976). See chap. 1, "Origins," for an overview of Eastern European immigration to America.

2. The Immigration Act of 1924, also known as the National Origins Act or the Johnson-Reed Act, was signed by President Coolidge. It limited the number of immigrants who could be admitted from any country to 2 percent of

the number of people from that country living in the United States as listed in the census of 1890. It was aimed at limiting the number of southern and Eastern Europeans, who had been entering the country in large numbers since the 1890s.

3. The facts cited about Dr. Kirsner's parents and their family life come from interviews with Dr. Kirsner, his sister Gertrude London, and his nephew Burton Resnic.

4. For an account of the founding and construction of Peter Bent Brigham Hospital, see Michael Bliss, *Harvey Cushing: A Life in Surgery* (New York: Oxford University Press, 2005).

5. See JBK, *Origins and Directions of Inflammatory Bowel Disease* (Dordrecht: Kluwer Academic, 2001), part 1, p. 15.

6. See Lucius Beebe, *Boston and the Boston Legend* (New York: D. Appleton Century, 1936), 139.

7. See Oscar Handlin, *Boston's Immigrants: A Study in Acculturation* (New York: Atheneum, 1968), 164.

8. See Thomas H. O'Connor, *The Boston Irish: A Political History* (Boston: Northeastern University Press, 1995).

9. See Theodore H. White, *In Search of History* (New York: Warner Books, 1978), part 1, "Boston: 1915-1938," 47.

10. Information and transcripts from the English High School kindly provided by Sammi Harrington, the guidance secretary/records, January 26, 2006.

11. Recollections of Morris Kirsner were taken from the transcript of an interview conducted in Boston in 2002 and kindly furnished by Dale Smith, Department of Medical History, Uniformed Services University of the Health Sciences, Bethesda, MD.

12. Information on the early history and curriculum of Tufts medical school is from Henry H. Banks, M.D., *A Century of Excellence: The History of Tufts University School of Medicine, 1893-1993* (Boston: Tufts University, 1993).

13. Henry H. Banks, "In the Beginning," *Tufts Medicine, a Centennial Issue; Tufts University 1893-1993*, 10; quotation is from a talk given in 1908 by Dr. Charles P. Thayer, one of the medical school's founders.

14. White, *In Search of History*, 55.

15. *Tufts Medical News*, January 1932, 4. A copy of this article was kindly supplied by Dale Smith, who discovered it in the Tufts Medical Library.

16. "Hospitals Approved for Internship," *JAMA*, August 27, 1932, 748.

2 ✳ Woodlawn Hospital, 1933–1935

One can imagine the sense of excitement and perhaps trepidation that the young man experienced boarding a train in Boston and leaving behind everything he had known for the first 24 years of his life. He remembers a very warm and supportive send-off from his parents and siblings.

The stock market crash of October 1929 was having its effect throughout the country, and the Chicago that Dr. Kirsner was going to in the summer of 1933 was no exception. In April 1931, when Anton J. Cermak became mayor of Chicago, the city was on the verge of bankruptcy. In 1932 the city and county had 650,000 persons who were unemployed and in desperate straits. By 1933 employment in industry in the city had been cut in half. Mortgage foreclosures had jumped from 3,128 in 1929 to 15,201 in 1933. At the same time, 163 banks, mostly in outlying areas of the city, had closed, and land values, which in 1928 had risen to over $5 billion, had dropped to $2 billion in 1933.[1]

The South Side of the city, to which Dr. Kirsner made his way via the Illinois Central Railroad after his cross-country rail trip from Boston, had been the site of the Columbian Exposition in 1893. Now, forty years later, its man-made lagoons and islands would play host to the second World's Fair. An array of new modernistic and angular buildings had been erected with the latest building materials, including prestressed concrete, asbestos board, and sheet steel. Attendance averaged 100,000 per day, and by October 1934 when the gates of the fairground closed, 39 million people had seen the fair. The new intern would soon learn the public health consequences of these numbers.[2]

Woodlawn Hospital was located on the northwest corner of 61st Street and Drexel Avenue, in the heart of the Woodlawn district. In 1859, a mere 75 years earlier, when one of the first settlers, a James Wadsworth, moved into the area, it was a low-lying marshland with heavily wooded forest tracts and only five other homes. Woodlawn had been annexed to the city of Chicago in 1889. The World's Columbian Exposition of 1893 and the opening of the University of Chicago led to tremendous growth in the community. Travelers to the fair came by way of the newly constructed elevated tracks (the "L") or by way of the Illinois Central Railroad, which had fitted specially adapted cattle cars with wooden benches to accommodate visitors. By 1920 the mile square area was bounded by the Midway Plaisance to the north, Stony Island to the east, 67th Street to the south, and Cottage Grove to the west. The population of the Woodlawn area had grown to 20,000.[3]

A community newspaper clipping from September 27, 1927, announces the construction of a "New South Side Hospital" that will, in the language of the newspaper, "rise nine stories and will be equipped with every known scientific device for the alleviation of pain." The architect's drawing depicts a handsome but very regular building with a small arched entrance in the lower left corner of the building façade; the lower three stories are faced with white stone, and the upper stories are of red brick. The hospital, which occupied a lot 55 feet by 155 feet, was being erected by Woodlawn Hospital, Inc. and would contain 120 beds. The architect's plans were drawn up by Dwight Wallace, said to be an authority on hospital construction, and the building was estimated to cost $400,000. The building was expected to be ready for occupancy by March 1928. The hospital was being constructed by a group of prominent South Side medical and business men, and the surgeon Dr. Rollo K. Packard was the president of the organization.[4]

When Dr. Kirsner began his internship, he still believed that he was destined to be a general practitioner. Not feeling completely prepared to undertake this career, he was seeking the additional training and experience in patient care that an internship would afford him. He would live in the hospital and receive a salary of $25 a month plus meals. The living quarters for the interns were quite modest, on the top floor of the hospital, although he remembers that he and his fellow interns had the luxury of both a ping-pong and a billiard table. The list of approved internships published in the *Journal of the American Medical Association* in 1932 indicates that there were three approved interns in each new internship class and that the hospital had 170 beds, which included beds designated for surgical, medical, obstetric, and pediatric patients. The 1932 *JAMA* listing indicates that the salary above room and board was zero (this is at variance with Dr. Kirsner's recollection, unless the hospital thought it fitting in 1933 to increase the intern salary). Most of the hospitals in the 1932 listing paid interns no salary beyond room and board, and where salaries were paid, they were in the range of $20 to $35 a month. Morris Kirsner was in high school at the time, and he remembers that one of his responsibilities each week was to mail a letter their mother wrote to Joe which contained $5 to ensure that Joe had enough to eat or whatever else he needed.

As an intern, Dr. Kirsner's duties entailed performing and writing up a complete medical history and physical examination for patients admitted to the hospital, as well as writing orders to prepare patients scheduled for surgery the next day. He had to be available to make rounds with the attending doctors who admitted their patients to the hospital, and to respond to nurses' calls to see patients who required attention when their physicians were out of the hospital. Dr. Rollo Packard, who had started practice as a general practitioner, had developed into an excellent and well-regarded surgeon. He was the source of many of the hospital admissions, and seeing his patients both before and after surgery was an important part of the intern's responsibility. Although the hospital was expected to provide regular conferences to fulfill its teaching responsibility as part of the criteria for internship accreditation, as is often the case the pressures of patient care for the hospital's busy practicing physicians often took precedence over teaching responsibilities. Dr. Harry Olin, a Tufts graduate a decade before Dr. Kirsner and chief of the hospital's radiology department, took an interest in the eager new intern and proved to be a helpful guide in his learning how to read and interpret x-ray film. Dr. Kirsner also learned a great deal from helping two out-standing general internists care for their patients, Dr. Charles Elliot and Dr. Hugo Moeller. He also remembers his contact with a patholo-gist by the name of Jack Kirschbaum, who had been at the University of Illinois and trained at Cook County Hospital. He became good friends with Dr. Kirschbaum and felt he was a first-class pathologist with an interest in teaching.

The types of patients that he encountered at Woodlawn Hospital were typical of those seen at community hospitals at the time. They ranged from cases of pneumonia, tonsillitis, and sinus and mastoid infections to surgical cases of appendicitis and inguinal hernia re-pairs. It was the outbreak of amoebic dysentery in Chicago that year, and the difficulty the general practitioners on the staff had in diag-nosing and treating the disease, that made a strong impression on Dr. Kirsner.

By August of 1933 two cases of amoebic dysentery had been re-ported to the Chicago Health Department, and in December of that year Woodlawn Hospital admitted its first patient with the disease. While amoebic dysentery had been well described in the medical lit-erature in the early part of the century, few physicians had substan-tial experience with its diagnosis and treatment. Dr. Kirsner found himself treating a significant number of these patients, and there were many questions about appropriate treatment which the general practitioners on the staff could not answer. Experiences such as this began to alert the young Dr. Kirsner to the fact that there were limi-tations to the knowledge of a general practitioner and that he would have to aim higher.

As amoebic dysentery spread throughout the city and visitors to the fair exported the infection to other parts of the country, the situation assumed national prominence. The Illinois Department of Public Health disputed the existence of the so-called epidemic. Dr. Herman Bundesen, who was made commissioner of health in 1922 and who had directed important campaigns against venereal disease, tuberculosis, and infant mortality, found his reputation tarnished when he came under severe criticism by the Chicago Medical Soci-ety for his delay in notifying the city's doctors about the epidemic. The Chicago Medical Society's *Bulletin* further reported that on June

29 and July 2, 1933, excessive rainfall in Chicago had caused sewers in the Loop to burst, and sewage flowed back into the food storage compartments of a downtown hotel. This had caused the outbreak of amoebic dysentery. The report was highly critical of Dr. Bundesen for seemingly being unaware of the broken sewers for seven months. The implications for the numerous guests from around the country and the world who had stayed in the hotel while visiting the World's Fair that year were obvious.[5] During the course of the epidemic, Dr. Kirsner remembers, there was a patient who was diagnosed as having acute appendicitis, but on surgical exploration he proved to have a perforated intestine secondary to amoebic enteritis.

In the fall of 1933 "a charming young lady," Minnie Schneider, was admitted to Woodlawn Hospital with an ear infection. It was Dr. Kirsner's good fortune to be the intern assigned to her care for the few days she was hospitalized. Minnie Schneider had come to Chicago from Des Moines, Iowa, where her family was prominent in the community, to join the Chicago Opera Ballet. She had studied with outstanding ballet teachers--Adolph Bolm, who had danced with Anna Pavlova and the Ballet Russes, and Laurent Novikov, Pavlova's last dancing partner--and had a promising career ahead of her. Nancy Weiss, the daughter of Minnie's older sister Bea, who was living in Chicago with her husband, Louis Sauer, remembered that she and her girlfriends were thrilled when Minnie would come to her house and give them ballet lessons. Unfortunately, the Chicago Civic Opera program, which had been supported by Samuel Insull, a pioneer in the commercial distribution of electrical power in the city, had collapsed because of financial difficulties.[6] In 1933, when Dr. Kirsner first met Minnie, she was working as a secretary to Al Neiman, who was then selling women's clothing in Chicago but who had been one of the founders of the famous Neiman Marcus store in Dallas, Texas.

Dr. Kirsner, in his words, "fell totally in love with her" and began to see Minnie socially after she was discharged from the hospital. One suspects that Minnie Schneider was way ahead of the young intern. Dr. Kirsner recalls that she and a friend of hers invited both him and a fellow intern to dinner, and as Dr. Kirsner put it, "That furthered our relationship."

He remembers, too, that he had "plenty" of competition. In particular, a wealthy business man from Akron, Ohio, who had known her previously back in Des Moines, was also seeking her affection. To his good fortune, Dr. Kirsner won out, and he traveled with Minnie to Des Moines to meet her family.

There he found a very different home environment from what he had known in Boston. The Schneiders' house was full of a certain social liveliness he had not experienced before. The family's home life was open and convivial. Minnie's parents played a major role in the Jewish community of the city, and there was a steady stream of visitors to the house. Music was an integral part of family life: her brother Louis played the violin, and her brother Aaron played the saxophone. Minnie, besides being a dancer, played the piano.

Minnie's father had come to America and initially settled in Brooklyn. The family briefly relocated in Omaha, Nebraska, and then settled in Des Moines. Her father was a tailor and had risen to become the number-one suit maker in the city. Minnie's older brother, Louis, initially bent on entering the same vocation, had returned to New York to study colors and fabrics. This extra experience resulted in her father becoming co-owner of the best men's clothing store in the city, the premier Kadis-Schneider Men's Store. On his first visit to Des Moines to meet Minnie's family, Dr. Kirsner remembers, her father instinctively reached for the lapel of his sport coat to gauge the fabric between his thumb and forefinger. Apparently he passed the test.

Her brother Lou, who was very interested in the humanities, also obtained a law degree at Drake University. At one time he was responsible for bringing the San Carlos Opera to Des Moines. This event and other community-related activities won him the Junior Chamber of Commerce Award. His expertise in law included aspects of British patent law, and later during the Roosevelt administration he was asked by the secretary of labor, Anna Rosenberg, to help draft the country's first social security legislation.

During that first visit, the Schneiders' family physician suggested that Joseph come to Des Moines and join him in private practice. Dr. Kirsner was impressed that the family received their medical care at the Mayo Clinic, recognized even then for its clinical excellence.

Lou was establishing himself as a prominent lawyer in the community, and Dr. Kirsner remembers that he invited him to a meeting

of the Spectators Club. At these meetings, topics for extemporane-
ous speeches were written on slips of paper and placed in a top hat
at the entrance door. Attendees drew slips and were selected to give
a brief speech on the designated topic. Not surprisingly, Dr. Kirsner
was asked to speak, and again he felt that he passed another "test."
Lou and Minnie were also active in the Des Moines Community Center, run by a prominent woman named Mrs. Max Meyer, a staunch
Republican.

In his recollections of these early visits to Des Moines, Dr. Kirsner
remembers how impressed he was with the charming openness of
Minnie's family, and aware of his own limitations at the time. While
he may have felt that he was lacking in social graces and had been
somewhat of a "homebody," his relationship with Minnie would be
decisive in expanding his horizons.

On January 6, 1934, Minnie and Joe were married in Chicago in
the private study of the legendary Rabbi Solomon Goldman. Rabbi
Goldman, who had been born in Russia, was the rabbi of the Conser-
vative Ansche Emet Congregation. He was a notable scholar and a
leader in Chicago's Jewish community.

On a family income of his $25 a month, which would later increase
to $50 a month, and Minnie's $50 a week, they rented an apartment
in the nearby Kimbark Hotel. It was a one-room apartment, and they
were not allowed to do any cooking. Dr. Kirsner recalls that they were
very creative and learned to boil eggs in a coffee pot for breakfast.

Minnie's niece Nancy remembers her disappointment at not being invited to the wedding, for which she had gotten a new dress. She
also remembers that her parents allowed the newlyweds to spend a
long weekend alone in their apartment. Her mother had baked an
upside-down pineapple cake, which she left in the refrigerator for
the newlyweds. That the cake went unnoticed became a frequently
told family joke, and when Nancy and Paul Weiss arranged a surprise
fiftieth wedding anniversary party for the Minnie and Joe in 1984, it
featured an upside-down pineapple cake.

The Kirsners' honeymoon had to be postponed until the summer,
when they traveled to New York by train and then by ship to Boston.
There Joe's family got their first opportunity to meet his new bride.
As an indication of how independent Dr. Kirsner had become, he had

not even told his parents of his intention to marry. Morris Kirsner confirms that Joe simply called home and "shocked" his mother by telling her that he had gotten married. This reunion of Joseph and his family was a happy one, and they were charmed by his new bride.[7]

In the spring of 1934 Dr. Packard offered Dr. Kirsner an appointment as a resident at Woodlawn Hospital and an increase in his salary to $50 a month. Thanks to his careful and complete admission histories and physical examinations, and his diligence in caring for patients, he had become recognized as a promising physician, one for whom a future appointment as an attending physician at Woodlawn Hospital would be likely. His thoughts about his future in medicine were still unsettled, however, and while he sought to improve his skills in patient care, he was coming to realize that the role of a general practitioner would probably not be entirely satisfying for him. Teaching at Woodlawn Hospital was fragmentary, and he petitioned the staff to allow him to attend medical grand rounds at Cook County Hospital on Thursdays. He also volunteered at the West Side Medical Dispensary at Rush Medical College.

The Cook County Hospital and Westside Medical Center that Dr. Kirsner encountered in the 1930s still stands today on W. Harrison Street, just west of what is now Rush University Medical Center. The dramatic façade of the 2,700-bed hospital, nearly two blocks long, looks out over the Eisenhower Expressway. Built in 1912, the hospital looks today much as it looked then. Somewhat sadly, "The Old Lady of Harrison Street,"[8] as it was affectionately called, is now empty and unused, Cook County having recently built and opened a new facility, Stroger Hospital, in 2001. Even before the turn of the century, the hospital had offered a highly sought-after and competitive internship that required applicants to take a demanding written examination. The Westside Medical Center had developed over many years at this site and had a vibrancy lacking in a community hospital like Woodlawn. In the 19th century the famous surgeon Christian Fenger had a decisive influence on the development of pathology and surgery at County. His work in pathology was carried forward by men such as Ludvig Hektoen, R. Le Count, H. Gideon Wells, and Fredrick Zeit.[9]

In 1933, when Dr. Kirsner traveled by streetcar to the Westside Medical Center, Dr. Richard Herman Jaffe's pathology grand rounds had achieved high regard in the medical community. Jaffe was born in Vienna in 1888. By 1922, after extensive pathologic training in Germany and experience in World War I, he had been appointed as *Privatdozent* at the medical school of the University of Vienna. In 1922 he was convinced to accept a position at Grant Hospital and at the University of Illinois. By 1928 he was the director of the pathology and clinical laboratories of Cook County Hospital.[10] It was his Thursday morning pathology conferences at Cook County Hospital that Dr. Kirsner would attend. These sessions attracted interns, the entire medical staff of Cook County Hospital, medical practitioners from throughout the city, and out-of-town visitors as well.

Although now 24 years old and with the responsibilities of a married man, Dr. Kirsner was still concerned with finding a direction for his career in medicine. Showing the idealism that would characterize his entire medical career--and that was not uncommon in doctors of his generation--he volunteered to attend the Central Free Dispensary on his own time, making the difficult journey to the Westside Medical Center by public transportation. Organized by Rush Medical College in 1873, the dispensary had provided free medical care for indigent patients of Chicago from before the turn of the century and was now associated with Presbyterian Hospital. A 1923 photograph of the interior of the clinic shows that it had an open waiting room; the ceiling is lined with water pipes and naked lights, and a wrought-iron staircase descends to the floor in the middle of the clinic. The patients, dressed in winter coats and hats, sit waiting on wooden benches, staring back at the camera.[11] This clinic was not unlike the Boston Dispensary, which Joseph Kirsner had encountered two years earlier as a student in medical school.

While at Tufts School of Medicine, Dr. Kirsner had had only a limited awareness of the University of Chicago, confined to the popular textbook on gynecology and obstetrics used during his clinical years, which had been written by Joseph B. De Lee, the first professor of gynecology and obstetrics at the newly opened Lying-In Hospital. The proximity of Woodlawn Hospital to the university, along with its new medical school with its hospital and clinics, which had opened in 1927, had played no part in his choice of internship. It was through a University of Chicago medical student, Charles Busse, who was spending an elective clerkship at Woodlawn Hospital, that Dr. Kirsner learned about Billings Hospital and was encouraged to attend one of their grand rounds. There he witnessed an approach to clinical medicine that met the ideals for a scientific and comprehensive approach to patient care that he felt was lacking in his experiences at Woodlawn Hospital. He was impressed by the outstanding full-time faculty and the distinguished internists who attended the conferences, including Joseph Miller, Walter Hamburger, and Richard Capps. There was an intense enthusiasm for learning and excellence and an orientation toward research that immediately captivated his imagination.

Dr. Kirsner talked over his impressions of the university and his experiences at the Cook County conferences and the Central Free Dispensary with Minnie, who encouraged him to pursue a position at the University of Chicago. Early in the summer of 1935 he made an appointment with George F. Dick, the chairman of the Department of Medicine, and asked whether there was a position for him at the hospital. He was told that there were no openings for new staff that summer. Dr. Kirsner was enthusiastic about science and medicine and tried to convey to Dr. Dick his confidence in his ability to meet the standards of the University Hospital. Dr. Kirsner asked Dr. Dick to keep his name on file, his telephone number, and notes on their conversation.

He was left with a difficult period of uncertainty, wondering whether he should commit to a third year at Woodlawn or look for another position. He even explored the possibility of a fellowship program at the Mayo Clinic, but nothing came of it.[12] In August 1935 Dr. Dick called to tell him that one of the clinical assistants in medicine was unexpectedly leaving, and therefore he could offer him a position as an assistant in medicine at the hospital and clinic. It is remarkable that Dr. Dick remembered his name from that first, unsolicited visit. Objectively speaking, Dr. Kirsner was not coming from what would have been considered the most prestigious internship in the city, and he carried no particular recommendation. His sincerity and enthusiasm for an opportunity to prove himself must have made a strong impression on Dr. Dick. With this call, the fog of uncertainty that had seemed to shroud his future cleared, and Dr. Kirsner was revitalized by this opportunity. At the time, neither he nor Dr. Dick could have predicted the impact this appointment would have on the young physician, and the benefits that would accrue to the University of Chicago from the decades, now numbering more than seven, of service that would follow.

Notes

1. *The Encyclopedia of Chicago,* ed. James R. Grossman, Ann Durkin Keating, and Janice L. Reiff (Chicago: University of Chicago Press, 2004).

2. Emmett Dedmon, *Fabulous Chicago: A Great City's History and People* (New York: Atheneum, 1983).

3. Everett Chamberlin, *Chicago and Its Suburbs* (Chicago: T. A. Hungerford, 1874).

4. A copy of this article is in the Special Collections of the Harold B. Washington Branch of the Chicago Public Library.

5. The material on the outbreak of amoebic dysentery is taken from the Chicago Medical Society *Bulletin* of 1933, 511-13, and the minutes of the council of the Chicago Medical Society. These materials were kindly furnished to the author by Elizabeth Sidney, editor of *Chicago Medicine* magazine of the Chicago Medical Society.

6. See Dedmon, *Fabulous Chicago,* chap. 24, "Insull Builds His Empire," 317-32.

7. Much of the information concerning Mrs. Kirsner was kindly supplied to the author by her niece, Nancy Weiss, in an interview recorded in her home on July 15, 2006, in Valparaiso, Indiana.

8. John G. Raffensperger, ed., *The Old Lady on Harrison Street: Cook County Hospital, 1833-1995* (New York: Peter Lang, 1997).

9. See Thomas Neville Bonner, *Medicine in Chicago: 1850-1950* (Madison, WI: American History Research Center, 1957).

10. Biographical information on the career of Richard Herman Jaffe, M.D., was kindly supplied from the archives of the Hektoen Institute of Chicago, by Phyllis Wheeler, secretary to the CEO of the institute.

11. The photograph may be found in Jim Bowman, *Good Medicine: The First 150 Years of Rush–Presbyterian–St. Luke's Medical Center* (Chicago: Chicago Review Press, 1987).

12. From an interview conducted by Dale Smith on July 24, 2003.

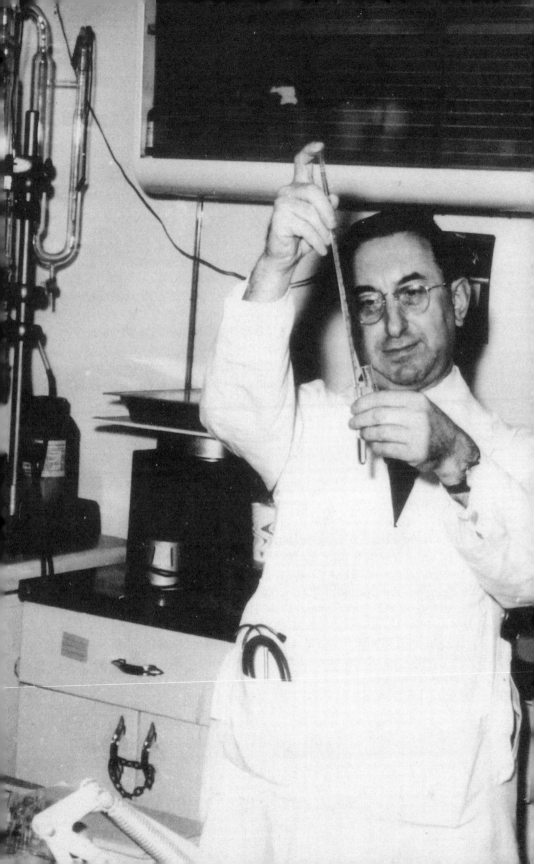

3 ✳ The University of Chicago, 1935

The medical world Dr. Kirsner entered in the fall of 1935 was the unique affiliation of the "new" University of Chicago's full-time research-oriented medical school and the "old" highly respected Rush Medical College (founded 1837), an association anticipated to produce outstanding physicians and significant medical research. Each school had arisen from the idealism, determination, and vision of outstanding men. Much of the original faculty at the University of Chicago had come from Rush.

In 1935 the medical school authorized for issuing degrees to the medical students trained at the University of Chicago was the joint responsibility of the university and Rush Medical College. Students gaining admission to the University of Chicago School of Medicine would spend the first two years of preclinical training on the South Side campus. They then would elect to spend the subsequent two clinical years either on the South Side campus or on the West Side, primarily at Presbyterian Hospital. A stone engraving on the entrance to the new medical school courtyard, displaying the twin seals of Rush Medical College and the University of Chicago, signified this relationship. Because the University of Chicago's new school of medicine and Rush Medical College provided the milieu that would foster Dr. Kirsner's development as an academic physician and would be the focus of his career, a brief history of these institutions is pertinent here.

Rush Medical College traced its origins a hundred years earlier to a 24-year-old surgeon named Daniel Brainard, who had arrived in Chicago in 1836 after graduating from the respected Jefferson Medical College of Philadelphia. In 1836 Chicago was but a village on the southwestern shore of Lake Michigan. The city was not yet incorporated, buildings were primitive, and streets were unmarked, unpaved roads. Soon after his arrival in the area, Brainard and several community leaders prepared a charter for a new medical school they anticipated would be essential for the future of the rapidly developing city. Brainard and his colleagues named the school after Benjamin Rush, the noted Philadelphia physician and humanitarian, originally trained in Philadelphia and in Scotland, who had cared for George Washington and was the only physician to sign the Declaration of Independence. Rush Medical College received its charter on March 2, 1837, two days before the incorporation of the City of Chicago.[1] The steady growth of Rush Medical College continued throughout the 19th century, and the school survived the catastrophic Chicago Fire of 1871 when its building on Dearborn Street and Grand Avenue was reduced to rubble. The school immediately reopened in the top-floor amphitheater of Cook County Hospital and was subsequently relocated to 18th and La Salle Streets. Rush, typical of the nation's medical schools of the middle and late 19th century, was known as a proprietary school of medicine. In such schools, the instructors were paid directly by the students for their lectures, and the school was supported by tuition fees. The growth of the school was accelerated by an affiliation with the new Presbyterian Hospital, which opened in 1884. By 1900 Rush Medical College had developed a reputation as one of the best medical schools in the nation.

The present University of Chicago (successor to the first University of Chicago, 1856-86)[2] was the creation of a small group of Baptist ministers including Thomas W. Goodspeed, H. L. Morehouse, William Rainey Harper, and Frederick Gates, and supported by the industrialist and philanthropist John D. Rockefeller, a staunch Baptist interested in education. Aided by Frederick Gates, secretary of the American Baptist Education Society and a strong supporter of a denominational school in Chicago, Rockefeller agreed to contribute $600,000 if the Baptist congregation of Chicago could raise another $400,000. This goal was reached through a citywide campaign generating major contributions from all ethnic groups, including the Sinai Congregation, which organized a fund-raising event at the Standard Club led by the distinguished rabbi Emil Hirsch. Marshall Field generously donated 10 acres of property just north of the Midway Plaisance of the Columbian Exposition for the location of the new school.

Thomas W. Goodspeed urged the trustees to name the brilliant William Rainey Harper as the first president of the university. Harper had previously taught at Vassar College, and one of his students was Rockefeller's oldest daughter, Elizabeth. By this time, Harper was a 33-year-old professor of semantics at Yale University and had become a personal friend and cycling companion of Rockefeller's. He was also a recognized scholar and an expert in five Semitic languages (Hebrew in particular). Spurred by Rockefeller's gift of an additional million dollars, initial plans for a college were expanded to a "university" that would not only educate students but further knowledge through the research of its graduate schools. By the time the university opened on October 1, 1892, President Harper, paying larger than usual salaries, had persuaded several college presidents to leave their schools and join the 120 faculty members who greeted the nearly six hundred students who entered the university. He had also recruited a group of outstanding scientists who formed the Ogden Graduate School of Sciences. The Ogden School would later provide the basic science training for the medical school students.

An affiliation between Rush Medical College and the new University of Chicago had been proposed as early as 1892. Prominent Chicago physicians Dr. E. Fletcher Ingalls and Dr. Frank Billings of the Rush faculty approached President Harper to promote an affiliation that they hoped would further the standing of Rush Medical College. This union was affirmed in 1898. The agreement allowed the university to select and examine students and to "consider" the names of all instructors on the faculty.

Another important part of the agreement was that Rush would raise the requirements for admission to two years of college. By 1901 the university was providing two years of preclinical training on the South Side, and the subsequent two years of clinical training were at Rush. During the preclinical years, students were enrolled in the Ogden Graduate School of Sciences. The Ogden School was established by President Harper in January of 1891 in honor of W. M. Ogden, the first mayor of Chicago. Ogden had been a trustee of the first University of Chicago and had bequeathed his estate to the university. The dean of the graduate school was the physicist H. Gayle, and the faculty included such distinguished scientists as Franklin P. Mall (anatomy), A. J. Carlson (physiology), Ludvig Hektoen (pathology), Howard Taylor Ricketts (pathology), discoverer of rickettsial diseases, and Albert A. Michelson (physics), the first American to win the Nobel Prize in Physics.

Harper viewed the affiliation with Rush as temporary and emphasized that Rush Medical College should not take from the agreement any encouragement that they would become the university's medical school. Harper's intention was to found a hospital and medical school on the university's campus as soon as funds were available. Both Gates and Rockefeller were not enthusiastic about the affiliation with Rush. Gates, though not a physician, had read William Osler's textbook of medicine and was impressed with how little of the scientific method was incorporated into the practice of medicine. Gates had a vision of a medical school committed to the scientific research and teaching that he felt was emblematic of all great university departments. Both Rockefeller and his adviser Gates wanted a medical school with a full-time faculty situated on the campus of the University of Chicago. Rockefeller was a believer in homeopathy and was not about to support another allopathic medical school, the method followed at Rush and at most other American medical schools in that era. In 1905, the year before his death from colon cancer, Harper appointed Dr. Frank Billings, then dean at Rush, as the first professor of medicine at the university.[3]

Abraham Flexner's 1910 report *Medical Education in the United States and Canada* was a seminal event in medical education in the United States. Flexner was not a physician but a medical educator. Born in Louisville, Kentucky, in 1866, he had received his B.A. degree at Johns Hopkins in 1886 and an M.A. at Harvard in 1906. Between 1913 and 1938 he was an officer of the Rockefeller Foundation's General Education Board, formed by Rockefeller in 1902. The General Education Board granted endowments to medical schools in cooperation with the Rockefeller Institute.[4] Flexner's views on medical education and medical research had been shaped by his survey of university-dominated research and medical education in Germany and by interactions with his brother Simon, director of the Rockefeller

Institute for Medical Research in New York. The Flexner Report, sponsored by the Carnegie Foundation, reviewed the status of 155 medical schools in North America and stimulated extensive reform. So striking were the deficiencies of many of the proprietary schools highlighted in the report that they closed outright. The proprietary schools that survived this process did so by virtue of an affiliation with or complete absorption by existing universities. Flexner's model for an ideal medical school included a faculty employed as full-time university professors, committed to both research and teaching and not involved in the private practice of medicine.

In 1916 the third University of Chicago president, Harry Pratt Judson, sought advice from the General Education Board on planning a medical school on the South Side campus, as had been envisioned by President Harper as early as 1897. The board promised to support this plan and recommended that Abraham Flexner be invited to visit to evaluate the conditions of medical education at the University of Chicago and Rush Medical College. Flexner also favored the development of a full four-year medical school on the South Side university campus and a postgraduate school of medical education at Rush. He envisioned a 250-bed hospital on the South Side that would be sufficiently endowed so as to avoid dependency on payments from its patients. The financial requirements for this venture were defined, and by May 1917 pledges were sought for the required $5.3 million estimated as necessary to endow the program. The project was quickly oversubscribed, but World War I brought the plan to a temporary halt.

After the war the board of trustees of the university again took up the plan for a campus medical school and hospital. By 1921 plans were being prepared for a building that would accommodate the hospital and three departments: medicine and surgery would be the new entities; the Department of Pathology was already located on campus in the Ricketts Building as part of the Ogden Graduate School of Sciences. The site of the structure would be north of the Midway at Ellis Avenue and 59th Street. It would occupy two blocks and require the city to approve the closure of Ingleside Avenue. In 1923 Dr. Franklin C. McLean, recently returned from the Peking Union Medical College in China, a school also supported by the Rockefeller Foundation, was appointed by President Ernest DeWitt Burton as professor of medicine and director of the clinic.

By 1925 the architectural plans--which now included Abbott Memorial Hall, a separate building for physiology, chemistry, and pharmacology to be located on 58th Street--and bids for construction were completed. Ground-breaking and dedication of the cornerstone took place in May and October of 1925. The six-story quadrangular structure was completed in October of 1927; its bed capacity would be 215 patients, divided evenly between medicine and surgery. The first two patients entered the hospital on October 3, 1927, and the formal dedication of the hospital and medical school was celebrated on October 31 and November 1. The hospital was named Billings Hospital, in dedication to Albert Merritt Billings, a relative of Dr. Billings who had donated $1 million toward the construction of the medical school, and also as an honor to the vision of Dr. Frank Billings, who had led the campaign to raise $5 million for the project.[5]

The original faculty included the chairman of the Department of Medicine, Dr. Franklin C. McLean, and the chairman of the Department of Surgery, Dr. Dallas Phemister (Dean Smith had initially been chosen to fill this position, but he withdrew to move to Johns Hopkins University School of Medicine). Included among the original nine faculty members in the Department of Medicine was Dr. Walter Lincoln Palmer, who in January 1936 would become Dr. Kirsner's mentor in the world of academic medicine.

The first five years following the dedication in 1927 were a period of remarkable growth at the Medical Center. The Bobs Roberts Memorial Hospital for Children was funded and built just south of Billings Hospital along 59th Street and opened on May 1, 1930, with a capacity of 80 beds. Dr. Frederic W. Schultz was appointed chairman of the newly formed Department of Pediatrics. Chicago Lying-In Hospital, a 140-bed hospital, opened in May of 1930. Dr. McLean and the university president, C. Max Mason, had approached the General Education Board for support in the endowment of a new Department of Obstetrics and Gynecology. Abraham Flexner again supported the proposal. The project was furthered by an independent grant from Julius Rosenwald of the Sears Roebuck Company. Dr. Joseph Bolivar De Lee became the first chairman of Lying-In Hospital. Dr. De

Lee, the son of Polish immigrants, had been born in 1870 in New York City and came with his family to Chicago as a boy. He had worked tirelessly throughout his professional career to provide maternal care to destitute pregnant women of the city of Chicago. Dr. De Lee delivered the first baby to be born at Lying-In on May 25, 1930. As noted earlier, Dr. Kirsner's only knowledge of the University of Chicago School of Medicine while still in Boston was the introduction he and his classmates at Tufts Medical School received through their use of Dr. De Lee's classic textbook on obstetrics and gynecology.

The McElwee-Hicks Building housing a 100-bed orthopedic facility was built as an L-shaped structure on the corner of 59th Street and Ellis Avenue adjacent to Billings Hospital. This new orthopedic facility resulted from the affiliation with Rush Medical College and with the Home for Destitute Children that had been arranged in 1911. The Home for Destitute Children started in 1892 thanks to the efforts of Emma E. Stelle. By the turn of the century, the home, located at 1653 Maypole Street near Paulina Avenue, was caring for 106 children suffering chiefly from orthopedic diseases. Supported by a further grant from the General Education Board, the orthopedic surgical section opened in 1931, and all the patients from the home on Maypole Street were transferred to the new orthopedic wing. Dr. Nathaniel Allison, who had been appointed professor of surgery (orthopedics) in 1929, was the chairmen of the new department.

Thus, by 1932 the Medical Center had expanded to a facility of 535 beds. It was graduating students who had elected to spend their four years entirely on the South Side campus, and its completely full-time faculty program was along the lines of Johns Hopkins University School of Medicine, the first of its kind in the United States.

* * *

In September 1935 Dr. Kirsner made his way to Dr. Dick's office, where he was told that he would be working as an assistant in medicine in the allergy clinic of the general medicine section under Dr. Knute Reuterskiold. His yearly salary would be $1,000. Minnie had given up a promising ballet career and was working for $50 per week as an executive secretary to Al Neiman to help support the family.

Dr. Reuterskiold proved to be uninspiring to his new assistant, who was excited by his new opportunity and eager to become involved in research. Dr. Kirsner would always remember Dr. Reuterskiold's response when questioned about his own research: "Research, we no longer do research, we know all there is to know." After this startling and disturbing remark, Dr. Kirsner knew he was not where he wanted to be, and immediately began to seek another position in the Department of Medicine. Dr. Reuterskiold left the University of Chicago several years later.

The brief period of time he spent in the allergy section was not without its intellectual rewards. His main contact was with the departing medical assistant to Dr. Reuterskiold, Dr. Clarence Bernstein Jr., a graduate of Johns Hopkins who was involved in modest allergy research. The association with Dr. Bernstein was productive, and the first several papers in Dr. Kirsner's bibliography, which begins in 1937, dealt with clinical and investigative aspects of allergy. The publications include a clinical paper on oral pollen therapy, one on a study of anaphylaxis in reaction to colloidal sulfur in guinea pigs, and one on insulin-induced hypoglycemia.[6] Through this early research experience, Dr. Kirsner came to appreciate emerging concepts in the science of immunology, and this would lay the groundwork for what would be his major research interest: the immunology of the gastrointestinal tract.

In addition to the allergy clinic, he saw patients in the general medical clinic. He welcomed the opportunity to teach and learn through his interaction with students. He was not an attending physician, and his role was comparable to that of a senior medical resident today. A patient he saw in the allergy clinic in 1936 with an acute attack of asthma complicated by subcutaneous emphysema of the chest wall (a condition dramatically recognizable by the feeling, likened to the crunching of Rice Krispies, when swollen areas of the skin are palpated). The patient was hospitalized and subsequently made a complete recovery. This rare clinical complication of asthma stimulated a review of the literature, and Dr. Kirsner's first published case report in the *Journal of the American Medical Association* (*JAMA*) in 1937.[7] This paper provides an early example of his thorough and scholarly approach to a problem, as well as a look at the style of case reports published in the medical literature in this era. The paper begins with a comprehensive review of the topic in the medical literature dating back to the turn of the century, including articles published in foreign languages. Noteworthy also is his careful documentation of the clinical history, including the patient's occupation as an caretaker for birds in the Department of Zoology at the University of Chicago; physical examination; and the clinical course. The report includes the results of intradermal skin testing to bird products obtained from the animal laboratories, black-and-white photographs of the patient at the time of admission, and complete follow-up information on his recovery and return to work as an animal caretaker following the use of a protective air-filtering respirator.

* * *

In 1935 the Department of Medicine scheduled medical grand rounds every Wednesday afternoon in Room M-137 of the hospital. For Dr. Kirsner, it was the educational highlight of the week. medical grand rounds attracted a large audience, including not only the faculty of the medical school but such leading Chicago internists as Dr. Richard Capps (Rush), Dr. Joe Miller (Northwestern University), and Dr. Walter Hamburger (Michael Reese Hospital). Dr. Kirsner was impressed by members of the Department of Medicine, notably Dr. Walter Lincoln Palmer. When he learned that Dr. Theodore Heinz, an assistant to Dr. Palmer, was leaving the University of Chicago to enter private practice in Castle Rock, Colorado, he approached Dr. Palmer to ask if he could work with him. Although Dr. Kirsner knew little of gastroenterology as a specialty, and Dr. Palmer had only limited firsthand knowledge of the young assistant in medicine, he decided to give Dr. Kirsner the opportunity. Thus, in January 1936 he joined Dr. Palmer and the Section of Gastroenterology, which included Dr. Marie Ortmayer and the endoscopist Dr. Rudolf Schindler, who had been recruited from Munich, Germany, in 1934.

This association would have a decisive impact in shaping Dr. Kirsner's career in gastroenterology. In June 1936 Dr. Palmer was 40 years old and on his way to a remarkable career with a lifetime of achievement that would establish him as a leader in American medicine and gastroenterology. He was chairman of the American Board of Internal Medicine, the organization charged with the certification of physicians trained in the specialty of internal medicine. He later was elected president of the American Gastroenterological Association and the American College of Physicians. Dr. Palmer was a natural leader and became president of every medical organization he joined.

His background could not have been more dissimilar from that of his new assistant. Dr. Palmer, born in Evanston, Illinois, in 1896, was the son of a country physician, Walter Aaron Palmer, who graduated from Rush Medical College in 1892. In 1903 Dr. Walter Aaron Palmer moved his family from Evanston to Castle Rock, Colorado. His son could remember making house calls with his father in a horse-drawn carriage. Accepting a Distinguished Alumnus Award from his alma mater, Rush Medical School, in 1980, he observed that if his father "had been born a few years earlier, and if my lifetime had been stretched out end to end in tandem, they would have reached from the Fort Dearborn massacre to the present and beyond. From the huts of the Pottawatamie Indians to the magnificent skyscrapers and the beautiful homes and factories which cover the southern shore of Lake Michigan."[8] In 1936 he had already been married for 10 years to Elizabeth Ricketts, the daughter of one of America's great medical investigators, Howard Taylor Ricketts, for whom the organism that was the cause of the rickettsial disease Rocky Mountain spotted fever had been named. Robert Howard Palmer, the first of Walter Lincoln Palmer's three sons—all destined to become physicians—was then five years old. Robert Howard Palmer became a gastroenterologist and member of the Department of Medicine and the Section of Gastroenterology at the University of Chicago. His second son, Donald Walter Palmer, born in November 1936, became a rheumatologist. His third son, Henry Palmer, became an excellent internist in private practice in Chicago, a faculty member of Rush University Medical School and Rush Presbyterian St. Luke's Medical Center. Dr. Henry Palmer remembers that as an adolescent he "babysat" for the Kirsners' son, Robert, in their home.

Dr. Walter Lincoln Palmer began his college education at Colorado College and in 1917 transferred to the University of Chicago. By 1919 he had earned his bachelor's and master's degrees from the University of Chicago. He went on to earn his M.D. degree from Rush Medical College and his Ph.D. in physiology from the University of Chicago in 1926, working with the legendary Anton J. Carlson. As an intern at Presbyterian Hospital on Chicago's Near West Side, he had received his introduction to gastroenterology training under one of the first great American gastroenterologists, the outstanding clinician Bertram Welton Sippy, who had achieved worldwide attention for his treatment of peptic ulcer disease. Palmer had been a member of the Medical Enlisted Reserve Corps of the U.S. Army during World War I, and in 1936 he was an associate professor of medicine and assistant marshall of the University of Chicago. With the opening of the University of Chicago Hospital and Clinics, he had become the first chief of the Section of Gastroenterology, one of the first such academic units in the country.

Dr. Anton J. Carlson, with whom Dr. Palmer had earned his Ph.D. investigating the mechanisms of pain in peptic ulcer disease, was responsible for training an entire generation of scientifically oriented gastroenterologists. Swedish born, Dr. Carlson had started out as a carpenter and a blacksmith, then a minister, becoming ultimately, through a circuitous route, a scientist. He was affectionately and reverentially known for his famous question, "Vat is de evidence?" with which he would terrify speakers at scientific meetings.

Through this training, Palmer became a leader in bringing scientific discipline to the specialty of gastroenterology, a branch of medical practice that had relied too often on individual opinion and uncontrolled empirical observations. But it was Dr. Palmer's clinical skills and humanistic approach to the patient that made a powerful and lasting impression on Dr. Kirsner.

Dr. Kirsner worked closely with Dr. Palmer. Their day would begin at seven thirty in the morning when they made rounds on patients hospitalized on the gastroenterology service. Each patient's progress and care during the preceding 24 hours were thoroughly reviewed, a process lasting until nine thirty or ten. They would then begin their morning outpatient clinic, which occupied a dozen rooms on the second-floor clinic area of the hospital. There was pressure to complete seeing all the patients by noontime, since the chest physicians occupied the same clinic space in the afternoon. Dr. Kirsner and Dr.

Palmer initially did their own patient histories and physical examinations; later they were assisted by gastroenterology fellows. Later, in the 1970s, gastroenterology fellows training with Dr. Kirsner could recall his pointing to charts that were by then thicker than a Chicago telephone book, dating back to the 1930s, and wondering whether one could ever replace the information contained in those records. Inspecting one of these thick charts, Kirsner's fellows could see the characteristic blue fountain-pen writing with which he carefully recorded the patient's "chief complaints" and history as the first entry in the chart. After their clinic was completed, they would perform the proctoscopic examinations that had been scheduled for patients that day.

When Dr. Kirsner began his training in gastroenterology in 1936, gastric intubation and aspiration of gastric contents, rigid open-tube proctoscopic examinations, and early techniques of esophageal dilatation (some developed by Bertram Sippy) for esophageal strictures and achalasia (a disease of the esophagus characterized by muscular spasm at the lower end of the esophagus interfering with swallowing) were the sole procedures available to the gastroenterologist. Diagnostic tests included single-contrast x-ray studies of the stomach and colon. The exciting new addition to their diagnostic armamentarium was the introduction of semirigid gastroscopy by Rudolf Schindler, newly arrived from Munich.

Clinical activities would continue until two thirty or three in the afternoon before they would stop for lunch. The doctors' cafeteria was a wonderful place remembered by Dr. Kirsner for its pleasant collegiality enjoyed by house staff and faculty and for the "gourmet lunches" with homemade pies and ice cream. As a testimony to the quality of the cafeteria food, one of the gastroenterology fellows, who went on to become a professor of medicine at Case Western Reserve Medical School, is etched in Dr. Kirsner's memory for the enormous lunches he consumed, invariably including a large steak. With the country still in the depths of the Depression, it was probably a house officer's best opportunity for a complete meal each day. He would remember that Dr. Palmer loved cottage cheese and ice cream. Over time, as Dr. Palmer and Dr. Kirsner added fellows to the program, they would all share the lunchtime break as a group.

After lunch they would return to their offices. Dr. Palmer had an office on the fourth floor, and Dr. Kirsner remembers his own "office" as being more like "a closet with a single window" next to Dr. Palmer's. Beyond the office was a storeroom that Dr. Kirsner soon converted into a simple laboratory. They would discuss their research and various clinical problems, in addition to dealing with correspondence, including reports to referring physicians, and preparing lectures and papers. Sick patients were seen again in the late afternoon before leaving, and they would generally not arrive home until after six thirty in the evening. If a lecture was to be prepared or a scientific paper written, this was an era when doctors could safely walk back to the hospital at night to select slides, follow up again on a sick patient, or continue work on a paper.

That these were memorable years for both men can best be understood from a letter Dr. Palmer sent Dr. Kirsner on June 19, 1984. The letter, which Dr. Kirsner has kept to this day, congratulates Dr. Kirsner on the Diamond and Gold Celebration Annual GIRF (Gastro-Intestinal Research Foundation) Ball. As a postscript, he adds: "Of course to my mind Minnie shares all this. I recall with pleasure the evenings you and I would work late in my office and the phone would ring with a call from either Minnie or Elizabeth wanting to know where their respective spouses were. They were always very nice and understood! WLP."

As a result of their hard work and dedication to patient care, the demand for the two doctors to see patients steadily increased. Initially, a hospital-bed quota was set for each service, and they were always trying to persuade the hospital administration to allow them more beds. At first, the gastroenterology quota was limited to seven beds, but more beds were made available as their clinical programs expanded. For Dr. Palmer, who had already established a significant reputation in the Chicago area, this problem was particularly acute, and he would admit patients to nearby Woodlawn Hospital as well.

The environment at the hospital was ideal. The faculty was full-time, and no one discussed salaries, understandable since they were so low. Remembering this time, Dr. Kirsner liked to think that patient care and teaching were more important to the faculty than monetary compensation. Some years later, describing their clinical activities in an article published in *JAMA* as a part of a series entitled "Rememberings," Dr. Kirsner recalled that in 1936 "a hospital bed cost $25.00 per day, professional fees were minuscule. Patients remained in the hospital for several weeks, or as long as months and even longer: indeed, as long as it was necessary to solve the problem."[9] Doctors saw new patients daily in the outpatient clinic at a charge of $4 per initial visit. Return visits were $2, or often no fee was charged. Laboratory studies were free, and lengthy patient consultations too were without charge.

There was a negative side to this liberal practice. The hospital and clinics had been established to operate on the income generated from their endowments, but those had disappeared during the Great Depression. During their first five years of operation, the hospital and clinics' annual expenditures ranged from $600,000 to $800,000 and exceeded the total annual income, including that derived from the endowments, by an average of $250,000. By 1932 hospital patient days were up to 64,000 at a cost of $8.26 per day, and outpatient visits were 126,000 at a cost of $1.85 per visit. These losses, translated into dollars at the time of the hospital's 50th anniversary in 1977, were the equivalent of $20 million. The number of outpatient visits and hospital days indicates that though the number of hospital faculty members was small, their patient load was remarkably high.[10]

A traditional activity of the Department of Medicine was the chief resident teaching rounds that stressed bedside medicine as part of an exercise emphasizing clinical pathophysiology. The hospital's senior resident in medicine was an outstanding individual, Dr. Louis K. Alpert, who had come to Chicago originally from Yale. Dr. Kirsner regularly joined the house staff and students for these rounds on Saturday afternoon, and his popularity with both groups increased. He became a well-recognized member of the junior faculty and found an excellent outlet for his zeal to teach and motivate students. His success is reflected in the numerous occasions he was chosen by the graduating medical school class to have his photograph included in the class photograph. These large framed documents are made up of individual photographs, with honored members of the faculty on the upper half of the picture, and the graduates on the lower half. These pictures of graduating medical school classes still decorate the corridors of Billings Hospital, and Dr. Kirsner's photograph appears often over the years.

In 1935 Billings still did not have a designated emergency room. Outpatients who needed to be seen at hours when the clinics were closed might be seen in an empty room on the fourth floor that had been set aside for this purpose. Dr. Kirsner recalls one evening early in his career when he examined a young man suffering from abdominal pain who had been referred to the gastroenterology department as an emergency. He made a tentative diagnosis of appendicitis and had the temerity to call the chief of the Department of Surgery, Dr. Dallas B. Phemister, directly at home. Dr. Phemister walked over to the hospital that evening and saw the patient with Dr. Kirsner and, agreeing with the diagnosis, took the patient into surgery that evening. The incident forged a bond of friendship and respect that continued through the remainder of Dr. Phemister's career at Billings.

Dr. Kirsner remembered that Dr. Dick told him on the first day he reported for work in 1935, "We expect you to take care of patients and to teach medical students, but unless you do creditable and excellent research, do not expect to remain here." With this expectation, the Department of Medicine gave him a budget of $100 a year for his research. Dr. Dick's words would echo in his mind for many years to come. The limited support necessitated that he seek funds for research in the form of contributions from patients and friends. Discovering an unused storeroom at the end of the hall on the fourth floor, he removed the old furniture it contained and set up his basic laboratory. The purchase of equipment was aided by a $500 grant from Dr. Alfred Barol, chief pharmaceutical consultant of the Wyeth Company of Philadelphia.

During these early years, he was caring for a homeless patient in the clinic named Edwin Rice, who had come to Chicago from Tennessee and was suffering from a severe recurrent duodenal ulcer. The hospital allowed Dr. Kirsner one free bed a year for research. The patient was hospitalized, and Dr. Kirsner was able to study in detail the biochemical effects of the then commonly used "Sippy Powders" on acid-base balance and renal function. He remembered that when, as a medical student, he worked at North Grafton State Hospital, some of the hospitalized patients had been trained to perform simple laboratory tests such as a urinalysis; so he began to train Mr. Rice to perform such simple tests. As his research progressed and his funds increased, he acquired another unused room just opposite his laboratory, and he hired a young woman as a technician to work in this second laboratory. After six months, his patient Mr. Rice had fallen in love with her, and they made plans to be married. Mr. Rice had been in hospital clothes for an entire year and had no clothing of his own. Dr. Kirsner gave him one of his two suits to wear at the wedding. Shortly thereafter, the couple disappeared, and Dr. Kirsner never heard from them again. However, the biochemical studies were of high quality and were published in the *Journal of Clinical Investigation*, the *Journal of Biochemistry*, and the *Journal of Digestive Sciences*.[11]

Toward the end of his first year at the university, the chairman of the Department of Medicine, Dr. Dick, called him into his office to compliment him on his performance. This came as something of a relief, since earlier in the year Dr. Dick had spoken to him about an opportunity in private medical practice that had become available in Tulsa, Oklahoma, and suggested that he might wish to give this consideration. Dr. Kirsner had replied, "Dr. Dick, I don't want to go to Tulsa, Oklahoma, I want to stay here." Relating the conversation to Minnie that evening, he worried that this might be a signal that he might not be remaining there much longer. Fortunately, these anxieties proved to be unwarranted.

Dr. George Dick was an imposing person; he was over six feet six inches tall and bald, and as Dr. Kirsner's wife noted, "He never smiled." He had come to the University of Chicago from Presbyterian Hospital. Born in Fort Wayne, Indiana, in 1881, he had graduated from Rush Medical College in 1905. He and Howard Taylor Ricketts were among some of the outstanding basic science faculty that the famous Chicago pathologist Ludvig Hektoen, an early director of the McCormick Institute for Infectious Diseases, had assembled.[12] At the McCormick Institute Dr. Dick and his wife, Gladys, had found the cause of scarlet fever, devised a susceptibility test, and developed an antitoxin to treat it. He had been appointed a clinical professor at Rush Medical College and in 1933 became chairman of the Department of Medicine at the University of Chicago, where he served until 1945. He aroused considerable controversy when, in 1927, he and Gladys patented their method for the "Dick test" in the United States and applied for a patent in England. However, they derived no personal remuneration, since an independent charitable body had acquired the patent.

Dr. Kirsner hoped that his summons to Dr. Dick's office at the end of his first year might result in a raise in his yearly salary of $1,000. After complimenting him on the outstanding work he had been doing, Dr. Dick handed him a new gray Parker fountain pen. Recounting the meeting and the gift to his colleagues, Dr. Kirsner quickly learned that Dr. Dick was the physician for several members of the Parker family in Janesville, Wisconsin, and had a large box full of Parker pens in his desk that he distributed throughout the department. In his talk to the assembled guests at the 95th birthday celebration held in his honor at the University of Chicago, Dr. Kirsner referred to this incident and then displayed the vintage 1937 Parker pen for the audience to see. He said, "It no longer works, but I would not give it away for anything less than a million dollars." There were no "takers," and Dr. Kirsner continues to keep the "special" pen in his desk at home.

During his early years at the University of Chicago, Dr. Kirsner appreciated that his clinical skills were under the severe scrutiny of his colleagues, and he realized that he needed to prove himself as a clinician as well as an investigator. He knew that when he was asked to consult on a patient he would be recognized for making a correct diagnosis and recommending appropriate therapy. Fortunately, he succeeded on several occasions and was gradually accepted as a valid member of the Department of Medicine recognized for his clinical skills.

Gastroenterologists in the 21st century enjoy a precision in diagnosis unheard of during the 1930s when Dr. Kirsner began his career. Endoscopic examination of the stomach was in its infancy, and endoscopic examination of the colon, as well as endoscopic visualization of the pancreatic and biliary ducts, remained far in the future. Computerized axial tomography (CAT) scan and magnetic resonance imaging (MRI), radiologic procedures that today are taken for granted, were undreamed of at that time. Clinicians had to rely on their knowledge of the clinical course of disease and careful bedside skills in obtaining meaningful histories from their patients and performing careful physical examinations to arrive at a diagnosis. It was a time when physicians not uncommonly had to depend upon surgical exploration of the abdomen to determine a patient's correct diagnosis.

In 1936 a patient suspected of having pancreatic cancer was admitted to the neurosurgical services at Billings Hospital for a cordotomy, a surgical procedure that involved transecting pain fibers in the spinal column to relieve intractable abdominal pain. At the referring hospital, the patient had undergone a surgical exploration and was found to have a mass in the region of the pancreas thought to be a cancer. Dr. Kirsner was asked to see the patient and during his examination observed that he was vomiting copious amounts of clear watery fluid. With this clue, he tested the fluid for acidity with Topfer's reagent (a test solution that turns red when added to gastric secretions containing hydrochloric acid) and found the concentration of acid in the patient's gastric secretions to be extremely high. This fact, along with his careful history and examination of the patient, led him to consider the possibility that a large ulcer in the duodenum had perforated into the pancreas, creating an inflammatory mass. He advised the neurosurgeons to cancel the cordotomy, and he treated the patient with antacids and antisecretory medications. Subsequently, the patient underwent a vagotomy and gastroduodenostomy (surgical bypass of the ulcer), which allowed the ulcer to heal and the patient to recover. Dr. Kirsner felt that his success in managing this case was noticed by his colleagues and contributed to establishing his reputation as a clinician. Years later the patient suffered an attack of acute appendicitis and again underwent abdominal surgery to remove the ruptured appendix. On this occasion, diagnosis of the earlier perforated ulcer was confirmed, as well as the absence of pancreatic cancer. He lived another 20 years before dying of a massive heart attack.

By the end of 1936, Dr. Kirsner had found the direction he had been seeking in his medical career. In the next seven years he would fully develop his skills as an academic gastroenterologist, investigator, and teacher.

Notes

1. For an account of the 19th-century history of Rush Medical College, see Jim Bowman, *Good Medicine: The First 150 Years of Rush–Presbyterian–St. Luke's Medical Center* (Chicago: Chicago Review Press, 1987).

2. The "first" or "old" University of Chicago was located at 35th and Cottage Grove near Lake Michigan on a site donated by Senator Stephen A. Douglas. It underwent bankruptcy in 1886.

3. For an excellent account of the early history of Rush Medical College and the history of its affiliation with the University of Chicago, see Malachi J. Flanagan, *To the Glory of God and the Service of Man: The Life of James A. Campbell, M.D.* (Winnetka, IL: FHC Press, 2005).

4. See Abraham Flexner, *I Remember: The Autobiography of Abraham Flexner* (New York: Simon and Schuster, 1940).

5. For an excellent account of the establishment of the Medical Center on the campus of the University of Chicago, see C. W. Vermeulen, *For the Greatest Good to the Largest Number: A History of the Medical Center of the University of Chicago, 1927-1977* (Chicago: University of Chicago, 1977); a copy is in the John Crerar Library, University of Chicago.

6. Bernstein, Jr. C and Kirsner JB, Oral pollen therapy, *Allergy* 8:3:3-8, March 1937; Kirsner JB, Anaphylactoid reactions to colloidal sulfur in guinea pigs, *Lab Clin Med* 22:10:1026, July 1937; and Kirsner JB and Bernstein, Jr. C, The relationship of insulin hypoglycemia to the method of administration and the type of insulin, *Lab Clin Med* 23:9:944-49, June 1938.

7. Kirsner JB, Subcutaneous emphysema in bronchial asthma: Report of a case, *JAMA* 108:2020-22, June 12, 1937.

8. From a transcript of Dr. Walter Lincoln Palmer's remarks at the 1980 Rush Medical College Commencement Banquet, in the author's possession and in the archives of Rush University.

9. Kirsner JB, Gastroenterology comes of age (in retrospect), *JAMA* 260:2: 244-46, July 8, 1988.

10. Vermeulen, *For the Greatest Good*, "Financial Crisis," 40.

11. Kirsner JB, Nutter PB, and Palmer WL, Studies on anacidity: The hydrogen-ion concentration of the gastric secretion, the gastroscopic appearance of the gastric mucosa and the presence of a gastric secretory depressant in patients with anacidity, *J Clin Invest* 14:619-25, July 1940; Kirsner JB and Palmer WL, The effect of various antacids on the hydrogen-ion concentration of the gastric contents, *Am J Dig Dis* 7:3:85-93, January 1940.

12. Thomas Neville Bonner, *Medicine in Chicago: 1850-1950* (Madison, WI: American History Research Center, 1957), 104.

4 * The Making of a Gastroenterologist, 1936–1942

Through his association with Dr. Palmer, Dr. Kirsner was introduced to the specialty of gastroenterology and quickly determined that diseases of the gastrointestinal tract would be the area of medicine to which he would devote his life's work. It is of interest to understand how the specialty of gastroenterology appeared to Dr. Kirsner in 1936, and how knowledge of the gastrointestinal tract and its diseases had evolved. It is also interesting to review the apprenticeship of academic physicians and specialists in the field in the years 1936-42, when Dr. Kirsner was establishing his credentials as a gastroenterologist. He was one of the first candidates to be examined by the newly developed subspecialty board of gastroenterology.

The Early History of Gastroenterology

The history of mankind's attempts to understand the gastrointestinal tract and its diseases dates back to the beginning of the recorded history of medicine. The appearance in the United States of physicians, mostly trained in Germany, devoted to the treatment of gastrointestinal illness and the growth of the specialty of gastroenterology are more recent. In January 1936, when Dr. Kirsner began his training with Dr. Palmer, the specialty of gastroenterology was underdeveloped. Much of the information about disease of the gastrointestinal tract rested on the strength of individually held, clinically derived opinions. Understanding of the underlying pathophysiology of disease was limited; research was minimal and therapy was empirical. In spite of these limitations, a significant tradition was already evolving. Progress in the understanding of digestive diseases paralleled advances in science through the 18th and 19th centuries into the early decades of the 20th century. The application of advanced technology to medicine would demand physician-scientists who would concentrate their efforts in circumscribed aspects of a rapidly evolving specialty.

During the 19th century, knowledge of the digestive system and its diseases accumulated from diverse observations in different countries. Building on the work of early anatomists and pathological findings at autopsy, physicians were gradually addressing issues of function and physiology. Fascinated by this early history, Dr. Kirsner would later write a series of articles and books on the historical evolution of the modern scientific foundation of gastroenterology.[1]

Among the more publicized of the early discoveries were the meticulous observations on gastric function made by U.S. army surgeon Dr. William Beaumont, observations made possible by the gastro-cutaneous fistula that his famous patient, the French-Canadian trapper Alexis St. Martin, developed after being accidentally struck in the upper abdomen by a shotgun on June 6, 1822.[2] Beaumont was able to document the effect of emotions on the appearance of the gastric mucosa and the role of gastric secretion in digestion. He used chemical methods to analyze the gastric contents and recognized the importance of the gastric mucosa in the production of hydrochloric acid.

Progress in the understanding of gastric function was furthered by the development of flexible tubes that could be passed orally into the stomach to sample gastric contents, a method introduced by Carl Ewald. The evolving sciences of bacteriology, microscopy, and histology all furthered the study of gastrointestinal diseases. The discovery of anesthesiology and the application of antiseptic surgical techniques in the second half of the 19th century allowed surgeons access to the abdominal organs and led to the surgical treatment of disease. The discovery of x-rays by Wilhelm Conrad Roentgen in 1895 revolutionized medicine and gastroenterology by allowing imaging of the skeletal system and internal structures.[3] The use of x-rays by the innovative physiologist Walter Cannon to visualize the digestive system quickly followed.[4] By the turn of the century, the use of electricity for illumination and progress in the development of lens systems were beginning to allow investigators, primarily in Germany, to develop instruments capable of examining the esophagus and upper portions of the stomach. By 1930 these efforts had resulted in the construction of the semiflexible gastroscope and its clinical application by Rudolf Schindler.[5]

On June 3, 1897, during the annual meeting of the American Medical Association (AMA) in Philadelphia, a group of eight physicians interested in the gastrointestinal tract met in the office of Dr. David D. Stewart to form the American Gastroenterological Association (AGA) to promote the study of the digestive tract and its diseases.[6] By 1897 specialty associations already existed in ophthalmology (1864), otology (1868), neurology (1875), dermatology (1876), laryngology (1879), surgery (1880), internal medicine (1886), urology (1886), orthopedics (1887), and pediatrics (1888). Dr. Charles D. Aaron, of Detroit, is credited with assembling this first meeting in Philadelphia and is considered to be the founder of the AGA, as noted in the official history of the association, written by the medical historian Dale C. Smith for its 100th anniversary.[7] Dr. Aaron was also recognized as the founder of the organization by Dr. John C. Hemmeter, a founding member of the association and chairman of the panel on the history of the association, in his introductory remarks on the occasion of the thirtieth anniversary. Dr. Hemmeter read a brief letter from Dr. Aaron (now lost) retelling what had motivated him to found the association.[8]

Dr. Aaron was born in Lockport, New York, in 1866 and was an 1891 graduate of the University of Buffalo. He supplemented his medical education in New York City in the 1890s and was greatly influenced by lectures on the digestive system presented by Max Einhorn of New York. He also visited clinics in Berlin given by Carl Ewald and by Ismar Boas. He invited Max Einhorn to attend this initial meeting of the AGA, and Einhorn was elected one of the 14 founding members of the association, as was Julius Friedenwald, the outstanding clinician and Johns Hopkins University professor of gastroenterology.

The status of the AGA during its first decade was sufficiently unstable that its survival was in doubt. By 1907 the organization could boast only 50 active members, plus 2 honorary and 2 corresponding members. Twenty-five percent of the members enrolled during the first seven years, including two former presidents, had resigned.

However, by 1904 Samuel J. Meltzer had become an important source of stability and strength for the organization. Meltzer, born in Courland, Russia, in 1851, played a major role in helping to establish gastroenterology as a scientific discipline in the United States. Before immigrating to New York in 1883, he had studied the mechanisms of swallowing with Hugo von Kronecker, a student of Karl Ludwig's. Samuel Meltzer was the prototype of a clinical scientist and gastroenterologist. He was a figure of enormous stature in American medicine and the founder of the most prestigious organizations dedicated to medical research in the country, including the American Association of Physicians, the American Society for Clinical Investigation, and the Society for Experimental Biology and Medicine. In 1904 he joined the Rockefeller Institute as head of the Department of Physiology and Pharmacology. Dr. Kirsner has noted that "in 1884 while in general practice in New York, Meltzer was the physician who delivered the infant Burrill B. Crohn [discoverer of Crohn's disease] (perhaps destining him for gastroenterology at birth!)."[9]

Aaron had hoped that the association he was encouraging would become a section of the AMA. At that time, however, the AMA was focused on including more physicians in the organization and was not interested in developing specialty branches, so Aaron had to develop a separate organization. (Later, the AMA established a section of gastroenterology and proctology.) Aaron, with A. L. Benedict and with assistance from Dr. Charles G. Stockton, both from Buffalo, proceeded to finalize the structure of the American Gastro-enterologic Association (as it was first titled). Stockton was elected the first president of the AGA and presided over the first meeting of the association in Washington, D.C., on May 2, 1898. The concept of physicians devoting themselves exclusively to digestive disorders was considered premature by many at the time. In 1900 Frederick C. Shattuck, professor of medicine at Harvard, expressed skepticism that "enough special knowledge and technical skill was involved in the diagnosis and treatment of digestive disorders to warrant the separation into a true specialty."[10]

The first three decades of the 20th century were an uneasy period for medical specialties. The medical profession in general and the AGA in particular struggled with issues related to the definition and legitimacy of specialists. The educational qualifications and certification and licensing process for physicians were still in a state of flux, and it is not surprising that the AMA was not in a position to deal with similar problems as they related to a subspecialty of internal medicine. William Osler had defined internal medicine as "the wide field that remains after the separation of surgery, midwifery, and gynecology."[11] The AGA encompassed a varied membership: academicians who were primarily physiologists and dedicated to the research activities of the time, clinicians who might be regarded as internists with a particular interest in digestive disorders, surgeons who also had a particular interest in gastrointestinal surgery, and the then-rare physician who was able to limit his practice to patients with gastrointestinal diseases. The last group presented a particular problem. Were they internists? As serious students of digestive disorders, how could they distinguish themselves from self-styled "stomach specialists" of the day who threatened to downgrade the field? They had yet to define their skills and qualifications at a level that would reassure general practitioners and internists that their patients would indeed benefit from being referred to a gastroenterologist.

For gastroenterology, and internal medicine in general, the early tensions related to the certification of specialists gradually resolved over time. Specialty boards such as the Board of Ophthalmic Examiners and the Otolaryngology Board had formed earlier, in 1916 and 1924, respectively; but these were in more readily identifiable fields, since they were circumscribed anatomically and characterized by unique technologies. In 1934 the AMA, in conjunction with the Advisory Board for Medical Specialties, defined the essential requirements for specialists. The twelve fields they approved for specialty certification did not at first include gastroenterology, which according to the Advisory Board belonged within the field of internal medicine. In response, the members of the AGA acted through the AMA to establish committees to consider the formation of an examining board of gastroenterology. Progress in establishing board examinations in internal medicine proceeded slowly, and it was not until 1937 that the American Board of Internal Medicine was ready to examine candidates. Although the American Board of Gastroenterology had been incorporated, it never examined any candidates. In 1937 its members became a subspecialty committee of the American Board of Internal Medicine. The founders included 89 gastroenterologists who were certified without examination. In 1940 another 21 gastroenterologists who had petitioned for admission were also certified without examination. The American Board of Internal Medicine issued its first certificates in the specialty of gastroenterology in 1940, but a standard for postgraduate training in the specialty of gastroenterology had not been established.

Today these training programs are referred to as fellowships or fellowship programs in the various subspecialty disciplines of internal medicine such as cardiology, hematology, and pulmonary diseases. Candidates must first obtain sufficient training in internal medicine to qualify for board certification as internists before they can be accepted into an approved fellowship program of generally two to three years' duration. The fellowship program must be satisfactorily completed before candidates are qualified to take the subspecialty board examination.

Initially, the exact structure of approved training programs was less well defined with respect to clinical experience in the care of patients and the performance of diagnostic and therapeutic procedures. In 1940, after passing a written examination in the field of internal medicine, candidates were first examined in internal medicine by a member of the American Board of Internal Medicine and then by a member of the subspecialty committee in gastroenterology. Candidates were required to examine an unknown patient, interpret clinical data on that patient, and then answer the examiners' questions on the underlying physiology, the diagnosis, and the appropriate therapy. In gastroenterology they were further required to interpret selected radiographs, endoscopic data, and findings from pathologic specimens.

The first joint examination was held in 1941, and four of the eight candidates passed. One of the four who passed was Joseph B. Kirsner. Oral examinations were contingent on passing the written examination in internal medicine, which consisted of an entire day of written essay questions. Dr. Kirsner took his oral examination at Cook County Hospital. The first patient in internal medicine was a man with congestive heart failure. The two examiners were Reginald Fitz

Jr., of Boston, and Walter Lincoln Palmer. Dr. Palmer excused himself from examining Dr. Kirsner on the patient with a gastrointestinal disorder but did examine him in internal medicine. Dr. Kirsner succeeded in accurately identifying a heart murmur caused by a stenosis (narrowing) of the mitral valve in the first patient he examined. In the second patient he identified a hiatal hernia associated with gastroesophageal reflux, a diagnosis that had not been considered previously. Dr. Palmer graciously called Dr. Kirsner's wife and suggested that she "take Joe out for a nice dinner, since he has done splendidly and passed with flying colors."

Rudolf Schindler and the Origins of the American Gastrointestinal Endoscopy Association

Dr. Rudolf Schindler, who had arrived in the United States in 1934 with his family as a refugee from Nazi Germany, was the second individual at the University of Chicago to play a major role in Dr. Kirsner's development as a specialist in gastroenterology. Through their interaction, Dr. Kirsner learned the technique of gastroscopy and the application of this relatively new procedure in the investigation of gastrointestinal disease. Their relationship would lead to Dr. Kirsner's selection as one of the founding members of the national organization known today as the American Society for Gastrointestinal Endoscopy, but originally known as the American Gastroscopic Club. For these reasons, the life of Rudolf Schindler and the role he played in the early years of the Section of Gastroenterology at the University of Chicago require a brief review.

As a member of the small Section of Gastroenterology, Dr. Schindler regularly attracted many national and international visitors to observe the technique of gastroscopy as practiced in his clinic. In his office he mounted a large framed map of the world and routinely placed pins to designate the city and country of origin of his visitors. Rudolf Schindler, rightfully credited as being the father of modern endoscopy, was born in Berlin in 1888 to parents of a mixed religious background: his father was a Jewish banker, and his artistically gifted mother, Martha Simon, was Lutheran. He received a liberal education and was indeed a polymath. He learned to play the piano at an early age and especially liked classical music, with a marked fondness for Mozart. He was a philatelist, a collector of shells, and mastered seven foreign languages. After attending the Kaiser Wilhelm Gymnasium he obtained his medical degree from the University of Berlin at the age of 22. During World War I he served as a battalion surgeon of the 12th Bavarian Infantry Regiment and a pathologist of the 6th Army. He contracted dysentery himself and also saw many soldiers with abdominal complaints. As a consequence of his military service, he became convinced of the importance of gastritis in the health of military personnel and persuaded the German military command to recognize this as a legitimate cause of disability.

Schindler initially used the rigid Elsner gastroscope to examine patients.[12] On a sunny day in 1924, Dr. Marie Ortmayer, a colleague of Dr. Palmer's and a student of Dr. Bertram Sippy's, was passing a bookstore in Vienna on her way to the Allgemeines Krankenhaus (General Hospital) and saw in the window the German edition of Schindler's *Lehrbuch und Atlas der Gastroskopie.* Excited by the beautiful publication with its color illustrations, Dr. Ortmayer journeyed with fellow Chicagoan Dr. Grant Laing, on the staff of St. Luke's Hospital on S. Michigan Avenue, to Munich to meet and observe Dr. Schindler. She was very impressed with his skill and with that of his wife, Gabriele, who assisted by reassuring the patient and positioning the patient's head in exactly the correct manner to facilitate the passage of the instrument. Dr. Ortmayer reported her observations to Dr. Palmer and urged him to observe Schindler's gastroscopies when he visited Europe in 1926.[13]

By 1928, through his collaboration with Georg Wolf, a well-known instrument maker in Berlin, Schindler had devised his semirigid gastroscope, which achieved partial flexibility in the distal third of the instrument through a series of prisms and lenses placed at short focal distances so as to transmit a coherent image even when the instrument was deflected. Their collaboration had begun when Schindler sent Wolf a sketch of the proposed instrument which he had drawn on a tablecloth during dinner. Several months later, he received the first version of the instrument in the mail.

In 1932 Schindler was taken into protective custody by the Nazis and accused of being an enemy of the state. The Schindler family believed that a maid who had been dismissed for stealing silverware had gone to the Nazis and stated that Schindler was a subversive. For six months, his wife threatened the authorities with an international scandal. Schindler appealed to Marie Ortmayer to help arrange an appointment in gastroenterology at the University of Chicago. Support came from Dr. Palmer, Dr. George Baehr, of New York City and chairman of the Physicians Refugee Fund, and other Chicago physicians, along with financial support from Mrs. Charles Morse.[14] In the summer of 1934, Dr. Schindler and his family were able to immigrate to the United States, where he received an appointment as an assistant professor of medicine in the Section of Gastroenterology.

Schindler established a gastroscopy clinic, which met three days a week and examined an average of six patients during each session. He also instituted a series of seminars to further review and discuss his gastroscopic findings. Dr. Kirsner began attending the gastroscopy clinic, assisting Dr. Schindler and learning the technique of gastroscopy. For Dr. Kirsner's generation of gastroenterologists, the ability to observe the lining of the stomach and its anatomical features and to watch its peristaltic activity was a thrilling revelation which might be likened to being one of the first people to hear a recording of their own voice on the cylinders developed by Thomas Edison. Countless gastroenterologists would credit similar experiences as motivating them to enter the field of gastroenterology.

During these clinic sessions, Dr. Kirsner developed an appreciation of the important role and responsibilities of the endoscopist's assistant from Gabriele Schindler.[15] The interaction of the endoscopist and assistant was so important to the ease and success of the procedure that Schindler was never totally comfortable with anyone other than his wife assisting him. Gastroscopic examinations in 1936 were far from the almost routine procedure we know today. Schindler approached each procedure as an act of clinical investigation requiring considerable thought and analysis devoted to the performance and the assessment of the results. There was no possibility of endoscopic photography or endoscopic guided biopsy as yet, so the findings had to be documented with careful line drawings and subsequent representation by an artist, Gladys McHugh, who worked with Schindler. The procedures were not without significant hazard to the patient.

As an example, the introduction of a new intubation tip on the instrument led to several perforations, and procedures had to be temporarily suspended until the problem could be resolved. During this period it was customary when the gastroscopic clinic was in session to keep one of the nearby hospital elevators on hold so that patients could be rapidly transported to the operating room if a complication occurred. In one unusual incident that Dr. Kirsner observed, the instrument became impacted in the patient's esophagus and could not be removed. As the patient was being transported to the operating room, the jolt of the cart being pushed into the elevator dislodged the instrument, eliminating the need for a surgical procedure. Dr. Kirsner became adept at performing gastroscopy, and as time progressed, if Dr. Schindler was not available on a given day, Gabriele would call Dr. Kirsner to ask that he take over in performing the procedures scheduled for that day.

Socially, the Kirsners and Schindlers became good friends and often met to play bridge. Though neither couple were expert at the game, Schindler was enormously interested in winning, and special arrangements had to be made for him to have the right partner to secure victory and keep him happy. On one of these occasions, Minnie Kirsner "had the temerity to ask if Schindler had ever himself been gastroscoped. His response was that he had not encountered anyone 'good enough' for this responsibility."[16]

In 1941 Leon Schiff of the University of Cincinnati suggested to several individuals in the United States who were interested in gastroscopy that a gastroscopic society be formed at a meeting tentatively scheduled in June 1941 at the Cleveland Clinic. Schindler withheld his support from this effort because he felt that it might lead to gastroscopy becoming a separate specialty and thereby limit its availability. Over the next several months, Schindler communicated with members of major organizations, including the AMA, the American Surgical Association, and the Otolaryngology Society, to develop the rationale for the formation of a gastroscopic organization, defining the scope of its activities and the appropriate training and criteria for certifying gastroscopists. These inquiries received unreserved support. In drafting his rationale and objectives in forming a gastroscopy society, Schindler invited Dr. Edward Benedict, who next to Schindler was "probably the most enthusiastic supporter of gastroscopy in the United States, to criticize, correct and approve the letter."[17] In a manner that resembled a military campaign, Schindler utilized his wall map of visitors to secure broad geographic representation and invited the 16 physicians who would attend the first meeting. The attendees were Crawford Barnett (Atlanta), Edward B. Benedict (Boston), James Borland Sr. (Jacksonville), James B. Carey (Minneapolis), Allan L. Cohn (San Francisco), John H. Fitzgibbon (Portland, OR), Charles A. Flood (New York City), John T. Howard (Baltimore), Roger Keane (Portland, OR), Bruce Kenamore (St. Louis), Herman J. Moersch (Rochester, MN), John F. Renshaw (Cleveland), Leon Schiff (Cincinnati), and Roy Sexton (Washington, DC). In addition to Dr. Schindler, the University of Chicago was represented by Dr. Kirsner and Dr. Ortmayer.

The first meeting took place on November 9, 1941, in Schindler's home on Blackstone Avenue near the university. Schindler had informed the group that after the meeting, they would "retire to the Windermere Hotel where a excellent dinner could be had for $1.00–1.50."[18] He was emphatic that rigorous standards of training, experience, and expertise be established for membership in the organization. After considerable debate over the proper title for the organization, the group agreed upon the American Gastroscopic Club. The word "club" was selected because it seemed less pretentious than such terms as "society," "organization," or "association." Schindler, however, felt that the term "club" lacked dignity and was sensitive to some of the associations that the word carried in his native Germany. The bylaws of the American Gastroscopic Club, as initially conceived by Schindler, included a recommendation that the organization be disbanded after a 20-year period, an action that in the end was not taken, since the club was rapidly transformed into the powerful organization it is today, the American Society for Gastrointestinal Endoscopy, a leading resource in the gastroenterology world.

At that first meeting, Dr. Schindler was elected the first president and Dr. Kirsner the secretary-treasurer. After their meal at the Windermere Hotel, the group returned to Schindler's home, where he entertained them with his piano-playing skills and selections from Gilbert and Sullivan operettas.

Walter Lincoln Palmer was most helpful in the early years of Dr. Schindler's career in Chicago, especially in helping him further develop, translate, and publish an American edition of his *Lehrbuch und Atlas der Gastroskopie* in 1937. Palmer never performed gastroscopy himself, but he remained a strong supporter of the procedure. Schindler rose to the rank of associate professor, but later was refused tenure. He and Dr. Palmer disagreed on the clinical importance of gastritis, and there were also personal tensions arising from Schindler's dogmatic and autocratic manner. In 1942, Palmer, as chairman of the AMA Section of Gastroenterology and Proctology, presented and published an article in *JAMA*, "The Stomach in Military Service," which was critical of Schindler's ideas on the topic. Perceiving this paper as a lack of support, Schindler moved to Los Angeles and the College of Medical Evangelists, which later became Loma Linda University.

He spent the next fifteen years teaching and providing support to instrument companies, as well as serving as a consultant to the Veterans Administration. In 1958, at age 70, in order to remain active in teaching, Dr. Schindler learned Portuguese and assumed a professorship at the University of Minas Gerais in Belo Horizonte, Brazil. He returned to the United States after two years because of his wife's ill health. Gabriele died in 1964. Dr. Schindler subsequently married a longtime friend from Munich, Marie Koch. He returned to that city, where he died in 1968.[19]

Dr. Kirsner's bibliography includes only one article coauthored with Rudolf Schindler. In 1940 they published in the *American Journal of Digestive Diseases* a preliminary article on gastroscopic findings in atrophic gastritis and on the effects of liver extract and iron therapy.[20] The paper reflects Schindler's long interest in gastritis, which occupies a major chapter in his textbook on gastroscopy. Schindler points out that his visual observations of gastritis in 1923 were the first to be made on a living patient since those of William Beaumont in 1838. The Schindler-Kirsner publication describes nine patients with atrophic gastritis based on the observations made during gastroscopy. (Biopsies of the gastric mucosa at this time were not feasible.) The first patient received no treatment, and the lack of improvement on repeat gastroscopy served as a control for the group. The remaining eight patients are described in considerable detail. There is no discussion of the relationship of the gastroscopic findings to the patient's symptoms. The paper is interesting for the detailed clinical history of each patient and the detailed descriptions of the gastroscopic examinations. Four of the eight patients showed visual improvement that was described as "spectacular." The response was felt to have resulted from "Lederle's liver extract," given as a series of weekly intramuscular injections, and in one of the cases from oral therapy with ferrous sulfate. In the patients who responded to this therapy, discontinuation of treatment led to a deterioration in the gastroscopic findings and a return of gastritis on repeat gastroscopy. The authors' conclusions are cautious and emphasize the need for control observations and eventual histologic (microscopic) studies of the gastric mucosa to confirm the validity of the observed improvement.

Pursuing a Doctoral Degree

In discussions with Dr. Palmer, Dr. Kirsner recognized that his academic career and his capabilities as an investigator would be furthered by pursuing a Ph.D. in the Division of Biological Sciences at the university. His experience at Tufts University Medical School had not included an exposure to medical research, and pursuing a doctorate degree would allow him to acquire the laboratory and basic science skills necessary to accomplish meaningful research. There were problems to be solved, including qualifying for the program and financing the three to four years of study that would be necessary. Dr. Kirsner certainly did not have the means or the salary to pay the tuition. Dr. Palmer persuaded the university to arrange a program of "tuition remission." This of course did not excuse him from the qualifying examination, including passing a test on his proficiency in French and German.

The subject Dr. Kirsner chose to study for his Ph.D., alkalosis, was a significant complication of the Sippy "acid-suppressing" treatment of peptic ulcer disease during the 1920s and 1930s. The "Sippy Powders" were combinations of sodium bicarbonate, magnesium oxide, and calcium carbonate. Since sodium bicarbonate is readily absorbed from the gastrointestinal tract, and since ulcer patients ingested large amounts of these powders during their treatment, they frequently developed the milk-alkali syndrome, characterized by a major elevation in blood pH (alkalosis) and evidence of renal insufficiency. The title of Dr. Kirsner's Ph.D. thesis, completed in 1942, was "A Study of Alkalosis with Special Reference to the Electrolyte Composition of the Blood Serum and the Role of the Kidney." It is apparent from the title that this topic required a thorough understanding of the body's fluid and electrolyte balance as well as renal physiology. His studies brought him into contact with outstanding investigators in whose laboratories he would learn the techniques necessary to complete his degree: Alf Alving, a renal physiologist; Dr. Eleanor Humphrey's, a superb histopathologist in the Department of Pathology; E. S. Guzman Barron, of the Department of Biochemistry; and the famous physiologist A. J. Carlson (discussed in chap. 3).

It is important that we recognize that in the 1930s laboratory studies that we now take for granted—such as the comprehensive measurement of blood electrolytes, magnesium, calcium, phosphate, creatinine, and blood urea nitrogen, as well as the blood pH—were far from routine. Billings Hospital had an excellent clinical biochemistry department supervised by Katherine Knowlton. She proved invaluable in performing many of the biochemical analyses. The age of automated laboratory analysis still lay in the future.

Dr. Kirsner's agreement with Dr. Palmer and the Division of Biological Sciences required that he continue to fulfill his clinical responsibilities in the Section of Gastroenterology while at the same time taking courses, passing examinations, and acquiring the skills and knowledge that would allow him to complete his thesis. When his dissertation was completed, he showed the manuscript to Professor Carlson. After reviewing the substantial research that had been done, Carlson returned the thesis to him and remarked, "Vell, Kirsner, you have been chasing a rabbit around the block, and you finally caught him."

The demands on his time during this period, and the stresses the program placed on him, were tremendous. Like all candidates for a doctorate degree, he had to appear before a panel of professors from the Division of Biological Sciences and the Department of Medicine to defend his thesis publicly. In discussing this event, he always enjoyed impressing medical students and young physicians by telling them how he was asked to derive the complete Henderson-Hassel-balch equation on the blackboard for his examiners, which he successfully accomplished.[21]

Peptic Ulcer Disease

When Dr. Kirsner joined the Section of Gastroenterology, peptic ulcer disease was Dr. Palmer's major interest, and the disease occupied most of their attention. Dr. Palmer's career had included a broad exposure to the clinical problem of peptic ulcer disease. He had begun his postgraduate medical training at Presbyterian Hospital, the major teaching hospital of Rush Medical College. There he was introduced to and subsequently worked with Dr. Bertram Welton Sippy,[22] whose name became synonymous with his comprehensive acid-suppressing program for peptic ulcer disease and the "Sippy Powders" that were used to treat ulcer patients. By the time of his death in 1924, Sippy had comprehensively described the natural history of the disease and formulated an approach to its complications. During the years that Palmer trained and worked with him, Sippy was at the height of his career and with his associates ran a practice that filled as many as 100 beds at Presbyterian Hospital and another 105 beds at three other hospitals in the city. Dr. Palmer was thoroughly indoctrinated in the Sippy approach to treatment, which included long hospitalizations averaging six weeks, an initial period of bed rest with oral intake limited to frequent milk and cream with alkaline powders during the waking hours, and nightly aspiration of the gastric contents to remove the "irritating" hydrochloric acid and to measure the free and total acid contents of the specimens to monitor the effectiveness of the therapy. Beyond a careful history and physical examination, precise diagnosis of peptic ulcer disease was limited to radiologic examination of the upper gastrointestinal tract (stomach and duodenum) utilizing barium contrast material. By today's standards, these radiologic examinations, which were oriented toward detecting an ulcer crater and following its disappearance, would be considered quite crude. They were performed with thick barium contrast material that did not allow the mucosal detail that we are accustomed to seeing in today's examinations.

Although the existence of gastric ulcers had been well recognized in the 19th century, it was not until the first decades of the 20th century that the frequency of duodenal ulcer disease was fully appreciated. The British surgeon Berkeley G. A. Moynihan played a major role in the recognition of the importance of duodenal ulcer disease, such that for a time it was referred to as "Moynihan's disease."[23] It is difficult for physicians today to appreciate the magnitude and severity of the problem in those early decades of the last century. The severity of peptic ulcer in the first half of the 20th century reflected both a higher incidence of the disease than is seen today and a lack of effective treatment. In an important publication on peptic ulcer disease in 1942, Dr. Kirsner—now the senior author—and Dr. Palmer noted that "between 1929 and 1939 approximately 1,350 patients with peptic ulcer disease were treated at the Albert Merritt Billings Hospital by the Sippy Program."[24]

The importance of gastric hydrochloric acid in the pathogenesis of peptic ulcers is encapsulated in Karl Schwarz's dictum of 1910 that famously stated, "No acid, no ulcer." Dr. Palmer had studied the problem of the mechanism of pain in peptic ulcer, the subject of his Ph.D. work in A. J. Carlson's laboratories. (The importance of acid as a mechanism of pain challenged the notion put forth by Walter Cannon, and later by Julian Ruffin of Duke University, that motility was the important mechanism of pain.) This was the rationale behind the intensive acid neutralization program of alkali powders that was the hallmark of the Sippy Program and the meticulous attention to the study of "free and total acid" in the aspirated specimens of gastric contents. Several of Dr. Kirsner's publications from his first five years at Billings Hospital studied the effectiveness of various antacid preparations on the hydrogen ion concentration of the gastric contents. These studies aimed to evaluate the efficacy and safety of the new aluminum hydroxide and phosphate preparations that were being introduced to replace the absorbable Sippy Powders.

The clinical importance of Dr. Kirsner's work on alkalosis for his Ph.D. is best appreciated in his 1942 publication in the *Archives of Internal Medicine* entitled "Alkalosis Complicating the Sippy Treatment of Peptic Ulcer Disease," written with Dr. Palmer. Reading this report, one learns that patients were routinely given 32 grams of sodium bicarbonate and 10 to 32 grams of calcium carbonate daily. The report documents 135 episodes of alkalosis in 111 patients. Thirty-seven of these episodes are judged to be severe, and it is noted that the authors of the report have previously reported four patients who died as a result of the alkalosis that developed as a complication of therapy. The paper reports thorough investigation of renal function and the reversibility of the impaired renal function associated with alkalosis. The nightly aspiration of the gastric contents, resulting in the removal of large amounts of sodium, potassium, and chloride in the gastric fluid, is a contributing factor in the development of alkalosis.

From today's perspective, the importance of this report is not just that it recognizes that alkalosis developed as a frequent complication of the Sippy Program (awareness of the syndrome had been reported as early as 1923 while Bertram Sippy was still alive), but that it reflects Dr. Kirsner's approach to a clinical problem. He did not focus on a single organ system but viewed the problem from the standpoint of a medical scientist, reflecting the best traditions in the field of internal medicine. As a result of these studies on the milk alkali syndrome, the use of sodium bicarbonate was discontinued in the therapy for peptic ulcer disease and replaced by aluminum- and magnesium-containing antacids such as aluminum and magnesium hydroxide (products like Maalox and Gelusil).

Forty-five years later, in 1983, the Australian clinician Barry Marshall, unburdened by the dogma that gastric acid was the critical factor in causing peptic ulcer, and his pathologist colleague Robin Warren at the Royal Perth Hospital, would publish their discovery of the short spiral curved bacillus that came to be known as *Helicobacter pylori* and suggest its importance as a cause of gastritis and peptic ulcer disease.[25] Although the *Helicobacter* species had been observed earlier in animals, this finding had been dismissed as an unimportant nosocomial (hospital-acquired) infection. It would take another 15 years after their rediscovery of *Helicobacter pylori* for the medical world and the gastroenterology community to fully recognize the importance of this finding in the development of gastritis, peptic ulcer disease, and gastric cancer (also gastric lymphoma). Reflecting on his experience in treating peptic ulcer disease at the University of Chicago, Dr. Kirsner feels now that they were so focused on gastric hydrochloric acid and psychological factors in the pathogenesis of peptic ulcer disease that they overlooked the possibility of infection. He remembers a female patient whose gastric acidity he had studied serially and who temporarily developed unexplained achlorhydria (lack of gastric acid). In retrospect, this phenomenon may have been the result of a *Helicobacter pylori* infection, a possibility he and his colleagues did not consider at the time and that made sense only after the discovery of *Helicobacter pylori*. Marshall and Warren were eventually awarded the Nobel Prize in Medicine for their discovery.

Early Encounters with Inflammatory Bowel Disease

In January 1936, at the beginning of Dr. Kirsner's career in gastroenterology at the University of Chicago, a forty-year-old woman was admitted to Billings Hospital suffering from ulcerative colitis.[26] The patient was severely undernourished and extremely ill. When Dr. Kirsner asked Dr. Palmer about the disease and its causes, he replied that little was known about the nature and treatment of the disease. After several weeks of limited care, the patient continued to do poorly; she steadily declined and eventually died. Therapy at the time was limited to sulfonamides, intravenous fluids, and blood transfusions. Measures that today would have saved such a patient—total parenteral nutrition (intravenous hyperalimentation), powerful antibiotics, immunosuppressive drugs such as 6-mercaptopurine, azathioprine, cyclosporin, and infliximab (Remicade), along with modern surgical techniques—did not exist.

The patient and her illness made a profound impression on Dr. Kirsner and generated a determination to better understand this mysterious disease. This interest became a lifelong dedication to the study of inflammatory bowel diseases (ulcerative colitis and Crohn's disease), the basic mechanisms of the disease, and the development of more effective treatment. He pursued this interest quite independently of Dr. Palmer, whose primary concerns continued to be in the area of peptic ulcer disease. Beginning in 1939, when his first published paper on ulcerative colitis appeared, articles on ulcerative colitis and Crohn's disease gradually replace those on peptic ulcer disease as the dominant topic in Dr. Kirsner's bibliography.

A review of the medical literature shows that by 1930 there was increasing clinical recognition of inflammatory bowel disease and its complications. Reports of ulcerative colitis had appeared during the 19th century, perhaps beginning with the case report of a patient with interesting forensic ramifications described by Samuel Wilks in 1859. William Osler mentioned the disease only briefly in the 1904 edition of his famous textbook of medicine, *The Principles and Practice of Medicine*. A landmark event in the historical recognition of the importance of ulcerative colitis occurred in 1909 with a symposium held in London, "Sporadic Ulcerative Colitis," which reviewed the cases of 317 patients collected between 1888 and 1907 from seven prominent hospitals: Guy's, London, St. Mary's, St. Thomas's, St. Bartholomew's, St. George's, and Westminster. By 1913 radiologists in Basel and Vienna had described the radiologic appearance of advanced ulcerative colitis with bismuth as a contrast agent. In the 1920s a report from the Mayo Clinic described their experience with 426 patients and included the identification by Edward Rosenow and J. A. Bargen of *Diplostreptococcus* as a possible cause of the disease. Numerous extraintestinal manifestations of ulcerative colitis, such as ophthalmologic complications (uveitis), pyoderma gangrenosum, and erythema nodosum, as well as toxic dilation of the colon were being recognized, and the association of ulcerative colitis and colon cancer was becoming apparent. As early as 1913, J. Y. Brown of St. Louis was recommending a temporary ileostomy to place "the colon at rest." This operation increased in popularity during the 1930s and 1940s, but it was unsuccessful in causing the colonic inflammation to subside.

The search for an infectious etiology of ulcerative colitis is reflected in the early papers on the subject that Dr. Kirsner coauthored with Dr. Palmer and other colleagues, especially the bacteriologist Gail M. Dack and the virologist E. C. Rodaniche. Considerable attention was focused on the organism *Bacterium necrophorum*, an anaerobic microorganism frequently isolated from patients with ulcerative colitis which Dr. Dack had cultured using meticulous microbiologic techniques. Later, studies indicated that this organism was not specific for ulcerative colitis and was often identified with ulcerated or necrotic colon tissue. Early clinical reports published during the last half of the 1930s by Dr. Kirsner and his colleagues included the results of therapy with the new sulfonamides, in particular sulfaguanidine, on *Bacterium necrophorum* and the course of the disease. The studies reflect an approach, thorough for its day, on the pharmacology of these new drugs with assays of serum and fecal levels of the drug and microbiologic effects on the stool. With Dr. Rodaniche, Dr. Kirsner examined the Rosenow-Bargen "intestinal *Diplostreptococcus*" theory for ulcerative colitis, with negative results. The development of the Frei test for *Lymphoganuloma venereum* and the tendency of this disease to affect the rectum led to publications seeking to uncover a relationship between the two diseases, but none was found.

These experiences alerted Dr. Kirsner to the possibility that the pathogenesis of inflammatory bowel disease might lie beyond a specific microbial pathogen. The increasing numbers of reports from the Section of Gastroenterology on inflammatory bowel disease reflected the increasing number of patients with ulcerative colitis and Crohn's disease that were being referred to the university. In 1975 Dr. Kirsner published his first comprehensive book on these diseases, *Inflammatory Bowel Disease,* a textbook that has gone through six editions. The most recent edition, published in 2004, is a multiauthored book reflecting the impressive growth of scientific knowledge in the study of inflammatory bowel disease.[27]

Family Matters

In 1937 Minnie was expecting, but as her pregnancy progressed, it became apparent that she had developed the dreaded complication of eclampsia and almost died from the illness.[28] An emergency cesarean section was performed, but the infant son did not survive. In 1941 Minnie was pregnant again, and she was cared for at the University of Chicago by Dr. William Dieckman, a recognized authority on eclampsia. Nevertheless, eclampsia again developed, and a second cesarean section was required, seven months into the pregnancy. Their infant son weighed only two-and-one-half pounds, but he survived. After he spent four weeks in the hospital, the Kirsners were able to take their son, Robert, home. For a year they were uneasy about having visitors come to their apartment for fear that the baby might acquire an infection. Later Dr. Kirsner would reflect on the difficulties of this time and particularly credit his wife for the devotion with which she cared for their infant son. These family pressures added to the stress he experienced as he continued to work on his Ph.D. and address the continuing demands of patient care in the hospital.

Graduation Ceremonies, 1942

In the winter of 1942, Dr. Kirsner's mother, Ida, made her only trip to Chicago to be present at the university's commencement ceremonies. The 208th convocation took place on March 20th, 1942, in Rockefeller Chapel.[29] Dr. Joseph Kirsner was awarded his doctorate of philosophy by the dean of the Division of Biological Sciences, Professor Robert Redfield. Dr. Kirsner was one of ten candidates to receive their Ph.D.'s that day from the Division of Biological Sciences. It is interesting to note the unusual topics of study chosen by doctoral candidates in the division that year, including "Growth Factors for *Pasturella pestis*," "Effects of Pentathol on the Fetus," "The Effects of Alcohol on Acquired Resistance to Pneumococcal Infection," and "Studies on the Anti-pernicious Anemia Principle."

The ceremonies began with the colorful opening processional of the faculty in full regalia. The opening prayer was given by the convocation chaplin, John Thomas McNeill, professor of the history of European Christianity in the Divinity School. Dr. Edith Abbott, dean of the School of Social Service Administration, gave the convocational address, "New Frontiers in Public Welfare." The ceremonies concluded with an address by the president of the university, Robert Maynard Hutchins. For Dr. Kirsner, the most memorable moment of the emotionally charged ceremony was receiving his Ph.D. diploma from President Hutchins, whom he admired and respected.

A photograph taken on the day of the commencement in front of Rockefeller Chapel shows Dr. Kirsner with his mother. Her modest attire and a quiet expression hide the joyous emotions she must have experienced on that day. One imagines the pride she must have felt observing the accomplishments that her eldest son had achieved in less than a decade since he left Boston. She must have taken great pleasure in her daughter-in-law and their newborn son, Robert. Ida Kirsner was a remarkable woman and was remembered with admiration by many of Joe Kirsner's friends from their neighborhood in Boston. Her entire focus was on the welfare of her family. But for Dr. Kirsner's mother, in spite of the joy of the day's events, there were also the alarming reports coming from her relatives in Ukraine, and she must have also been experiencing a sense of apprehension about the terrible war that had engulfed Europe and the Pacific.

Notes

1. Comprehensive accounts of this subject may be found in JBK, *The Scientific Growth of Gastroenterologic Knowledge during the 20th Century* (Philadelphia: Lea and Febiger, 1994); JBK, *The Development of American Gastroenterology* (New York: Raven Press, 1990).

2. For an account of this historic event, see William Beaumont, *Experiments and Observations on the Gastric Juice and the Physiology of Digestion* (1893) (New York: Dover, 1959; Birmingham: Classics of Medicine Library, 1980).

3. Wilhelm Conrad Roentgen, "On a New Kind of Ray" (1895), translated in *Source Book of Medical History,* comp. Logan Clendening (New York: Dover, 1942).

4. W. B. Cannon's contribution to gastroenterology, *Gastroenterology* 63:878-89, 1972.

5. See "The Metamorphosis—Rigid to Flexible (1900-1930)," chap. 5 of Irvin M. Modlin's *A Brief History of Endoscopy* (Milan: MultiMed, 2000).

6. A comprehensive history of the early years of the American Gastroenterological Association can be found in Dale C. Smith, *The American Gastroenterological Association: 1897-1997* (Bethesda: AGA, 1999). The history of American gastroenterology is comprehensively detailed in JBK, *The Development of American Gastroenterology.* A further source of interest is Bockus, HL, Comments on the early development of gastroenterology in the United States of America, *Perspect Biol Med* 14:2:228-37, Winter 1971.

7. Smith, *The American Gastroenterological Association,* 1.

8. It should be noted that Julius Friedenwald, who was in attendance at the meeting on June 3, 1897, in a history of the first 10 years of the AGA published in *Gastroenterology* 42:722-31, 1962, lists all the members in attendance and describes their background, but does not credit Dr. Aaron as being the founder of the AGA.

9. JBK, *The Development of American Gastroenterology,* 169-71.

10. Shattuck, FC, Specialization in medicine, *JAMA* 35:723-26, 1900.

11. William Osler, "Internal Medicine as a Vocation," in *Aequinimitas and Other Papers That Have Stood the Test of Time* (New York: W. W. Norton, 1963).

12. Fascinating accounts of Rudolf Schindler's life and his role in the development of gastroscopy can be found in Davis A, Rudolf Schindler's role in the development of gastroscopy, *Bull Med Hist* 46:150-70, 1972; Modlin IM and Farhadi J, Rudolf Schindler—a man for all seasons, *J Clin Gastroenterology* 31:2:95-102, 2000; Gordin ME and Kirsner JB, Rudolf Schindler, pioneer endoscopist, *Gastroenterology* 77:354-61, 1979.

13. See Marie Ortmayer's account of these events: Some early reminiscences, *Endoscopy* 16:4:201, May 1970.

14. In addition to assisting in the Schindlers' immigration to Chicago, Mrs. Charles Morse and Mrs. Martha Fischer were supportive of research leading to the diagnosis of early gastric cancer and underwrote a portion of the publication costs of the colored plates of Schindler's *Lehrbuch* when the work was translated and published in English.

15. Assisting at gastroscopy—an historical account, *Gastrointestinal Endoscopy* 57:3:381-83, 2003.

16. See Gordin and Kirsner, Rudolf Schindler, pioneer endoscopist.

17. Gerstner P, The American Society for Gastrointestinal Endoscopy: A history, *Gastrointestinal Endoscopy* 37:2:S1–S26, 1991 (quotation on S2).

18. Gerstner, ASGE: A history.

19. See Davis, Rudolf Schindler's role.

20. Schindler R, Kirsner JB, and Palmer WL, Atrophic gastritis: Gastroscopic studies on the effects of liver and iron therapy, preliminary report, *Arch Int Med* 65:78-89, January 1940.

21. The equation relates the pH or concentration of hydrogen ions in a solution to the ratio of base to weak acid in that solution. This and the Krebs cycle are the bane of first-year medical students in biochemistry.

22. For a more complete accounting of the life of Bertram Sippy, see Palmer WL, Bertram Welton Sippy (1866-1924), *Gastroenterology* 77:152-55, 1979.

23. For an appreciation of the historical significance of the eponym, see Spiro HM, Peptic ulcer: Moynihan's or Marshall's Disease? *Lancet* 352:645-46, 1998.

24. Kirsner JB and Palmer WL, Alkalosis complicating the Sippy treatment of peptic ulcer disease, *Arch Int Med* 69:789-807, May 1942.

25. Marshall BJ, Unidentified curved bacillus on gastric epithelium in active chronic gastritis, *Lancet* 1:8336:1273-75, 1983; Marshall BJ and Warren JR, Unidentified curved bacilli in the stomach of patients with gastritis and peptic ulceration, *Lancet* 1:8390:1311-15, 1984.

26. Dr. Kirsner has made a major contribution to the understanding of inflammatory bowel disease through a series of publications reviewing the history of these diseases and summarizing his experiences at the University of Chicago. To cite three representative examples: *Origins and Directions of Inflammatory Bowel Disease: Early Studies of Nonspecific Inflammatory Bowel Diseases* (Dordrecht: Kluwer Academic, 2001); Historical antecedents of inflammatory bowel disease, *Inflamm Bowel Dis* 2:73-91, May 1996; and Inflammatory bowel disease at the University of Chicago: Early experiences, a personal historical account, *Inflamm Bowel Dis* 11:4:407-16, April 2005. For more on this interest of Dr. Kirsner's, see chapter 14.

27. *Kirsner's Inflammatory Bowel Disease,* 6th ed., ed. R. Balfour Sartor and William J. Sanborn (Edinburgh and New York: Saunders, 2004).

28. In preeclampsia, the woman has dangerously high blood pressure, swelling, and protein in the urine. If untreated, this syndrome will lead to eclampsia, which progresses to kidney failure and ultimately convulsions.

29. Details of the 208th convocation ceremonies at the University of Chicago are in the Special Collections Department, Regenstein Library, University of Chicago.

5 ∗ World War II, 1943–1946

The decade from 1933 through 1943 saw Dr. Kirsner evolve from a
newly graduated physician of Tufts School of Medicine destined for
general practice in New England to an academic physician: a specialist confident in his skills in gastroenterology and internal medicine,
a recognized teacher, and a credible investigator beginning to make
important clinical and laboratory contributions to the medical literature. During this decade the storm clouds of war had gathered
over Europe and Asia, and armed conflict had erupted in China,
Spain, and Eastern Europe. America watched with increasing concern the rise of the National Socialist Party in Germany, the rise of
Mussolini's Fascist Party in Italy, and the growing aggression of Japan
in Southeast Asia. September 1939 marked the German advance into
Poland and the declaration of a state of war between Germany and
Britain and France. While America tried to remain neutral, Hitler
advanced swiftly through Europe, overrunning Belgium, France, the
Netherlands, Scandinavia, and Greece. The German invasion of Rus-
sia on June 22, 1941, dissolved the 1938 Nazi-Soviet Nonaggression
Pact, which had allowed Germany to overrun Central Europe. For
Dr. Kirsner and his family, there was the ever more alarming aware-
ness of Nazi anti-Semitic policies depriving Jews of their rights as
citizens, and the unbelievable reports of atrocities occurring in the
cities and death camps of Central Europe. U.S. neutrality ended on
Sunday, December 7, 1941, with the Japanese attack on Pearl Harbor.
The United States declared war on Japan on December 8. Three days
later, December 11, Germany and Italy declared war on the United
States, sparing President Franklin D. Roosevelt the need to convince

the American people of the necessity of war with Germany as well, and Congress passed a joint resolution accepting the state of war "which had been thrust upon the United States."

Dr. Kirsner's parents, who for years had corresponded with close relatives still living in Ukraine, lost contact with them and later learned of their probable disappearance into the Nazi death camps. Dr. Kirsner and Minnie were deeply troubled by these events, and Dr. Kirsner decided it was his duty to volunteer to serve his country. News of his desire to enlist became known in the Medical Center, where his abilities as a clinician and his status as a rising star were highly appreciated. He received a message to come to the office of the chancellor, Robert Maynard Hutchins, in the Harper Building.[1] In 1929 Hutchins had been selected, at the age of 29, to be the president of the university. As dean of Yale Law School, he had been recognized not only for his brilliance but also for his outspokenness. On the Midway he had achieved a reputation for his low opinion of physicians and was known to regard them as tradesmen. Physicians had more than once felt his censure if they did not meet the standards he had set for the university. His vision of the kind of medical school he wanted for the university had culminated in October 1939 when he announced that the university would close Rush as an undergraduate school of medicine in 1942 and that the University of Chicago Medical School would be the sole medical school for the university.[2]

One can imagine the trepidation that Dr. Kirsner must have felt as he proceeded down the long corridor in Harper to keep his appointment in Hutchins's office. Hutchins told him he had learned of his intention to enlist in the army and said he thought Dr. Kirsner ought to remain at the university, where he would be needed for his clinical abilities and teaching skills. Hutchins stated "that important things were happening at the university." (Only years later would Dr. Kirsner come to learn of the existence of the Manhattan Project, which may have been on Hutchins's mind at the time).[3] Dr. Kirsner agreed to stay another year at the university and reevaluate his decision to volunteer. Hutchins understood and assured him that "he would always have a place at the university." Dr. Kirsner never knew how the chancellor had learned of his desire to enlist; he had talked with Dr. Palmer about his plans but had not received from him any advice or expression of regret. News of personal matters often traveled quickly in the Medical Center, though, or perhaps it was because he had once seen Hutchins's wife as a patient and on one occasion had even made a house call. This would be Dr. Kirsner's one and only personal meeting with the university's most prominent president.

During the subsequent year the deteriorating situation in both Europe and the Pacific, plus his family's confirmation of their worst fears about their relatives still in Europe, left him with no doubt in his determination to go ahead and volunteer for early overseas military duty. Recruitment posters of this era stressed the theme "Remember Pearl Harbor." For most Americans the enemy was Japan, the nation that had attacked the United States without provocation. For Dr. Kirsner and the more than 500,000 Jews that entered the U.S. armed services, the enemy was Nazi Germany.[4] Even with a young son at home, he had Minnie's full support. For him, this war had become a sacred duty, and he knew his skills as a physician were needed.

In September 1943 Joseph B. Kirsner, a 34-year-old assistant professor at the University of Chicago, having written a number of published papers and becoming recognized in a growing number of national medical organizations, was inducted into the Army Medical Corps as a first lieutenant. Dr. Kirsner has in his possession a letter from an A. C. Bachmeyer addressed to the Office of Army Procurement and dated September 4, 1943, stating that Joseph B. Kirsner is "especially qualified in gastroenterology," and further that he is "fully competent and highly skilled in the use of the gastroscope." Dr. Kirsner was rapidly advancing in the field of gastroenterology and might have asked for preferential treatment in securing a favorable assignment or consulting role. But he did not and accepted his assignment as a first lieutenant assigned to Carlisle Medical Officers Barracks in Pennsylvania, where he reported for duty on November 4, 1943.

One of the defining moments for men entering the armed services occurred when they were issued their "dog tags." Dog tags served as a stark reminder that they might indeed be killed in action, and that this simple device might serve as the only means of identifying their remains. Engraved in metal were data that defined the soldier and provided lifesaving information as well. The information included the wearer's name and service number, blood type, racial demographics ("white" or "negro"), and religious affiliation.

The religious classifications dated back to 1899 federal immigration records and included only four choices: Protestant, Catholic, Hebrew, or blank. "Hebrew," or H, stood for "Jew."[5] The term Hebrew conveyed a biblical overtone and a time before the Middle Ages in Europe made "Jew" a term of rebuke. When Napoleon Bonaparte issued his 1808 proclamation regarding the rights of the Jews of France, he avoided the term Jew in favor of Hebrew for this reason. On dog tags, the H was useful for pastoral matters and assured 36 hours' leave for Rosh Hashanah and Yom Kippur. Grimly, it also assured the wearer that a Magen David (Star of David) would mark their grave in case of their demise. Dr. Kirsner had never thought of himself as a "Hebrew," but he did not hesitate to select the H. Not all Jews did the same. A survey of military chaplains indicated that officers were less likely to identify themselves as Jews. Dr. Kirsner remained firm in his choice, even though rumors circulated that the Germans would shoot POWs whose dog tags identified them as Jews. There are documented instances of Jewish servicemen who became POWs being singled out by the Nazis, separated from their units, and sent to hard labor camps.

It was the mission of the U.S. Army facility in Carlisle to convert civilian medical and dental personnel into "military officers." This mission was accomplished in six- to eight-week cycles processing 1,600 medical and dental officers. One wonders how Dr. Kirsner, somewhat older than his fellow trainees and accustomed to setting his own work schedule and used to his own disciplined and regular work habits, adjusted to functioning as part of a military unit. True, the army had its own proscribed discipline and routine, but as anyone who has served on active duty in the armed services knows, an atmosphere of "hurry up and wait" often prevails. There was also the difficulty of learning to live in an open barracks with strangers after having experienced the pleasures of a home and the attentions of a wife for almost a decade. We tend to forget the uncertainties that this generation of men experienced when they joined the service in 1942. The United States was only in its second year of the war, the outcome was yet unknown, and men entered the service with no certainty as to how long a tour of duty they faced, as well as the very real fear that they might not survive the ordeal.

Dr. Kirsner and his new colleagues would have to learn the culture of the military. The newly inducted officers had to learn how to wear their newly issued uniforms, when to salute, the uniform code of military justice, and how to fire a rifle or pistol—for many, something that was totally foreign. These subjects were far removed from the hallowed halls of the teaching hospital. Then there was physical conditioning, learning to march in platoons, to: perform basic maneuvers, to run obstacle courses, and to climb barrier walls. The latter was made more fearsome by the recollection that one of the medical officers had collapsed and died on the other side of the wall. Dr. Kirsner vividly remembers vainly protesting when they were commanded to experience crawling under barbed wire with "live" machine-gun fire overhead.

The training also involved courses on aspects of military medicine and public health. During one of the courses reviewing aspects of the medical literature, the class was being conducted by a young major who was discussing the gastrointestinal tract. The instructor referred to a paper that Kirsner and Palmer had published on the management of gastrointestinal bleeding from peptic ulcer disease. The instructor's summary misstated the meaning of the paper. To quote Dr. Kirsner's recollection of the incident:

> Prudence dictated that I should keep quiet, but for some reason completely unknown to me, I was belligerent about the matter, raised my hand like a schoolboy and said, "Major, you are incorrect." The class was startled, the major was surprised; he looked at his notes, and he said, "Who are you?" I said, "I am Kirsner." Naturally this created an uproar in the audience, at which point the major abruptly dismissed the class; and I had visions of being summarily court-martialed or sent to a battalion aid station. This did not happen and I continued on with the program.

A similar incident occurred during a course on public health. The courses were taught by a didactic method that resembled reciting a catechism. On a review of some 100 questions, Dr. Kirsner answered 99 correctly and found his answer faulted on only one question, which dealt with the ·definition of "vectors" of disease. At this time there were a group of five "much-decorated" Brazilian officers who, although they routinely disturbed the rest of the barrack with their loud talking and late hours, did possess five dictionaries among them. Reflecting his habit of scholarship, Dr. Kirsner consulted the dictionaries and found that the definitions supported his interpretation as to the correct answer to the question. The military colonel conducting the review of the examination was surprised by the first lieutenant who raised his hand and challenged the answer that the colonel had given as the correct one. The colonel was not happy at having his authority questioned in front of the class. He addressed Dr. Kirsner, "Young man, by whose authority do you challenge this response?" Kirsner produced the several dictionaries loaned by the Brazilian officers and said, "By the authority of these dictionaries," holding them up and reading their names. There were large cheers and applause. The colonel dismissed the class. Kirsner's comrades were sure he had crossed a line, and again he was certain he would be sent to a battalion aid station or receive some similar form of retribution. Several sleepless nights passed and nothing happened. Kirsner would later learn that these encounters had become legendary at Carlisle, and the first question instructors would ask a new class was, "Are there any professors in the class?"

From Carlisle, Dr. Kirsner was sent on December 17, 1943, to O'Reilly General Hospital, Springfield, Missouri, where he was assigned to make rounds in medicine and await a permanent assignment. He remained there for about six weeks, but because he had requested early overseas duty, he was then sent to Fort Dix, New Jersey, to complete his training. As related in a privately published book, *15th General Hospital '43–'45*, in March of 1943 a handful of men assembled at Fort Dix that "would eventually blossom forth into a well rounded compact unit—the 15th General Hospital."[6] The commanding officer, Col. John P. Bachman, MC, was from Hartsdale, New York, and had already experienced the "horrors of war" on December 7, 1942, at Pearl Harbor. Initially there were seven officers and 30 enlisted men. During the fall of 1943, the unit acquired its professional staff: surgeons, internists, dentists, radiologists, nurses, and laboratory staff. After 12 days on high alert, on the evening of Tuesday, February 29, 1944, the entire unit was transported to New York Harbor and went aboard the *Queen Mary,* which had been refitted for troop transport.

Dr. Kirsner found himself in a stateroom with infantrymen whose bayonets and rifles were stacked in a corner. He managed to get himself appointed as an assistant to the physician in the sick bay, where he spent the rest of the journey sharing in the responsibility of routine sick-bay calls.

On the morning of March 1, at 11:45, "the engines throb—the ship begins to move and there's a mad rush to the portholes for a last glimpse of the New York skyline and the Statue of Liberty." The ship proceeded rapidly on a zigzagging course under the ever-present threat of submarine attack. On the morning of March 7, the crew came on deck to the welcome sight of an escort of destroyers flying the Union Jack and the Scottish hills rising out of the mist. The next day the troops went ashore to a tune of a Scottish fife band. There followed a long train ride to the Midlands of England to a town called Ellesmere. A short trip brought them to Otley Deer Park and the first sight of operations for the hospital, in a building erected as part of the Lend Lease Act of 1941. Dr. Kirsner's medical specialty board certification served him well, and he was placed in charge of the unit's gastroenterology service.

V-mail—little letters that could reach the most out-of-the way destination in about 10 days—from the troops in England were carefully censored, since the military wished to keep the movement and location of troops secret from the enemy. Writing by V-mail, Dr. Kirsner tried to inform his wife where he was stationed in England. He wrote Minnie interesting facts about the foxglove plant and about William Withering, credited with the discovery of digitalis. Minnie was confused by his description of the medication but showed the letter to Dr. Palmer, who knew that William Withering had discovered the medicinal effects of tea brewed from the foxglove plant in Ellesmere, and that this was Dr. Kirsner's covert way of telling her where he was stationed. This anecdote speaks to the relationship as mentor and friend maintained by Dr. Palmer with the Kirsners. Although Dr. Kirsner was at the time not part of the activities of the section, Minnie still felt comfortable in asking Dr. Palmer for help in understanding the letter.

It was a lonely period as he and the men of the 15th General Hospital waited for the impending invasion of Normandy. He remembers a visit from Col. William Middleton, a professor of medicine and chairman of the Department of Medicine at the University of Wisconsin. Together they made rounds on the hospital's inpatients. Such an infrequent occurrence brought to mind the pleasure he had experienced at the University of Chicago in making rounds with Dr. Palmer.

On June 6 the 15th General Hospital received the news that D-day had begun. A week later the unit began to see grim evidence of the cost of war as injured soldiers began to pour into the hospital. Quoting from the history of the 15th General Hospital: "Everyone pitches in and goes to work to help these kids who staked their lives against a madman's dream of world conquest. We toil and sweat and marvel at the wonders of plasma and penicillin. Now its [sic] work and no play and we're only too happy to do it."

On July 15 the unit was moved first to Blanford, England, remaining idle for six weeks and then on August 18 to a staging area, Eastleigh, enduring "filthy hovels" that served as tent quarters. Finally (again quoting from the history of the 15th General Hospital), "in the early hours of the 23rd of August, with destroyer escort, we set sail for the coast of France. Dawn breaks and we, along with a vast armada are off Utah Beach Normandy. It takes us all day to debark—down cargo nets—there are no piers here." After coming ashore the unit marched six miles in driving rain to temporary quarters at Saint-Marie-du-Mont, billeting in a cow pasture for the next ten days. They were then loaded on a train to Garche, a "hospital train—capacity 300; into that put 700 officers nurses and enlisted men." There, as guests of the 203 General Hospital they enjoyed private rooms, hot showers, and good meals.

The town of Garche was near Paris and home to one of the largest hospitals in Europe, the Raymond Poincaré Hospital. For the moment the duties for his outfit were rather light, and Dr. Kirsner managed to unofficially attach himself to the French army medical command. In this capacity he was able to make rounds at the hospital. He also made rounds on the floor that housed Nazi prisoners of war. This was both an interesting and a disturbing experience. He found the prisoners still filled with hostility and hatred even though they were being treated with care for their wounds. He remembers one officer who was clearly suffering from the infected wounds that would shortly take his life, and in spite of the sympathy that Dr. Kirsner tried to show the German officer, the man said to him, "I hate you."

With the German armies in retreat toward the Rhine in August 1944, the fate of Paris became a matter of concern. Eisenhower was focused on destroying the German armies and did not wish to become involved in any subsidiary operation that would divert manpower or resources, no matter how important it was from a sentimental or political point of view. General de Gaulle intervened, and disregarding Eisenhower's instructions, he secretly ordered General Pierre Koenig to seize the capital as soon as he could. Hitler had ordered the devastation of the city, but the German commander General Dietrich von Choltitz negotiated a surrender that allowed the Germans to withdraw. On August 25, 1944, General Leclerc, whose armored division was under Eisenhower's command, followed by the U.S. 4th Infantry Division, entered the City of Light.

After the liberation of Paris, Dr. Kirsner was able to visit Paris with some of his army buddies. They were befriended by a Frenchman who took them for a good dinner. This sounded great after living for so many weeks on K rations and C rations.[7] In a café they had a "beef" dinner, which they later learned was horse meat. Dr. Kirsner had to admit that it tasted pretty good, but it was an experience he would not repeat.

By September 1944 his unit had removed on to Liège, Belgium, where they first stayed at the Hotel Moderne. Before the war, the Hotel Moderne had been quite grand and had an elegant dining room with large glass windows overlooking a garden. When the hotel came under rocket attack, the physicians would learn of the capacity of shattered glass to create severe shrapnel wounds. They also learned that the heavy lead content of the glass made it possible to locate embedded fragments of glass on an x-ray. The 15th General Hospital occupied a hospital building at the top of one of the seven hills bordering the southern portion of Liège. The building had housed a German hospital facility that had been abandoned in the face of the Allied advance. The hill was named "coronary hill" after an enlisted man who had collapsed and died after running up it; his autopsy revealed that he had died from a ruptured coronary artery. According to the history of the 15th General Hospital, the hospital was called Saint Laurent and the text notes, "But it's desecrating the name of a Saint to apply it to the pig sty we found. So cleaning, mopping, scrubbing the 15th goes to work and soon we have something resembling an Army Hospital."

In the hospital Dr. Kirsner found a Schindler gastroscope that the Germans had left behind. Although he hoped to be able to use the instrument, after cleaning and attempting to set it up he found that it had been damaged beyond his ability to repair it. He found it ironic that the German medical corps was using an instrument, the Schindler gastroscope, pioneered by a man they had persecuted.

Dr. Kirsner remembers working closely with Lt. Col. Herbert Pollack, MC, who was chief of the medical service. Dr. Pollack was an expert on nutritional deficiencies, and Dr. Kirsner felt that he had been instrumental in his being assigned to the 15th General Hospital. Another officer with whom he had a close working relationship was Maj. Mitchell Oestreich of Chappaqua, New York. Dr. Oestreich was the chief of the radiology department and had designed what was felt to be the best x-ray setup in the European theater of operations. He was also a man of many talents: he was an avid photographer, gave classes in German and French, organized community singing and played accompaniment on his mandolin, and performed the duties of Jewish chaplain.

The history of the 15th General Hospital describes the German reconnaissance planes, referred to as "Bedcheck Charlies," that flew over the city each evening and the ack-ack guns that attempted to drive them away. The threat grew more ominous when robot bombs, unmanned rockets loaded with explosives, began to pass overhead. The 15th General Hospital celebrated Thanksgiving that November in rare form, but they awakened the next morning to the "blackest day in the history of the 15th. On that fateful morning, which was the most infamous in our collective lives, a winged death came hurtling from the skies into our midst. This messenger of destruction from a hate-saturated people found its mark in front of our Pharmacy building and sixteen lives bent on missions of mercy were obliterated." Countless others were injured, but because the pharmacy was in the center of the hospital and the patients were on the periphery, no patients were lost. One of the medical personnel who perished in the explosion was a good friend, Maj. Michael A. Rafferty, from Camden, West Virginia, who was chief of the hospital's laboratory service and had occupied an office adjoining Dr. Kirsner's. Dr. Kirsner would never forget this event. The bomb had entirely destroyed the office where he normally started his day before making rounds. He could never understand why he was not in his office that morning, but always felt it was the hand of providence that had spared him. It renewed his dedication to his belief that he had an almost religious calling to his service in medicine.

Also among the men killed in this incident was a member of the pharmacy staff at Billings Hospital, T/Sgt. Joseph S. Zabella Jr. Minnie learned of his death a few days later when she went to the pharmacy to pick up some medication. Knowing that Joe was part of the same unit caused her great distress, but again she able to turn to Dr. Palmer, who made the appropriate calls and learned that Joe was safe.

The damage to the hospital was so severe that patients had to be transferred to other military hospitals in the vicinity of Liège. Dr. Kirsner and the personnel of the 15th General Hospital were then regrouped and relocated in another facility. The 15th General Hospital was stationed close to the Meuse River when the Germans launched what became known as the Ardennes campaign—the Battle of the Bulge—which was to be their last major offensive of the war. It was a surprise thrust of men and machines through Belgium's Ardennes forest in an attempt to cut the Allied forces in two. The battle, which began on the morning of December 16, 1944, involved more than a million soldiers. After initial success, the armies of Montgomery to the north and Bradley to the south forced the Germans to withdraw, and by January 16, 1945, the Ardennes front was reestablished. German casualties were 120,000 dead, wounded, and captured. During this phase of the war in Europe, there was considerable anxiety in the unit that they might face the challenge of heavy casualties, but this did not occur. Later, as the 15th General Hospital continued to provide support for the 1st Army as it advanced through the highly dangerous Siegfried Line, the hospital experienced the full impact of the war and would receive as many as 1,000 casualties a day. The entire staff was involved in the care of war wounds. Dr. Kirsner and the cardiologist Capt. Frederick J. Lewy, MC, of New York City, continued to care for all the medical problems, which were dwarfed by the number of battle causalities requiring surgical treatment. Dr. Kirsner felt that he was now directly witnessing the horrific casualties of war.

The history of the 15th General Hospital describes Dr. Lewy (Fred) as a "historian and literateur [sic]" remembered for his "patient efforts to hammer into us, in a deep deliberate voice some knowledge of German." This same volume, which, like a high school yearbook, includes a photograph and a short commentary on each officer, describes Capt. Joseph B. Kirsner, MC, as a "delver into the mysteries of the alimentary canal, from stomatitis to proctitis, master of all sphincters and diagnostician of borborygmi. . . . With this background most logical to be called G.I. Joe." It also mentions that he was the hospital librarian, "but try and get a book from him," and that in Ellesmere he gave "early promise of being a dart thrower."

During the advance of the 1st Army through the Siegfried Line, the 15th General Hospital was one of five 1,000-bed general hospitals positioned near Valenciennes near the Belgian border with Germany and the Remagen bridge. Eisenhower had anticipated a major campaign to cross the Rhine with the potential for heavy casualties. Early in March the Allies received an unexpected gift when they learned from a POW that Hitler planned to destroy the Remagen bridge on March 7, 1945. The Allies rushed to capture the bridge, which was the major crossing point over the Rhine in that area. They were successful, although two explosions partially damaged the structure. For 11 days the Allies were able to cross the bridge before it collapsed, thereby gaining a foothold in Germany. Hitler was furious over this failure to destroy the bridge, and court-martialed and executed four of the officers he held responsible.

On May 7, 1945, the remnants of the Third Reich surrendered unconditionally. At this time Dr. Kirsner was consulted on the refeeding of Holocaust survivors by Professor L. Brull and Paul Roskamp, chairman of the medical staff of Liège University. The injudicious refeeding of profoundly malnourished internees had resulted in several fatalities from gastric perforation.

With the Allied victory in Europe, Dr. Kirsner was able to enjoy a brief stay in a small town on the Riviera, La Ciotat. For some American soldiers, V-E meant going home, but for most it was either occupation duty in Germany or transfer to the Pacific theater. Dr. Kirsner was assigned to the 229th General Hospital, an outfit that was being assembled from the Medical Corps in Europe and stationed near Marseille. The hospital was part of a force that would sail across the South Atlantic and through the Panama Canal to arrive in the Philippines, presumably as part of the preparation for the invasion of Japan. The 229th General Hospital embarked on the USS *General D. E. Aultman* and departed from Marseille on July 22, 1945, sailing around the coast of Gibraltar and into the South Atlantic. In addition to the 229th General Hospital, the *Aultman* embarked with the 1367th Engineers and various port companies totaling 3,298 troops. The ship was named for a brigadier general who had served in the Spanish-American War and later as an artillery commander in France during World War I. It was built in the Kaiser Shipyard in Richmond, California, and commissioned in May of 1945. The vessel had a complement of 426 officers and crew, and a troop capacity of 3,343.

One of the younger medical officers assigned to the 229th General Hospital was Murray Dworetzky.[8] Dr. Dworetzky had with him a folder in which he had collected two years' worth of Cabot clinical pathologic cases from the *New England Journal of Medicine*. Once they were aboard ship, he gave the folder to Joe and said, "Maybe you can do something with these." As the ship slowly crossed the Atlantic, Dr. Kirsner organized a daily voluntary meeting of the medical officers aboard to read and discuss one of the case histories. This academic exercise helped the medical officers keep up their skills and knowledge.

Dr. Dworetzky recalled that he and all the other junior medical officers looked up to Joe as the unofficial chief of medicine. Herb Ensworth, who had come from Cornell and ultimately settled in private practice in Ithaca, New York, was the unit's official chief of medicine, but Joe was the man they would call when they needed additional help in diagnosis and treatment of a difficult case.

After two years in Europe, Dr. Kirsner, like many of his colleagues, was ready to go home. Among the several thousand troops aboard the *Aultman*, there was a universal prayer as they were going through the Panama Canal that the ship's propellers would somehow be damaged in the narrow passageway and they would be sent home to the

United States. As the ship entered the third of the locks, a propeller was indeed damaged, and there was great cheering and enthusiasm. The ship had temporarily lost power and ran aground at a very slow speed. It had to be lifted off the shore by shifting fluid in the ship's ballasts. The troops disembarked in Panama City and were stationed in Camp Coby for a week in August without the benefit of air conditioning while the ship went into dry dock for repairs. By August 12 the ship was able to proceed into the Pacific and toward New Guinea. Two days out of the Canal Zone, the ship received the report of Japan's surrender on August 11, 1945.

Another piece of good news that reached Dr. Kirsner by mail as his ship was passing through the Panama Canal was notification that his nomination as a member of the prestigious American Society for Clinical Investigation had been accepted.

After a sea voyage of 55 days, the USS *General D. E. Aultman* finally docked in Hollandia, New Guinea. Watching the steam rising out of the jungle, Dr. Kirsner found a jeep driver who would take him into the jungle to observe the vegetation and the remnants of the fighting that had taken place in the area. He was surprised to hear, in the middle of the New Guinea jungle, someone call out "Hello, Joe," and looking around he saw a native "climbing down from a tree" and wearing discarded army fatigues. Of course, the native recognized the jeep and Dr. Kirsner's uniform as belonging to the U.S. Army and had already learned to use the slang expression "GI Joe." Over the years, whenever Dr. Kirsner related this anecdote, he could count on the double meaning of the sobriquet "GI Joe" to draw a laugh.

The *Aultman* next proceeded up the South China Sea to Lingayen Gulf in the Philippines, where they landed on September 13, 1945, and established the 229th General Hospital in tents while they awaited further orders. Dr. Kirsner even had the luxury of a tent with a wooden floor. But the war in the Pacific had come to an end. On the morning of August 6, 1945, more than half the city of Hiroshima had been obliterated when the United States dropped the first atomic bomb. Three days later, on August 9, the city of Nagasaki became the victim of the second atomic bomb. On August 14 the Japanese War Council capitulated, and the next day Emperor Hirohito told his people, who heard his voice for the first time, via a radio broadcast, that the years of fighting had ended. It took until September 2 for the famous signing of the unconditional surrender to General Douglas MacArthur by representatives of the Japanese government on the deck of the battleship USS *Missouri* as it lay at anchor in Tokyo Bay. Later in life, Dr. Kirsner never had any doubt that the dropping of the atomic bombs on Japan was justified in view of the American and Japanese lives that would have been lost if America had been forced to fight on.

Dr. Kirsner found himself involved in the rehabilitation of American POWs, getting them in shape for their trip back to the States. On September 29 he wrote a letter to Dr. Palmer from the 29th Replacement Depot located 29 miles south of Manila.[9] The camp was devoted to the processing of repatriated Allied soldiers. He notes the progress these men have made in regaining weight and becoming nutritionally restored. He also spent several days in a second section of the camp helping to repatriate Dutch returnees. Here he saw the residual effects of malnutrition and cases of smallpox, and perhaps cases of beriberi heart disease. Speaking with Dutch physicians, he was able to get some idea of the tremendous caloric restrictions experienced by the prisoners. In addition, some of the Dutch POWs had been exposed to the atom bomb dropped on Nagasaki, and Dr. Kirsner saw severe burns on exposed parts of the body—the V of the neck, the arms, and below the thighs—that resisted the primitive therapy that was available. Many of these victims later died.

His letter also describes life in the Philippines, and he mentions tents with wooden floors and running water as well. There was good food and nightly movies. He comments on the good weather and a view of green rice fields, a lake, and two imposing mountains. He ends his letter by remarking to Dr. Palmer that his long letter reflects "the enormous amount of time I have wasted (or had been wasted by Army policy)." He further notes that he is looking forward to returning to civilian life and "doing some real work" (resuming his academic activities). Clearly, Dr. Kirsner was feeling frustration at seeing his career placed on hold during these years of war.

The 229th General Hospital was placed aboard another troop ship, traveling up the North China Sea to Japan. This trip was the most difficult sea voyage he had experienced. Many of the troops were violently seasick. Their unit was among the first Americans to arrive in Nagoya, in September 1945.

Nagoya, located in southern Honshu, was east of Kyoto at the head of Ise Bay. The city and the famous Nagoya Castle, built in 1610 when the Tokugawa shogunate established the city as the capital of the Owari province, had been all but leveled by Allied bombing. As their ship docked in the harbor, Dr. Kirsner was astounded at the extent of the devastation they could see from the ship. In the immediate port area, he noted that many of the large buildings had been completely destroyed. In what had been the city's financial district, the only recognizable features to survive the bombing were large safe-deposit vaults. The 229th General Hospital was able to locate one building that was still usable. It had been a telephone building and had 13 floors. Each floor would accommodate 100 patients. Dr. Kirsner had charge of the gastroenterology section, which took up an entire floor. He made daily rounds with a young lieutenant who served as his ward secretary. There was an outbreak of smallpox at this time, a disease Dr. Kirsner had never seen before and with which he was to gain experience on his ward.

Dr. Dworetzky confirms Dr. Kirsner's recollection of seeing U.S. service personnel with smallpox. In a letter published in the *New England Journal of Medicine* on March 28, 2002, he recounts that in October 1945 they began to see their first cases of smallpox and that over the next several weeks they saw 22 service personnel with the disease. The first case they saw was confirmed by autopsy. It seemed that all the victims had visited the hospital for other medical problems within two weeks of the onset of their illness. Since none of the eight patients who died had evidence on his arm of a smallpox vaccination, the cases were attributed to faulty vaccination technique. The hospital staff began to vaccinate themselves every three weeks, since they were uncertain about how effective their earlier vaccinations had been. They received a batch of vaccine from the Philippines that caused a substantial cutaneous reaction. These reactions were first interpreted as a primary reaction, but the vaccine was cultured and shown to have been contaminated by *Staphylococcus*.[10]

There was time to see some of Nagoya. There were several outings to Japanese restaurants, but these were carefully controlled and Dr.

Kirsner had little contact with the Japanese civilian population. On one occasion he ventured out on his own to visit the campus of Nagoya University. During this visit a curious incident occurred, frightening at first, but it fortunately ended quite happily. He was walking on the campus when a Japanese civilian suddenly approached him, gesticulating wildly. As the man approached, the thought ran through Dr. Kirsner's mind that he might have a knife or a gun, and there he was rather foolishly by himself and certainly without any protection. As the man drew closer, Dr. Kirsner could see that he was carrying a package and kept repeating "University of Chicago" in a heavy accent. It turned out that he wanted Dr. Kirsner to give the package to Dr. Percival Bailey, a prominent neurosurgeon at the University of Chicago, as a gift.[11] The man had been a student of Dr. Bailey's before the war. Dr. Kirsner carried the package through the remainder of his military service and brought it home to the United States. Later, at a dinner party at the home of a mutual friend, Dr. Edmund Jacobson, Dr. Kirsner presented the package to Dr. Bailey. He also had occasion to visit a local hospital in Nagoya and was impressed that conditions were such that the Japanese, having limited access to the newly discovered penicillin, were forced to recover as much of the precious drug as possible from the urine of patients to whom it had been administered.

In the summer of 1946, after almost three years of overseas duty, Dr. Kirsner was allowed to return home. He took an overseas voyage across the North Pacific and landed in Seattle. A cross-country train ride brought him to Fort McCoy, in Wisconsin, where he was released by the army into the Medical Reserve. He returned home to Chicago by rail in June of 1946. He was discharged with the military rank of major and had received three battle stars.

During those long three years Minnie had remained in Hyde Park and raised their son, Robert. She had a married sister, Bea Sauer, and her family living in the city, but was otherwise alone. She earned a little additional money through part-time work in the local Woodward's Bookshop. One wonders at the fortitude of the wives of servicemen whose husbands were overseas during the years of the war. For Minnie it was a period of uncertainty and anxiety over the safe return of her husband. At one time, to help extend their funds, Minnie rented a room in their apartment to a single woman who was working at the university. The woman seemed quite suitable, but Minnie became distressed that she never saw her take a bath. She discussed the matter with her brother Lou, who suggested that she tell the woman that she would have to vacate the room, since her brother was going to be staying in the apartment as part of his work, which involved traveling to Washington via Chicago. Later, when she was wheeling Robert in his buggy on the Midway, Minnie encountered a friend, Laura Fermi, the wife of the famous physicist. On relating the incident to Mrs. Fermi, she learned that the woman was working for what was then part of the Manhattan Project, and a requirement of her job was that she take showers twice a day, both on arrival at and departure from her job.

Joseph Kirsner had served his country well, and like so many servicemen of his generation he returned to civilian life with a maturity and a sense of patriotism and purpose that would characterize his generation. He was ready, as he put it, to "do some real work!"

Notes

1. Edward Shils, ed., *Remembering the University of Chicago: Teachers, Scientists, and Scholars* (Chicago: University of Chicago Press, 1991). See the chapter on Robert M. Hutchins for a concise account of his career at the University of Chicago.

2. See Jim Bowman, *Good Medicine: The First 150 Years of Rush–Presbyterian–St. Luke's Medical Center* (Chicago: Chicago Review Press, 1987), 81-85, describing these events.

3. See Eugene Goldwasser, *Jake: Leon O. Jacobson, M.D.* (Sagamore Beach: Science History Publications/USA, 2006). Chapter 6, "The Atomic Bomb Project," 25-28, gives an account of a physician's contribution to the Manhattan Project during the war years.

4. See Deborah Dash Moore, *GI Jews: How World War II Changed a Generation* (Cambridge, MA: The Belknap Press of Harvard University Press, 2004), esp. the preface and 25-27.

5. Moore, *GI Jews*, 76.

6. Unless otherwise stated, all quotations relating to the history of the 15th

General Hospital are from this privately published book, *15th General Hospital '43–'45,* Capt. Michael W. Leff, DC, editor in chief, and Maj. Mitchell Oestreich, MC, photography editor.

7. K rations were probably named for Dr. Ancel Keys, physiologist at the University of Minnesota, who in 1941 was asked by the U.S. War Department to design nonperishable ready-to-eat meals. The A rations were served in any area where food could be preserved under refrigeration. C rations included ten different meat compounds, the most celebrated of them being the ubiquitous Spam, stews, spaghetti, vegetables, dehydrated eggs, and potatoes. K rations comprised compounds that if nothing else were at least nourishing. There was even a D bar, which was hard as a rock and might take 30 minutes to consume.

8. The author wishes to acknowledge the help of Murray Dworetzky, who generously shared his observations of Dr. Kirsner both during the war and later at the University of Chicago. His observations were recorded in an interview conducted in February 2006.

9. The letter was published in the *Denver Medical Bulletin* in 1946. It had been submitted by Dr. Palmer under the title "A Very Interesting Letter Received by One of Our Colleagues." The author is indebted to Dale Smith for finding and supplying him with a reprint of the article.

10. Dworetzky M, Smallpox, October 1945, *NEJM* 346(17):1329-30, 2002 (bioterrorism issue).

11. Percival Bailey (1892-1973) was a neurosurgeon, physiologist, philosopher, and tireless investigator. He was a leading member of the Chicago scientific community of neuroscientists.

6 * Returning from War, 1946-1961

In August 1946, after three years away from home, Dr. Kirsner returned to civilian life and to his wife and their five-year-old son, Robert, a scene that was being repeated in all walks of life throughout the United States. In one sense, 1943 to 1946 was for Dr. Kirsner a somewhat distorted version of the traditional *Wanderjahr* enjoyed by the men of an earlier generation and a different class. He had seen parts of Europe and of Asia, he had seen humanity at its best and at its worst, and he had been part of the events that defined his century and cast a long shadow into the 21st century.

Minnie had kept their home going through three long and at times uncertain years. She had nurtured Bob from a frail, premature baby to a normal, active five-year-old. At age 65, Robert could still recall his mother frequently showing him a picture of his father, helmeted in full battle gear, wearing glasses and smiling back at the camera. Robert would recall this picture and his father's return from the service as being "really scary." But there were pleasures delayed that could now be enjoyed with the money that had been saved in military back pay. Minnie had always wanted a fur coat, which she now bought, and they also purchased their first automobile, a Chevrolet Impala.

For many returnees, separation from the military meant returning to civilian careers that were very different from what they had done in the military. The doctors in the Medical Corps, however, had at least continued to work as physicians through the war years. Many were young and would resume the completion of their training. Dr. Kirsner was among the more senior military officers who were al-

ready fully trained, and he had remained in contact with his specialty throughout the war.

Military medicine was of course far removed from the academic career he had been pursuing in Chicago. But although he had been unable to write papers during those years, his clinical experiences during the war had caused him to reflect on aspects of the etiology of inflammatory bowel disease. In spite of the enormous stress of war, he had seen no new instances of ulcerative colitis among military personnel; the only cases he had observed, in two servicemen, had existed prior to their enlistment. Also, in his tours of civilian hospitals in France and Belgium, again in spite of the hardship and trauma the civilian population had endured, he did not encounter any new instances of ulcerative colitis.[1] These observations would encourage him to begin to rethink his previous views on the importance of psychosomatic factors in the etiology of ulcerative colitis.

The return to civilian life and his academic career was undoubtedly accompanied by uncertainty and some anxious moments. If he had thought his office in Billings Hospital was small before—and he had characterized it as a closet—he now found to his amazement that the room had since been occupied by two additional physicians and their desks. But Dr. Kirsner was characteristically full of optimism. His accomplishments during the years after the war clearly reflect the enthusiasm, determination, and dedication that he applied to his work.

At Dr. Palmer's suggestion, in September 1946 a trip was arranged to visit several gastroenterology programs on the East Coast. Dr. Kirsner visited Stewart Wolf at Cornell, Tom Machella at the University of Pennsylvania, and Louis Zetzel's program at Beth Israel Hospital in Boston. Later he would also visit J. A. Bargen's active program in inflammatory bowel disease at the Mayo Clinic. The purpose of these visits was to update his knowledge of current training and research programs. Perhaps Dr. Palmer was already beginning to groom Dr. Kirsner for a larger role in the administration of the Section of Gastroenterology.

In 1943 and 1944, while he was in the military, 14 articles were published with Dr. Kirsner's name as either the lead author or a contributing author. These articles dealt largely with peptic ulcer disease and represented a publication lag of work that had been completed during the prewar years. Starting in 1947 with a few articles, including an extensive three-part article that appeared in monthly installments reviewing the literature on peptic ulcer disease from July 1946 through 1948, he produced a steady stream of publications: 25, primarily on peptic ulcer disease, gastric cancer, and ulcerative colitis. Notable also were the first two of a series of articles, published in the *Journal of Biological Chemistry,* on the metabolic consequences of ulcerative colitis, the result of studies on amino-acid metabolism in patients that he had performed with the expert help of Leonard Sheffner.[2] Leonard Sheffner was a talented Ph.D. biochemist from the University of Illinois whom Dr. Kirsner had recruited into the Section of Gastroenterology to pursue these basic investigations. Hiring a scientist like Sheffner reflected his conviction that the clinician scientist needed the thinking and technical skills of basic scientists to ensure quality research. His experience during the war observing the extreme nutritional problems of Dutch POWs in the Pacific and Nazi concentration camp survivors had convinced him of the important role nutritional factors played in the care of patients with debilitating illnesses like chronic ulcerative colitis. Utilizing biochemical techniques specifically adapted to their research, the studies he and Sheffner performed resulted in, as Dr. Sumner C. Kraft would characterize it in his tribute to Dr. Kirsner's work in the study of inflammatory bowel disease, "comprehensive investigations of protein balance . . . , including the direct measurement of individual amino acids in the foods eaten and in the blood, urine and feces documenting the tremendous protein and other nutrients losses even in patients with only moderately active IBD."[3]

There were also important papers on gastric secretion and the therapy of peptic ulcer disease. Of particular importance were the articles written with Erwin Levin and Walter Palmer evaluating the results of limited Roentgen radiation of the fundus of the stomach aimed at suppressing gastric acid secretion—a key objective in the treatment of peptic ulcer disease at the time.[4] Today this approach may seem surprising, given our awareness of the adverse affects of ionizing radiation, but it reflects the severity of duodenal ulcer disease in this era and the lack of effective medical therapy. The absence of effective therapy is highlighted by the frequency with which physicians resorted to a surgical approach to chronic peptic ulcer disease, despite the attendant debilitating physiologic consequences associated with subtotal gastric resection.

American Gastroscopic Club

The American Gastroscopic Club (see chap. 4 for a fuller discussion) held its first annual meeting on June 7, 1942, at the Claridge Hotel in Atlantic City after the annual meeting of the American Gastroenterological Association (AGA). Gastritis was the principal topic on the agenda. At that time there were 109 members in the club. Because of World War II, the club did not hold another formal meeting until 1945. Meeting in informal sessions, the officers and governing board discussed issues related to availability of x-ray facilities, surgical resources, and standards for proper training, including the observation of at least 50 procedures; having an understanding of the proper indications, contraindications, and differentiation of benign and malignant gastric ulcers; and the interpretation of endoscopic observations.

From 1943 to 1946 Edward Benedict of Boston served as the second president of the club, following Dr. Schindler. Dr. Benedict started the publication of *Bulletin of the American Gastroscopic Club*. The importance of the *Bulletin* grew, and the membership appointed H. Marvin Pollard of the University of Michigan and Roy Sexton of Washington, D.C., as editor and associate editor, respectively. The club undertook a special project, *A Comprehensive Bibliography of Every Publication Related to Modern Gastroscopy*, which was completed in 1950 under the supervision of Dr. Kirsner and Dr. Julian Buser. Dr. Buser had been a member of his medical team in Japan, and after the war he had come to the University of Chicago, where he received his training in gastroenterology and for a time was a member of the Section of Gastroenterology. They collected 501 articles and books published between 1943 and 1949, an indication of the growing national recognition and interest in endoscopy. One thousand copies of the bibliography were printed and distributed to hospitals and medical libraries throughout the country.[5]

In 1946 Dr. Kirsner resumed his position as secretary of the Gastroscopic Club and was elected president of the organization from 1949 to 1950. Dr. Kirsner had never considered endoscopy and the performance of gastroscopy to be the main focus of his clinical and research efforts, however. He coauthored three papers with Dr. William Ricketts and Dr. Palmer on aspects of gastritis in 1949 and 1950 that were published in *Gastroenterology,* the *American Journal of Medical Science,* and the *American Journal of Medicine.*[6]

As noted above in chapter 4, the American Gastroscopic Club was rapidly transformed into the organization it is today, the American Society for Gastrointestinal Endoscopy. The ASGE plays a major role in gastroenterology and ensures the appropriate and safe application of endoscopic techniques in the care of patients.

American Association for the Study of Liver Diseases (AASLD)

Hepatitis had been a significant problem among the Allied servicemen of World War II. The more than 60 instances of hepatitis that resulted from contamination of the yellow-fever vaccine had also served to focus attention on the problem and its morbidity among members of the armed forces. The introduction of the Menghini percutaneous needle liver biopsy and the advent of new biochemical tests to assess liver function or recognize liver disease had led to increasing interest in the study of liver disease after the war. The American Society for Experimental Pathology began to devote one of its sessions to the liver in the late 1940s. In the autumn of 1948 the library of the Hektoen Institute for Medical Research of Cook County Hospital was the site of the first informal conference of what would become the American Association for the Study of Liver Diseases (the AASLD), which celebrated its fiftieth anniversary in 2000.[7]

Approximately 30 participants attended the annual meeting of Chicago's Central Society for Clinical Research held each fall in the Drake Hotel, at the foot of Chicago's Magnificent Mile. Hans Popper would ask each of the participants working with him to describe their research, and visitors also described their liver-related activities.[8] Popper, the dynamic founder of the society and the dean of American hepatology, was born on November 23, 1903, in Vienna, then the capital of the Austro-Hungarian Empire.[9] His father was a prominent physician, and Popper received a classical education. His father served in World War I, and the family suffered destitution and hunger because of the postwar inflation afflicting Germany. With his father's return to civilian life, the family's situation improved, and Popper was able to enter the University of Vienna in 1922. His interests were initially in biochemistry, and he published several articles as a student. After graduation in 1928, he spent his first five years in anatomical pathology, a path to a career in academic medicine.

With the growth of the National Socialist Party in Germany and the spread of Nazi ideology into Austria, life became increasingly stressful. In 1940 Popper fled Europe on the maiden voyage of the *New Amsterdam* to New York. He was accepted at Chicago's Cook County Hospital as a research fellow at a stipend of $150 a month. Taking advantage of the wide spectrum of liver disease at Cook County Hospital, he was able to pursue his interest in hepatology, which dated back to his years in Vienna. He was a productive investigator, and his work received wide recognition. In 1943 he was appointed chief of the pathology service at Cook County Hospital and professor of pathology in its Graduate School of Medicine, where he also founded the Hektoen Institute of Medical Research.

During the summer of 1949 Popper proposed to attendees at the informal meeting held the previous autumn that a more structured meeting take place at the Hektoen Institute during the afternoon and evening before the next Central Society meeting. The chief collaborators in this venture included Hugh L. Butt of the Mayo Clinic, Fred Hoffbauer from Minneapolis, Fenton Schaffner of Chicago, and Leon Schiff from Cincinnati. The meeting was preceded by the usual Thursday morning clinical pathologic conference held in the amphitheater of the Department of Pathology. Among the 42 attendees of the 1949 meeting were Dr. Kirsner and Dr. William Ricketts of the University of Chicago. Topics discussed included the differential diagnosis of jaundice, newer tests of liver function, experimental investigations, and new concepts of hepatic structure. The dinner session was devoted to an enthusiastic conversation about creating an American registry of pathology at the Armed Forces Institute of Pathology. There also was a lengthy discussion on the funding of future liver conferences and the establishment and incorporation of a society that would be called the Association for the Study of Liver Diseases (ASLD; later renamed the American Association for the Study of Liver Diseases, AASLD). Plans were made to hold the next meeting in 1950 before the Central Society meeting. The ASLD was incorporated in the state of Illinois on March 23, 1950, at a meeting of the preliminary council at the Hektoen Institute. The article on the history of the AASLD written by Hans Popper in 1982 and published in the journal *Hepatology* includes a reproduction of a photostat of the original application for incorporation. Dr. Joseph B. Kirsner's signature is clearly visible among the 10 signatures on the document.

The doctors' lounge at Cook County Hospital was the site of the first meeting of the ASLD, which was attended by 75 physicians, 59 of whom were members. The evening session was followed by a short business meeting. The total income of the society for that year was $110, and the expenses were $74.85, leaving the new society with a net worth of $35.15. The annual membership dues were $2, and at the second meeting, on November 1, 1951, with membership steadily increasing, current members were urged to submit their dues, since many were already in arrears. Today the AASLD has a membership of over 3,000 physicians. It is recognized nationally and internationally through its publication of the journal *Hepatology*, its promotion of first-rate scientific research in the field of hepatology, and its educational programs in continuing education and public awareness of liver diseases.

The Development of Corticosteroids

Throughout the 1940s, treatment of a patient with ulcerative colitis or Crohn's disease was largely limited to supportive and symptomatic management, including attention to nutritional deficits and correction of anemia through blood transfusions. The available sulfonamides benefited some patients, but properly conducted controlled trials of these medications had yet to be performed. Even the mainstay of medical therapy for patients with inflammatory bowel disease, sulfasalazine, commonly known as Azulfidine and a combination of sulfapyridine and 5–amino salicylic acid, had been synthesized only recently by biochemists at the Karolinska Institute and tested during the early years of the 1940s. The Scandinavian pediatrician and investigator Nina Swartz, in Stockholm, was testing the efficacy of this compound in patients with rheumatoid arthritis when she noted that those patients also suffering from ulcerative colitis experienced a remission of their colitis. For the patient, since the lack of effective therapy meant long periods of hospitalization and the ever-present threat of surgery and a proctocolectomy (removal of the colon and rectum and a permanent ileostomy), the discovery of sulfasalazine represented one of the first true therapeutic breakthroughs. A highlight of Walter Lincoln Palmer's 1948 Friedenwald Lecture to the AGA was his review of both his and Dr. Kirsner's current views on the etiology, clinical manifestations, and treatment of the disease.[10] Later in his career Dr. Kirsner would write extensively on the history of inflammatory bowel disease and review the wide spectrum of therapeutic agents that had been tried in a desperate search for an effective form of therapy.[11]

On April 20, 1949, the *New York Times* reporter William Laurence described a staff meeting at the Mayo Clinic where it was announced that preliminary tests of a hormone derived from the outer layer of the adrenal glands had opened up an entirely new approach in the treatment of rheumatoid arthritis.[12] Drs. Philip Hench, Charles Slocumb, and Howard Polley reported their experiences with 14 patients suffering from rheumatoid arthritis who had been treated with Kendall's Compound E, or what is now known as cortisone, which had been isolated by the biochemist Edward Kendall.[13] Movies illustrated the dramatic mobility of previously wheelchair-bound patients who, after receiving the new medication, were able to stand and walk. In October 1950 the Nobel Committee announced that Philip Hench and the two biochemists, Tadeus Reichstein of the University of Basel and Edward Kendall of the Mayo Clinic, who had isolated and elucidated the chemical structure of adrenal steroids would receive the Nobel Prize. The possibility that these compounds might benefit patients with rheumatoid arthritis had occurred to Hench as a result of his clinical observations that women suffering from the disease experienced a remission when they were pregnant.

The isolation of these compounds produced in minute amounts by the adrenal cortex was extremely difficult, and although only precious milligram amounts were available at first, their effectiveness was rapidly tested in many inflammatory diseases. The first patients with inflammatory bowel disease were treated at the Mayo Clinic. By November 1950 Dr. Kirsner and Dr. Palmer were able to present their preliminary experience with ACTH (adrenocorticotropic hormone, the pituitary hormone that drives the adrenal gland to produce its own array of corticosteroids) at the 23rd Annual Meeting of the Central Society for Clinical Research in Chicago.[14] In December 1950 Armour Laboratories sponsored a second clinical ACTH conference that covered a wide variety of topics, including basic investigation of the pituitary-adrenal axis, investigations on the effects of ACTH on kidney and electrolyte function, and clinical applications of both ACTH and cortisone in a wide variety of clinical situations. Dr. Kirsner and colleagues from the University of Chicago presented a paper on the effects of ACTH and related hormones on amino-acid metabolism.[15] There were two other papers on the use of ACTH in ulcerative colitis, from Harvard University and from the Wadsworth General Hospital Veterans Administration Center in Los Angeles.

In the October 6, 1951, issue of *JAMA* Dr. Kirsner and Dr. Palmer reported their early and encouraging results in patients with chronic ulcerative colitis using ACTH, and the usefulness of cortisone itself.[16] Clinical side effects, such as Cushing's syndrome with its typical redistribution of fat (facial puffiness and truncal obesity), cutaneous striae (red streaks over the trunk of the body), fluid retention, and hypertension, also were noted. The clinical response to the introduction of adrenal steroid therapy represented uncharted waters for physicians in the 1950s. One effect that greatly impressed Dr. Kirsner was the dramatic increase in the appetite of patients receiving steroids. In particular, there was a patient he carefully studied with Dr. Del Bergenstal of the endocrinology department. Metabolic protein balance studies, including measurement of urinary nitrogen, revealed that in response to steroid treatment, this patient was consuming and metabolizing an astounding 400 grams of protein and 8,000 calories a day.

Ironically, the Chicago area entered this story again on Thanksgiving evening 1950, when the suburb of Oak Park became the site of a racially motivated hate crime. An arson attempt was made against

Percy Lavon Julian (1899-1975), the first African American to buy a home in Oak Park.[17] Dr. Julian held a Ph.D. earned in Europe and was head of the soya products division of the Glidden Company in Chicago. In November 1950 he was hard at work on a method of synthesizing Compound S from naturally occurring plant sterols, work that resulted in a U.S. patent for the production of cortisone.

Over the next decade Dr. Kirsner would continue to report his experience with an growing number of patients with ulcerative colitis and regional enteritis treated with ACTH, cortisone, and hydrocortisone.[18] Today, corticosteroids, while helpful in the initial control of inflammation, are no longer acceptable for the long-term treatment of inflammatory bowel disease because of their side effects, particularly those related to osteoporosis and its associated complications.

Living in the Cloisters

When Dr. Kirsner returned from the service in 1946, he and Minnie and Bob lived at 5736 S. Drexel Avenue in a three-story apartment building that Dr. Kirsner liked to describe as a sort of "junior faculty building." The structure no longer exists, but it would seem the hierarchical view of university housing was an imprint that military life had left on his thinking. In 1952, concurrent with his achieving the rank of full professor, the family moved into the building that would be his home from that time on. Since he has continued to live in the building for over 55 years, and it is a unique building, a little of its background is warranted.

The Cloisters, at 5805 S. Dorchester, occupies the southwest corner of 58th Street and Dorchester Avenue.[19] The building, completed in November 1928, was designed by the architects Granger and Bollenbacher. The first residents to move in were owners in a cooperative plan. The 1927 prospectus for the building indicated that as of September 1, 1927, the land and the building still under construction were valued at $2.16 million.[20] The building was described as "Romanesque" in style, "akin to the Gothic Gray Towers" of the university. The lofty entrance arches of "warm-colored" Indiana Limestone were all handworked, and the garth flooring was of variegated slate. There would be a central enclosed garden court and fountain bounded by an open, arched passageway. The building was thirteen stories tall, with 84 substantial individual apartment units.

Owing to the Depression, the 1930s were a difficult time, and in 1935 the Cloisters Building Corporation declared bankruptcy. One year later, the 5805 Dorchester Corporation was established, which lasted until November 1950, when the University of Chicago bought the building. The location and ownership by the University of Chicago gave the building its aura of being part of the university community. Over the years prominent individuals who have resided there included James Henry Breasted, the founder of the Oriental Institute; Charles Huggins, a 1966 Nobel Prize winner in medicine; Gary Becker, a winner of the Nobel Prize in Economics in 1992; Shirley Jackson Case, one of the original owners and a professor of the New Testament and early church history; and Allan Bloom, professor of philosophy, author of *The Closing of the American Mind,* and the person on whom the protagonist in Saul Bellow's novel *Ravelstein* is based.

In 1952 the Kirsner family moved into 8F on the front side of the inner court. Robert recalls that when his parents were out for an evening he amused himself, unbeknownst to them, by dropping folded paper "water bombs" into the courtyard below. Subsequently, they moved to the top floor of the building, into the penthouse apartment or Top C. This large, open apartment with a circular view on the north and east sides of the building, affords a view of Lake Michigan and the parks along its shoreline, and in the distance, particularly on a clear day, a beautiful view of the Chicago downtown skyline.

Personal Life

In his foreword to his 1991 book *Remembering the University of Chicago,* Edward Shils, professor of sociology and member of the Committee on Social Thought at the University of Chicago, reflecting on the faculty of the university who did significant work from 1930 to 1970, writes that these were a group of men and women who devoted themselves seven days a week to their calling.[21] Anyone who came into contact with Dr. Kirsner during this period quickly become aware of the dedication he brought to his career. In his presentation before the AGA in San Antonio, Texas, on May 19, 1975, of the prestigious

Friedenwald Medal to Joseph Barnett Kirsner, Dr. Palmer impressed upon the audience, and subsequent readers of the address in *Gastroenterology*, that he had never met anyone with Dr. Kirsner's capacity for sustained hard work.[22]

However, he found time for recreation. There were many tennis courts around the university, and Dr. Kirsner became quite adept at the game, a facility he may have carried over from his youth in Boston, where he and his brother, Morris, played four-wall handball at the YMCA. Dr. Kirsner felt that handball was a demanding sport and remembered his brother as an outstanding competitor. He took Bob to the tennis courts and initiated him into the game as well. Robert Kirsner, now in his mid-60s, remembers his father as having a formidable backhand.

From the early years of their marriage, the Kirsners had been close friends with Martin Sandler and his wife, Lorraine. Martin Sandler's cousin was married to Minnie's brother Lou, who was a distinguished lawyer then living in Minneapolis. During the summers when Bob was away at camp, Minnie and Joe took regular vacations in the Lake Minnetonka area of Minnesota, where they stayed with the Sandlers in their cabin on the lake. Martin Sandler remembers that they played many tennis matches and that Joe regularly won. Dr. Kirsner remembers that he loved to go fishing on the lake. One summer, in 1951, he was sitting in a boat out on the lake, and, frustrated at not having had the slightest luck in catching any fish, he pulled a pack of cigarettes out of his shirt pocket and threw it into the water. He never smoked again. At the time Dr. Kirsner was regularly smoking both cigarettes and a pipe, and he credits this occasion, and the fact that his mentor Walter Palmer was a nonsmoker, for influencing his decision to stop. At 98 years of age and recalling this incident, he said he would like to embellish this story by adding that the fish immediately started biting, but this did not happen.

Gastroenterology Research Group

During the years following his return to civilian life and to academic medicine at the University of Chicago, Dr. Kirsner worked tirelessly to encourage basic research in gastroenterology while publishing extensively on clinical aspects of gastrointestinal disease. His bibliography from 1947 to 1955 lists over 175 publications written by himself or coauthored with colleagues in the Section of Gastroenterology. The topics include clinical aspects of peptic ulcer disease, the treatment of complications, and the search for a more effective means of reducing gastric secretion, then thought to be the key to successful treatment. The clinical challenge of differentiating benign from malignant gastric ulcers and the clinical value of exfoliative cytology of the gastrointestinal tract were frequent topics of his reports. Beginning in 1947, ulcerative colitis and regional enteritis assume a greater and greater importance in his list of publications. Many of the articles dealt with clinical aspects of these diseases, but he was also beginning to investigate the problem of the etiology and pathogenesis of inflammatory bowel disease. A paper presented in 1955 at the Central Society for Clinical Research summarizes his work on the experimental production of an immunological model of ulcerative colitis.[23] There were important studies on the basic biology of protein and amino acid metabolism in normal men, inflammatory bowel disease, and cirrhosis of the liver published as a series of articles in the *Journal of Biological Chemistry, Gastroenterology,* and the *Journal of Clinical Investigation.* These publications reflect his continuing interest in the basic science aspects of the pathophysiology of disease, nutrition, and both inflammatory bowel disease and liver disease.[24] His bibliography also reflects interest in both the clinical and the experimental aspects of a broad spectrum of gastrointestinal and hepatic disorders.

At annual meetings of the American Society for Clinical Investigation in Atlantic City in the spring, and those of the Central Society for Clinical Research in Chicago in the fall, he and his colleagues agreed that there was an underrepresentation of papers on basic research in gastroenterology. In addition, Dwight Wilbur, in his presidential address to the AGA in May 1955,[25] documented the lack of innovative research in digestive diseases and the limited funding of appropriate research. These perceived difficulties led Dr. Kirsner to found the Gastroenterology Research Group, whose meetings became an important part of the AGA's spring meetings, Digestive Disease Week. Taking place on the Sunday preceding the start of Digestive Disease

Week, the program of the Gastroenterology Research Group became a major seminar for basic research topics.[26]

Dr. Kirsner, working together with Basil I. Hirschowitz, then of the University of Michigan (later of the University of Alabama), and E. Clinton Texter Jr., of the Chicago Northwestern University Medical School, formed a steering committee to organize an initial meeting of the Gastroenterology Research Group at Thorne Hall on the Chicago Campus of Northwestern University and its medical school in November 1955. The meeting was attended by 150 physicians, a number that reflected the latent but significant interest in gastrointestinal research.

The program at this first meeting dealt with newer aspects of peptic ulcer disease research and techniques for studying the functions of the small intestine. Dr. Clifford J. Barborka, a member of the research committee of the AGA, opened the meeting, and Dr. Kirsner served as its chairman. He informed the audience that the purpose of the meeting was to provide a forum where ideas could be freely exchanged and new research stimulated. The speakers included Owen Wangensteen, the innovative chairman of the Department of Surgery at the University of Minnesota; Stewart Wolf, then chairman of the Department of Medicine at the University of Oklahoma School of Medicine; and Basil Hirschowitz. Drs. Wangensteen and Wolf confined their remarks to the study of gastric secretion, and Dr. Hirschowitz examined the role of ACTH and the adrenal cortex in peptic ulcer disease. The second session of the meeting, chaired by Dr. Texter, was devoted to the current status of and investigative techniques involved in research on the physiology of the small intestine.

The second meeting of the Gastroenterology Research Group was held in April 1956 in Haddon Hall in Atlantic City, New Jersey, in conjunction with the American Federation for Clinical Research and attended by over 300 investigators. This meeting focused on the techniques and study of the small bowel in health and disease. By 1959, at the ninth semiannual meeting of the American Federation for Clinical Research, at the Drake Hotel in Chicago, the program of the Gastroenterology Research Group was devoted to the biology of the colon mucosa. Dr. Kirsner's paper, "Hypersensitivity Reactions in the Colon Mucosa," reflected his interest in the search for an immunologically mediated model for inflammatory bowel disease, which he felt was key to understanding its pathogenesis. Later members of the group, in addition to Kirsner, Hirschowitz, and Texter, included Dr. Thomas Almy of Cornell, Dr. Charles F. Code of the Mayo Clinic, Dr. Perry Culver of Harvard, Dr. Alvin J. Cummins of the University of Tennessee, Dr. Nicholas Hightower of Scott & White Hospital in Temple, Texas, and Dr. Wade Volwiler of the University of Washington. Over the years, the strength of the Gastroenterology Research Group is reflected in the long list of distinguished scientist members of the AGA.

Miles Fiterman and His Importance to Gastroenterology

In 1954 Dr. Kirsner received a telephone call from Miles Fiterman, a prominent businessman in Minneapolis. Mr. Fiterman had been given Dr. Kirsner's name as someone to whom he could turn for the care of his young daughter, Valerie, then three years old, who had developed severe ulcerative colitis. Dr. Kirsner arranged for Valerie's transfer to the Bobs Roberts Memorial Hospital for Children of the University of Chicago under his care. At this time there were no pediatric gastroenterologists, and it was necessary for gastroenterologists to assume the care of both pediatric and adult patients with inflammatory bowel disease.

During Valerie's hospitalization, which lasted several months, Dr. Kirsner and her parents, Miles and Shirley, came to know each other very well. Miles Quinten Fiterman was born on May 15, 1920, in Deep River Falls, Minnesota.[27] He had met his wife when they were both 16 years old. A graduate of the University of Minnesota Law School, Miles had founded a flourishing company called Miles Pre-cut Homes, which were sold in 41 states. Miles repeatedly questioned Dr. Kirsner about current research into the cause of ulcerative colitis. Dr. Kirsner told him that there really wasn't much support for such research, a reply that engendered from Mr. Fiterman an unprecedented and generous burst of philanthropic activity. Miles financed and funded the publication of worldwide abstracts on ulcerative colitis and Crohn's disease which then were distributed free of charge to physicians nationally. In 1958 he established and funded the National

Foundation for Research in Ulcerative Colitis. He was instrumental in the publication of a pamphlet, *The Hidden Flame*, written by the noted science writer Victor Cohn of Minneapolis, which increased public awareness of inflammatory bowel disease.

These activities, and Dr. Kirsner's continued successful care of their daughter, including trips to Minneapolis to help during medical crises, strengthened their long-term friendship. In 1968, at Dr. Kirsner's advice, the prestigious Advisory Council of the National Institute of Arthritis and Metabolic Diseases, whose bylaws called for a layperson to serve on its board, appointed Miles to serve for a six-year period, contemporaneous with Dr. Kirsner's membership on the board. This proved to be a significant indoctrinating experience for Fiterman.

In 1967 the AGA named Miles as the first lay member of the society, and he and Shirley would often attend the annual meetings. In 1990 the Fitermans established the AGA/Miles and Shirley Fiterman Foundation Clinical Research Awards in Gastroenterology (honoring Dr. Kirsner) and in Hepatology (honoring Hugh Butt of the Mayo Clinic). The award annually provides $25,000 and a gold medal to awardees. Later they established a funding program for promising investigators in the field of gastroenterology and hepatology. In 1994 the Fiterman Foundation pledged an additional $100,000 each year for awards in the basic sciences. When Miles died after a long illness at 84 on June 21, 2004, Shirley assumed his place on the AGA's Foundation for Digestive Health and Nutrition. By this time the Fitermans had provided millions of dollars in support of research to 30 clinical and 20 basic science investigators, in addition to many other generous contributions.

Although Miles Fiterman died several years ago, the Fiterman family remains interested in continued advances in gastroenterology. Valerie Fiterman, during her initial hospitalization in Chicago, gradually responded to a program of nutritional support and antibiotics and was able to return to the care of her pediatrician in Minneapolis, where she eventually made a remarkable recovery. She has enjoyed good health since, and has married and has a family. She has assumed her parents' support of gastroenterology, and Dr. Kirsner last saw her at the AGA meeting in Chicago in 2006. Dr. Kirsner considers the Fitermans to be exceptional people, unstinting in their generous support of gastroenterology. The story of the Fiterman family is emblematic of the role the public can play in support of medical research and in setting up highly effective organizations (other examples are the Crohn's and Colitis Foundation of America and the Gastro-Intestinal Research Foundation).

Involvement in the NIH

The story of Dr. Kirsner's involvement with the National Institutes of Health (NIH) indirectly dates back to the closing days of World War II, when he was caring for patients at the 15th General Hospital in Liège. In the summer of 1944, as an Allied victory in Europe began to appear inevitable, President Roosevelt called into his office his deputy Vannevar Bush, the director of the Office of Scientific Research and Development (OSRD), a wartime organization under the Defense Department set up to deal with military-related research. Roosevelt asked Bush, "What's going to happen to science after the war?" to which Bush replied, "It's going to fall flat on its face." Roosevelt then said, "What are we going to do about it?" and Bush responded, "We better do something damn quick."[28]

Vannevar Bush (1890-1974), an outstanding electrical engineer educated at Harvard and MIT, had risen from being dean of the engineering school at MIT, to president of the Carnegie Institute in 1939, to chairman of OSRD during the war with a budget of $500 billion by the war's end. Bush sought a peacetime version of the OSRD with a fresh legislative charter that would strengthen the nation's military security through technological expertise. He felt that the technological weakness of the Allied forces had invited German aggression and that the financial support of the federal government was necessary to promote "world-class research." Bush drafted a letter in Roosevelt's name that shaped the relationship between government and civilian researchers for decades to come. The letter addressed four important questions about the government's obligation to science and engineering.

The first question dealt with releasing the thousands of scientific reports that posed no security threat, to stimulate commercial research. The second question was related to the support of medical research. The medical wing of OSRD had sponsored numerous medical innovations during the war. Two of the most notable related to better drugs for fighting malaria and the commercial production of penicillin. Bush took great pride in these activities of OSRD, and by 1945 penicillin had saved more lives than any medication previously developed. The third question related to the role that government would play in the future to aid research activities of public and private organizations. And the fourth question asked how the government could aid the task of developing scientific talent in American youth. For each question, Bush formed a select committee of 18 members, many of whom had been the recipients of OSRD contracts. The result of these deliberations was a report that Bush introduced titled *Science: The Endless Frontier.* The centerpiece of his introductory essay was the creation of a national research foundation. By this time, July 1945, President Roosevelt had died, and the report was given to President Harry Truman. The report was rapidly approved by the president and Congress and led to the establishment of the National Science Foundation and to financial support for the NIH.

When the Japanese surrendered on August 29, 1945, and World War II came to an end, 44 research grants that OSRD had with universities and with industry were transferred to the then-small NIH. The NIH traced its origins back to 1798, when President John Adams established the Marine Hospital Service on Staten Island for the relief of sick and disabled seamen. On May 26, 1930, the Ransdell Act converted the Marine Hospital Service to the National Hygienic Laboratory, an evolutionary step on the path to the formation of the NIH. The Ransdell Act authorized the construction of two new buildings and the creation of a system of fellowships. In 1935 Mr. and Mrs. Luke Wilson made a gift of 45 acres of their Tree Tops estate for the use of the NIH in Bethesda, Maryland, and by 1937 it had acquired eight divisions. In 1948 the Research Grants Office was created at the NIH to administer OSRD projects transferred to the Public Health Service (now part of the NIH) and to operate a program of research grants and fellowship awards.[29]

In the early 1950s Dr. Kirsner submitted a grant for research funds for the study of peptic ulcer disease. When this grant was rejected without explanation, he accepted the decision as an indication that he was still "rusty" as an investigator after his absence from academic medicine during the war. His subsequent research was focused on inflammatory bowel disease, not only on the clinical course of the disease but also on developing a suitable model of ulcerative colitis in experimental animals, the immunological mechanisms of the disease, and documentation of genetic (familial) aspects of inflammatory bowel disease. Dr. Kirsner was troubled when he learned that this second grant was also rejected without any explanation a year later, and he was ready to contact Illinois senators Everett Dirksen and Paul Douglas "to have the NIH investigated." He felt that, as a man who had served his country in both the European and Pacific theaters of war, he was entitled to an explanation of this rejection of what he knew was a sound scientific proposal. There was the further disconcerting effect that this new rejection made him question his future in academic medicine.

The dean of the Division of Biological Sciences at the university, Lowell T. Coggeshall, reassured Dr. Kirsner and said he would contact the NIH and let him know what he found out. Coggeshall (or Cogg, as Dr. Kirsner refers to him) was a popular dean of the medical school who served from 1947 to 1960 and subsequently became a vice president of the university. Dr. Kirsner went to the dean with this problem and not to the chairman of the Department of Medicine, Wright Adams, because Dr. Coggeshall, too, was a veteran of World War II.

Cog learned that the grants were being reviewed by basic scientists (physicists and biochemists) who were not familiar with the clinical diseases that were the focus of Dr. Kirsner's research proposals. Dr. Coggeshall contacted the director of the National Institute of Arthritis and Metabolic Diseases, Dr. Floyd Daft, who also recognized the problem. He and his deputy, Dr. Ralph Knutti, came to Chicago in 48 hours.

In May 1957 Ralph Knutti addressed the 58th Annual Meeting of the AGA and reviewed the history of digestive disease projects supported by the National Institute of Arthritis and Metabolic Diseases.[30] The institute had been formed in 1950 as one of the seven institutes making up the NIH. As early as 1951, projects related to the field of gastroenterology became of interest to the institute, but, as Dr. Knutti pointed out, they were of secondary interest only. He felt that by 1956 the institute had developed a small but sound program in gastroenterology funding. By June 1956 there were 60 research projects in gastroenterology that had received a total of $677,882. In addition, support for 15 medical doctors and two graduate training grants brought the total for financial support for gastroenterology to $752,882. Looking at these figures, we can see that Dr. Kirsner was competing for rather limited resources. Sixty research grants funded for $678,000 dollars comes to less than $11,000 a grant. The base salary for training grants was $3,800 a year.

Dr. Knutti and Dr. Daft met with Dr. Kirsner in Cog's office. Dr. Kirsner recommended that digestive disease be included in the NIH. He reviewed with them how important gastrointestinal problems had been in the army and to the national interest. Dr. Daft and Dr. Knutti quickly agreed. These discussions lead to the formation of the General Medicine Study Section at the University of Chicago in 1955. The initial membership included leaders in the field of gastroenterology—Dr. Kirsner, Franz J. Ingelfinger, Thomas P. Almy, Stewart Wolf, Julian Ruffin, and Wade Volwiler[31]—in addition to a superb group of basic and clinical scientists and physicians representing multiple medical specialties.

Dr. Kirsner would later learn that other investigators had been similarly frustrated when their research proposals submitted to the NIH were rejected. He, however, was the only one who had taken action to correct the problem.

It is interesting to read the April 30, 1957, letter from the acting surgeon general of the Department of Health, Education, and Welfare of the Public Health Service inviting Dr. Kirsner to serve on the newly formed General Medicine Study Section for a period extending to September 30, 1960.[32] This rather bureaucratic document outlines his responsibility for reviewing applications for research grants and determining which areas of research should be supported. The General Medicine Study Section was to be important in providing leadership in clinical research in gastroenterology, endocrinology, and nutrition and metabolic diseases among multiple medical specialties. Meetings were to take place three times a year in Bethesda, and "compensation was allowable at the rate of $45 per day for the time spent at the meeting and any field trips that prove desirable.

Members also receive transportation costs, plus $12 a day in lieu of actual and necessary expenses."

One of Dr. Kirsner's initial accomplishments as a member of the newly formed General Medicine Study Section was the organization of the first national conference on ulcerative colitis. This pioneering conference, "New Frontiers in Ulcerative Colitis," was held on Monday, January 6, 1958, in the Top-of-the-Park Room of the Woodner Hotel in Washington, D.C.[33] The meeting lasted the entire day with a luncheon and a dinner. It was supported by the NIH and the National Foundation for Research in Ulcerative Colitis, founded that year by Miles Fiterman. Dr. Kirsner was the chairman of the meeting and also gave one of the 10 scientific presentations that day. Welcoming remarks were to be given by Dr. James A. Shannon, the director of the NIH since August 1955, but unfortunately Dr. Shannon was not able to attend. Instead, Dr. Floyd Daft welcomed the group and pointed out that the General Medicine Study Section was then less than a year old but was already one the busiest study sections in the NIH and that "New Frontiers in Ulcerative Colitis" was their third conference.

The list of speakers and their topics contains the names of distinguished physicians who are still well known today, including Thomas Almy (Cornell), who spoke on the pathophysiology of ulcerative colitis; George L. Engel (University of Rochester), who spoke on the biologic and psychologic features of the ulcerative colitis patient; and Louis Weinstein (Tufts University), who presented his studies on bacteriologic aspects of the disease. Also present were basic scientists, including Robert A. Good (University of Minnesota) and Lewis Thomas (New York University), who spoke on aspects of the inflammatory reaction. Dr. Kirsner presented his work on experimental ulcerative colitis. Miles Fiterman was also present, and the National Foundation for Research in Ulcerative Colitis sponsored a celebratory dinner following the meeting. The entire proceedings of the meeting were published, under Dr. Kirsner's editorship, in the February 1961 issue of *Gastroenterology*.[34] The General Medicine Study Section, later expanded into several sections, continues to provide expert NIH-directed review of research applications in many specialty areas of medicine.

In 1956 Dwight David Eisenhower won a second term in office, overcoming a major myocardial infarction and disproving the public conception that a heart attack or myocardial infarction spelled the end of a man's active career. The nation's "first cardiologist," Paul Dudley White of Massachusetts General Hospital in Boston, had guided the country through the president's illness with his frank and informative press conferences.[35] Then, in June 1956, the president was hospitalized with a worsening small-bowel obstruction, the culmination of a long history of recurring episodes of abdominal pain. Lt. General Leonard Heaton performed a two-hour operation in the early hours of June 9, during which Crohn's disease involving the terminal ileum was discovered. Heaton decided to bypass the diseased segment of bowel and establish an anastomosis (or attachment) of the uninvolved or disease-free small intestine above the diseased terminal ileum to the likewise healthy-appearing transverse colon, rather than attempt a resection (removal) of the diseased intestine. He felt this was the safest course to take in man who had suffered a myocardial infarction less than a year earlier.[36] The decision was subject to considerable criticism by "Monday-morning quarterbacks," however. Dr. Kirsner, a recognized inflammatory bowel disease expert, was among those consulted by Washington, and he defended the surgeon's clinical judgment as appropriate to the situation. Eisenhower went on to finish his second term in office, and his ileitis remained quiescent for the remainder of his life. He died on March 28, 1969, just short of his 79th birthday.

In 1956, if little was understood by the public about the nature of heart attacks, even less was known about regional enteritis, as the president's illness was called. No spokesman was asked to step forward to inform the American public as Paul Dudley White had done earlier. Enquiries made to the NIH about what research was being done in this area did, however, lead eventually to the allocation of $100,000 in the form of 10 individual grants for research. Dr. Kirsner was the recipient of one of these grants. In retrospect, an opportunity to raise public awareness about inflammatory bowel disease and thereby strengthen research activity was overlooked. This responsibility was later undertaken by the Crohn's and Colitis Foundation of America.

NIH-supported funding in the training of gastroenterologists dates from 1956-57, and the Section of Gastroenterology at the University of Chicago was the first center to be funded under this program. The program led by Franz Ingelfinger at Harvard Medical School became the second recipient of a NIH-supported Training Grant in Gastroenterology. This important funding effort grew over the next 10 years to encompass 44 approved programs that had provided training for 637 physicians plus 103 individuals still in training. In 1969 an analysis of the program, published in *Gastroenterology* by George Scheele and George Kitzes,[37] reported that 24 percent of the trainees were involved to a major extent in research, 6 percent in teaching, 5 percent in "institutional care," and 38 percent in private practice. Analysis of those trainees who continued on to a significant career in research indicated that training extending into a third year had a greater yield than two years of training. The authors also recognized the need to provide trainees with advanced knowledge in an area of basic science tailored to their individual needs, and that such knowledge might require access to training beyond the resources of the individual academic program in which the trainee was based. The total budget for training of the National Institute of Arthritis and Metabolic Diseases in 1968 had risen to $16 million, funding approximately 290 programs. The average cost of these individual programs, $48,000, had increased at the rate of 6 to 8 percent each year, as opposed to the approximate 5 percent increase in funding during a comparable period of time. The report noted that most of the effort of training was directed at research in the small bowel and liver. Efforts involving the esophagus and colon were "nonexistent," and the report anticipated greater needs in basic science and "attendant methodological advances," as well as pediatric gastroenterology, epidemiology, and therapeutics. In 1965 Dr. Kirsner was appointed to the Advisory Council of the National Institute of Arthritis and Metabolic Diseases of the NIH and continued to be an active member until 1974.

European Trip, 1956

In the summer of 1956 the Kirsners were able to attend the International Congress of Gastroenterology meeting in London, where Dr. Kirsner was invited to present his studies on gastrointestinal exfoliative cytology. This meeting was a forerunner of what in 1958 would become the World Congress of Gastroenterology. Their son, Bob, now 14, was attending summer camp in Michigan, but Dr. Kirsner planned to show Minnie some of the places he had been during World War II: Ellesmere, Normandy and Garches, Liège and the Ardennes forest area. The Kirsners were friends of Mr. and Mrs. Henry Chumley, who owned a bookstore in Hyde Park. Frances Chumley was so enthusiastic about the trip that she made Dr. Kirsner a topcoat with no fewer than 18 pockets so that he could easily carry many miscellaneous items on the trip. He had planned to fly economy class, but a patient sent him money so that he could fly first class, and Dean Coggeshall also provided support for the academic part of the trip.

Minnie had wanted to stay at Claridge's hotel in London, and the hotel had requested that they transmit information on their "qualifications" to stay there. Minnie informed the hotel that Dr. Kirsner was the president of the American Gastroenterological Association and other local medical groups. They found themselves in a huge suite on the first floor (the king of Jordan was staying in the suite one floor above them). Feeling that it was all too expensive and far more elaborate than what they required, they asked the manager for a smaller suite but were told that none was available. Mrs. Kirsner responded that the Dorchester Hotel would accommodate them, and the manager of the Claridge's quickly located a smaller but quite satisfactory room for them. With the money saved, they were able to buy gifts for friends and family.

Before the conference started, they traveled from London to Frankfurt, Germany, where they enjoyed dining at an elegant restaurant that they went to first on their own and then on a subsequent evening as guests of a patient who joined them. They were able to visit Vienna and also Rome. In Rome they were looking forward to a visit with the pope that had been arranged by their good friend and patient Joseph Valenti. Dr. Kirsner found himself being asked for medical advice by a secretary of the Vatican, and subsequently they received an invitation to visit the pope at Castle Gandolfo, his summer residence. The Kirsners had brought items given to them by Catholic friends, which the pope graciously blessed. They were also taken out to dinner at Alfredo's and that same evening to a spectacular open-air opera performance, several miles outside of Rome. A remarkable day and evening for the Kirsners.

Notes

1. Kirsner JB, Inflammatory bowel diseases at the University of Chicago: Early experiences, a personal historical account, *Inflamm Bowel Dis* 11:4:407-16, April 2005.

2. Kirsner, JB, Palmer WL, and Scheffner AL, Studies on amino acid excretion in man, part I: Amino acids in urine, *J Biol Chem* 175:1:107-15, August 1948; Scheffner AL, Kirsner JB, and Palmer WL, Studies on amino acid excretion in man, part II: Amino acid in feces, *J Biol Chem* 176:1:89-93, October 1948.

3. Sumner C. Kraft, "Approaches to the Etiopathogenesis of Inflammatory Bowel Disease: A University of Chicago Perspective," chap. 8 of *Current Gastroenterology*, vol. 7, ed. G. Gitnick (Chicago: Year Book Medical Publishers, 1987), 350-55.

4. Ricketts WE, Palmer WL, Kirsner JB, et al., Radiation therapy in peptic ulcer, *Gastroenterology* 11:6:789-806, December 1948.

5. See Gerstner P, The American Society for Gastrointestinal Endoscopy: A history, *Gastrointestinal Endoscopy* 37:Suppl.2:1-26, 1991.

6. Ricketts WE, Palmer WL, and Kirsner JB, Chronic gastritis: A study of the relation between mucosal changes and symptoms, *Gastroenterology* 12:3:391-93, March 1949; Ricketts WE, Kirsner JB, and Palmer WL, The gastroscopic appearance of the gastric mucosa in peptic ulcer, *Amer J Med Sci* 217:542-44, May 1949; and Findley, Jr. JW, Kirsner JB, Palmer WL, et al., Chronic gastritis—a study of symptoms and gastric secretion, *Amer J Med* 7:2:198-206, August 1949.

7. Popper H, History of the American Association for the Study of Liver Diseases, *Hepatology* 2:6:874-78, 1982.

8. Schaffner FA, AASLD, the early days, *Hepatology* 27:1:303-5, 1998.

9. Schmid R, Hans Popper, in memoriam, 1903-1988, *Hepatology* 9:5:669-74, 1969.

10. Palmer WL, Chronic ulcerative colitis (Julius Friedenwald Lecture), *Gastroenterology* 10:4:767, April 1948.

11. Kirsner JB, Historical antecedents of inflammatory bowel disease therapy, *Inflamm Bowel Dis* 2:73-81, 1996.

12. See Gerald Weissman, M.D., "Cortisone and the Burning Cross: The Story of Percy Julian," *Pharos*, Winter 2005, 13-16.

13. Hench PS, Kendall EC, Slocumb CH, and Polley HR, The effect of a hormone of the adrenal cortex (17-hydroxy-11-dehydrocorticosterone) (Compound E) and the pituitary adrenocorticotropic hormone on rheumatoid

arthritis: A preliminary report, *Proc Staff Meet Clinic* 24:181-97, 1949.

14. Kirsner JB, Palmer WL, and Klotz AP, ACTH and cortisone in chronic ulcerative colitis: A comparison of clinical effects, *Proc Central Soc Clin Res* 23:58, 1950.

15. D. M. Bergenstal, R. L. Landau, and J. B. Kirsner, et al., "Effects of ACTH and Related Hormones on Metabolism," in *Proceedings of the 2nd Clinical ACTH Conference,* ed. John R. Mote, 2 vols. (New York: Blackiston, 1951), 1:250-63.

16. Kirsner JB and Palmer WL, Effect of corticotrophin (ACTH) in chronic ulcerative colitis: Observations in 40 patients, *JAMA* 147:541-49, October 6, 1951.

17. Weissman, "Cortisone and the Burning Cross: The Story of Percy Julian."

18. Kirsner JB and Palmer WL, Ulcerative colitis: Therapeutic effects of corticotrophin (ACTH) and cortisone in 120 patients, *Ann Int Med* 41:2:232-50, August 1954; Kirsner JB, Sklar M, and Palmer WL, The use of ACTH, cortisone, hydrocortisone and related compounds in the management of ulcerative colitis—experience in 180 patients, *Amer J Med* 22:2:264-74, February 1957; and Kirsner JB, Palmer WL, Spencer JA, et al., Corticotrophin (ACTH) and the adrenal steroids in the management of ulcerative colitis: Observations in 240 patients, *Ann Int Med* 50:4:891-927, April 1959, originally presented at 39th Session of the American College of Physicians, Atlantic City, N.J., April 30, 1958.

19. Information on the history of the Cloisters was kindly furnished by Denise R. Halverson in an interview conducted on January 27, 2006.

20. A copy of this prospectus was provided by Denise Halverson. It was prepared by Earle A. Shilton of 637 North Michigan Ave. for the Officers and Directors of The Cloisters Building Corporation.

21. Edward Shils, ed., *Remembering the University of Chicago: Teachers, Scientists, and Scholars* (Chicago: University of Chicago Press, 1991).

22. Palmer WL, Presentation of Julius Friedenwald Award to Joseph B. Kirsner, *Gastroenterology* 69:3:575-77, 1975.

23. Elchlepp JG and Kirsner JB, Studies on experimental ulcerative colitis, *Proc Central Soc Clin Res* 28:27-28, 1955.

24. Representative of these interests are the following papers: Scheffner AL, Kirsner JB, and Palmer WL, Amino acid excretion in patients with gastrointestinal disease during ingestion of various protein supplements, *Gastroenterology* 16:4:757-63, December 1950; Ricketts WE, Eichelberger L, and Kirsner JB, Observations on the alterations in electrolytes and fluid balance in patients with cirrhosis of the liver with and without ascites, *J Clin Invest* 30:11:1157-70, November 1951; Strub IH, Talso PJ, and Kirsner JB,

Intracellular and extracellular fluid and electrolyte alterations in cirrhosis of the liver with edema and ascites, *Gastroenterology* 28:2:163-75, February 1955; and Kirsner JB, Brandt MB, and Scheffner AL, Diet and amino acid utilization in gastrointestinal disorders, *Amer Diet Assn* 29:11:1103-8, November 1953.

25. Wilbur D, Research in gastroenterology, *Gastroenterology* 29:161-70, 1955.

26. Kirsner JB, The Gastroenterology Research Group, *Gastroenterology* 31:451-52, 1956.

27. Information on the life of Miles Fiterman taken from Butt H, Kirsner JB, and La Russo NF, Miles Fiterman, obituary, *Gastroenterology* 127:5:1286, 2004; and Ashlei Stevens, "Miles Fiterman Dies at 84," *New York Times,* June 25, 2004.

28. G. Paschal Zachary, *Endless Frontier: Vannevar Bush, Engineer of the American Century* (New York: Free Press, 1997), chap. 10, "The Endless Frontier (1944-1945)," 218-39.

29. Extensive information on the history of the National Institutes of Health is available on their Web site (http://www.nih.gov/about/).

30. Knutti, RE, Gastroenterology programs of the National Institutes of Arthritis and Metabolic Diseases, *Gastroenterology* 33:6:877-79, 1957.

31. Dale C. Smith, *The American Gastroenterological Association: 1897-1997* (Bethesda: AGA, 1999), 63.

32. Letter from JBK's papers; a copy is in the author's files.

33. Kirsner JB, Editorial: Commentary on the 1958 National Institutes of Health Conference on new frontiers in ulcerative colitis, *Inflamm Bowel Dis* 9:1:61-69, 2003.

34. Kirsner JB, New frontiers in ulcerative colitis (Symposium), *Gastroenterology* 40:2:281-369, February 1961.

35. For a review of President Eisenhower's heart attack from a physician's perspective, see Paul Oglesby, *Take Heart: The Life and Prescription for Living of Paul Dudley White* (Boston: Distributed by Harvard University Press for the Francis A. Countway Library of Medicine, 1986).

36. For an account of President Eisenhower's gastrointestinal illness and operations, see Heaton, LD, et al., President Eisenhower's operation for regional enteritis, *Ann Surg* 159:5:661-66, 1964; and Hughes CW, et al., A review of the late General Eisenhower's operations, *Ann Surg* 173:5:793-99, 1971.

37. Scheele GA and Kitzes G, Analysis of academic training programs in gastroenterology for the 10-year period 1957 to 1967, *Gastroenterology* 57:2:203-13, 1969.

7 ✳ Taking Charge, 1962–1971

In 1962 the University of Chicago still had in place a mandatory retirement age of 65, and Walter Lincoln Palmer, chief of the Section of
Gastroenterology, was approaching that age. By this time, Dr. Palmer's career had veered more toward activities involving the American
College of Physicians, while Dr. Kirsner was focused on gastrointestinal research activities and the American Gastroenterological Association (AGA). For a number of years, Dr. Kirsner had assumed more
and more of the responsibilities for both the training of fellows and
the research activities of the section, although Dr. Palmer still commanded a large and prominent gastroenterology referral practice.

Two years earlier, at a meeting in the offices of the dean of the
medical school, Dean Lowell T. Coggeshall met with the chairman
of the Department of Medicine, Wright Adams, and Dr. Palmer and
Dr. Kirsner. The purpose of the meeting was to discuss Dr. Kirsner's
assuming the position of head of the Section of Gastroenterology.
They discussed the future activities and goals of the section and Dr.
Palmer's role in the section after his retirement. The university wanted Dr. Palmer to continue his clinical activities at the hospital and
to use his faculty position as a base for his role in national societies.
By 1962 Dr. Palmer had served as president of the American College
of Physicians, the AGA, and was currently president of the Institute
of Medicine of Chicago, chairman of the American Board of Internal Medicine, and known throughout this country and abroad as a
leader in American medicine.

Dr. Palmer was reluctant, after so many years of being in charge
of the section, to accept a secondary role. He also mentioned that no

one had told his father, a country doctor, when to retire, and he saw himself as being in the same position. Instead, he decided to leave Billings and move his practice across the Midway to Woodlawn Hospital. There is a touch of irony in this decision, in that this was the community hospital where, 27 years earlier, Dr. Kirsner began his medical career in Chicago. In making this decision, Dr. Palmer would take with him many of the patients in his clinical practice and his associate Dr. Jean Spencer.

Dr. Palmer sent a letter to Dr. Kirsner on September 10, 1962, that is interesting on several levels. It gives us a picture of the manner in which the university approached Dr. Palmer's emeritus status, and also of the relationship between Dr. Kirsner and Dr. Palmer.

> Gradually my plans are crystallizing. I am to have a scientific office at home even though this may be difficult for Elizabeth to find space for books, files, and secretary. With the children gone, this should be possible some way or another. Dr. Jacobson has kindly assured me that one of the emoluments of the Emeritus state is a laboratory and that he will arrange for me to continue on the fifth floor or elsewhere.
>
> The clinical facilities of the Woodlawn Hospital will be available. The Staff has kindly made it possible for me to have office space on the second floor.

Reflecting on the past 35 years:

> The years have been happy ones, and productive as well, due in no small measure to your unfailing support and your unending labor. We are both proud of the work done, of the men trained, and of the group assembled. We both regret the dissolution induced in 1962 by forces beyond our control. You face the task of rebuilding the group, and of course, you will succeed in time. You certainly have my best wishes as well as eternal gratitude for all that you have done for me and for the group.
>
> You may not realize it, but the only picture of you in my files other than the group pictures is a snapshot of you in battle helmet. I would appreciate it greatly if you would do me a favor of a more formal photograph, if you have one, for placement in my book of celebrities.

During this period of transition, another important faculty member, Dr. Charles Clayman, also left the section to go into private practice. Dr. Kirsner was left alone to rebuild the section with the help of two recently graduated fellows, Dr. Sumner Kraft and Dr. Richard W. Reilly. The years from 1962 to 1971, when Dr. Kirsner would turn the section over to Dr. Irwin Rosenberg and become the deputy dean for medical affairs of the medical school and chief of staff of Billings Hospital, was a highly productive period in his life. During this time he established his reputation as a national leader in gastroenterology, a national and internationally recognized authority on inflammatory bowel disease. Through his efforts and through the work of the talented faculty he assembled, the Section of Gastroenterology at the University of Chicago would share in this recognition. Most importantly, the section would attract many talented fellows whose careers in gastroenterology would be launched through their association with Dr. Kirsner and their experience in the section. The transition, while placing greater demands on Dr. Kirsner, was one that he had in effect been "groomed for," given that from 1946 to 1962 he had gradually assumed more and more of the responsibility of administrating the section, including direction of the fellowship program, the bulk of the clinical activity, and direct involvement in and planning of research activities. In the years leading up to his retirement, Dr. Palmer had been away from the section for longer periods of time, since he was involved with national organizations and in visiting medical centers in South America, so it was natural that Dr. Kirsner had assumed greater responsibility over time.

Surveying Dr. Kirsner's bibliography for 1960 and 1961 gives one an overview of the areas in the field of gastroenterology that he and the members of his section were concerned with at the time. First were the clinical aspects of gastrointestinal disease. Publications included a broad array of review articles on such subjects as the causes and evaluation of the malabsorption syndrome, peptic ulcer disease, and inflammatory bowel disease, plus numerous chapters he wrote independently or coauthored with colleagues. With Dr. Palmer he wrote a chapter on the esophagus and the stomach for a major clinical textbook of the day, *Sodeman's Pathologic Physiology: Mechanisms of Disease.* He also wrote the comprehensive chapter "Diseases of the

Digestive Tract" for J. P. Greenhill's textbook *Obstetrics* (the continuation of Dr. De Lee's classic textbook, which Dr. Kirsner had studied in medical school). Other articles were individual cases or collections of cases documenting specific manifestations of individual diseases and published in *Gastroenterology,* the *American Journal of Digestive Diseases,* and the *American Journal of Medicine.* Topics included sclerosing cholangitis in ulcerative colitis, gangrenous skin lesions in ulcerative colitis, and a case report of cytomegalic inclusion disease in ulcerative colitis. Several articles reflected basic and clinical research underway in the department: two articles on the basement membrane of the epithelium of the colon and rectum published in *Science* and in *Gastroenterology,* an article on colon antibodies in ulcerative colitis published in the *Journal of Laboratory and Clinical Medicine,* and a major review article, "Hypersensitivity, Autoimmunity and the Digestive Tract," published in *Gastroenterology* and the forerunner of many articles on gastrointestinal immunology that reflected his and Dr. Kraft's laboratory research.

Dr. Kirsner was also beginning to write articles of a more philosophic nature that took a broader view of medicine and the care of the patient. Examples include "On Specialization and Gastroenterology" in *Pharos,* the journal of the Alpha Omega Alpha Society, and *JAMA;* and "The Treatment of the 'Untreatable' Patient," in the *Illinois Medical Journal,* also given as a talk, "Oration in Medicine," at the Illinois State Medical Society's annual meeting on May 25, 1960. And he was the editor of a symposium "Incipient Gastrointestinal Disease" in *Medical Clinics of North America,* as well as contributing an article on the recognition of the malabsorption syndrome.[1]

Fellows in the Section of Gastroenterology

The training of future specialists and academicians in gastroenterology was an important activity of the gastroenterology section. It constituted the third leg of the "three-legged stool" of academic medicine: patient care, research, and teaching. Hand in hand with advances in the "scientification" of medicine and enormous strides in the field of gastroenterology itself, fellowship training programs have evolved from not much more than apprenticeships to highly structured training programs designed to meet clinical and procedural requirements for accreditation; over time, they have been further subdivided into areas of subspecialty expertise.

In the 1930s Dr. Kirsner's initial exposure to the field was gained at the bedside, observing and working with Dr. Palmer. The gastroscopy clinic established at Billings by Dr. Rudolf Schindler afforded him the opportunity to learn gastroscopy at a time when few centers in the country could have provided such training. When the AMA and the American Board of Medical Specialists laid down the basic training requirements for fields in internal medicine, Dr. Kirsner was among the first candidates to be examined for certification in gastroenterology (see chap. 4).

With the demobilization of the armed services after World War II, more than 13,000 returning medical officers were seeking specialty certification. Help in meeting these demands came in part from the Servicemen's Readjustment Act, the GI Bill of 1944. The Veterans Administration ruled in 1945 that this program would apply to postgraduate medical education, and the funds made available to hospitals resulted in a dramatic expansion of residency programs.

In 1950 a committee chaired by Dr. Henry L. Bockus of the University of Pennsylvania medical school submitted a report to the governing board of the AGA reporting that there were then only 6 hospitals in the country with residency programs in gastroenterology and 29 fellowship positions at 15 institutions, where trainees on average devoted 50 percent of their time to research and 50 percent to clinical training.[2] The Bockus committee recommended one year of internship; one year, preferably two, of internal medicine residency; and a year of gastroenterology. Support for fellowship training from the NIH did not begin until 1956. The first two fellowship programs were established at the University of Chicago, under the direction of Dr. Palmer and Dr. Kirsner, and at Boston University, under the direction of Dr. Franz Ingelfinger. By 1969 there were 44 training programs in the United Sates, at a cost of $2 million annually. Dr. Kirsner was the chairman of the advisory committee to the NIH on fellowships.[3]

As director of the fellowship program at Chicago in the 1960s, Dr. Kirsner reviewed all the applications and recommendations for prospective fellows and interviewed each candidate before he or she was offered a position in the program. By this time, the fellowship program was highly structured, and trainees were given responsibility under faculty supervision for seeing patients in the outpatient clinic throughout their two-year fellowship, were assigned for three months each year to the inpatient service, and each year did a rotation on the inpatient consultation service. Fellows were also assigned on a rotational schedule to the hospital's proctoscopy clinic, the gastroscopy service, the liver biopsy service, and the section's esophageal dilation and esophageal motility services. Formal weekly clinical conferences, radiologic and pathological teaching conferences, and a section journal club were standard components of the fellowship program. In addition to the clinical portion of the fellowship experience, the fellows were assigned to one of the section's research laboratories, and the director of that laboratory served as a mentor, helping the trainee develop skills and experience in basic research.

Dr. Kirsner regards the approximately 200 fellows who trained in gastroenterology during his career as one of his most important legacies. The following sampling of these former fellows provides a picture of the section under Dr. Kirsner's leadership during these critical years.

* * *

The experiences of Dr. João Carlos Prolla of Brazil are worthy of note, since they reflect the experiences of other foreign physicians who came to the University of Chicago for training with Dr. Kirsner.[4] The recipient of an award from the W. K. Kellogg Foundation and the American College of Physicians Latin American Fellowship Program, Dr. Prolla came to the United States from Brazil in 1961. At the time he was an assistant at the Porto Alegre Medical School, in the southern part of Brazil, where he was a member of the gastroenterology department. He began his North American experience in New York on the service of Professor Thomas Almy at the Cornell University/Bellevue teaching unit in the summer of 1962. His initial training included a review course in internal medicine and polishing his precarious skills in English. Dr. Prolla then asked to be placed with Professor Henry Bockus in Philadelphia. Bockus's multivolume textbook was known throughout the world, and Dr. Prolla considered him the most prestigious American gastroenterologist. Dr. Almy disagreed and advised him to seek an appointment on Joseph B. Kirsner's service in Chicago, since Dr. Bockus was nearing retirement and Dr. Kirsner was both younger and a very capable clinician. Dr. Almy told Dr. Prolla that he would not regret the decision. Dr. Prolla quickly appreciated his good advice. Looking back 45 years later, he reflects "that meeting Professor Kirsner was one of the most important scientific and humanistic events of my life."

Dr. Prolla found Dr. Kirsner to be very patient with his limited language skills. Taking an initial history and physical examination from a new patient took him twice the time that the other first-year fellows needed, but Dr. Kirsner personally guided his steps in the clinic as he gradually gained the necessary confidence. Dr. Prolla was astonished by Dr. Kirsner's capacity to know and retain every detail of the medical, social, and personal life of his patients. He observed "that for Dr. Kirsner, a chart of greater than four pounds held no mystery." Dr. Prolla also was helped in his initial clinical steps by Dr. Kirsner's associate Dr. Reilly.

In 1963 Dr. Kirsner assigned Dr. Prolla the responsibility of supervising the GI cytology laboratory after the head of the laboratory, Dr. Howard Raskin, left the section to return to his home in Baltimore and the University of Maryland. GI cytology was being performed in very few centers in the United States, and the history of this technique at the University of Chicago dated back to the 1950s when Dr. Cyrus Rubin was a member of the section. In the early 1960s, the differentiation between benign gastric ulcers and malignant ulcers of the stomach was a major clinical problem for gastroenterologists. Early diagnosis of a malignant ulcer in time for the chance of surgical cure was a goal that was rarely achieved. When x-ray examination and endoscopic visualization without the possibility of biopsy were the only diagnostic tools available, gastric cytology afforded the hope of early diagnosis. While still affiliated with Harvard Medical School and at Beth Israel Hospital in Boston, Dr. Rubin had adopted the Papanicolaou (Pap) staining technique utilized for the diagnosis of cervical cancer and pioneered its application to the diagnosis of gastric cancer and malignant gastric ulcers.[5] While at the University of Chicago, he extended this technique to the esophagus, biliary tract, and large intestine.

When Dr. Prolla took over the cytology laboratory, he was aided by Leroy Cockerham, who, despite having no formal training, had formidable skill and experience in passing gastrointestinal tubes. Dr. Prolla was amazed at how easily Mr. Cockerham was able to place gastric tubes and perform esophageal and gastric lavage. When Dr. Prolla returned to Brazil in 1965, he had little success with GI cytology and realized that more than half the success of the procedure lay in the facility in passing the tubes and lavaging the GI tract.

Part of Dr. Prolla's experience included conducting a research project that required reviewing both the autopsy records of 148 patients who had died of leukemia in order to categorize the gastrointestinal complications and lesions they had suffered and also 158 references from the literature. This herculean task required many late hours in the medical records department, but it resulted in a presentation at the 45th Annual Meeting of the American College of Physicians in Atlantic City on April 8, 1964. Dr. Prolla was, in his words, "scared to death" at the thought of facing an audience of greater than 1,000 people and presenting his findings in English. Dr. Kirsner made him practice his presentation repeatedly so that by the day of his presentation, Dr. Prolla knew every word of his 15-minute paper by heart. When he came to write the paper up for publication, Dr. Kirsner repeatedly reviewed the manuscript in minute detail. The paper, including a page of color illustrations, was published in the *Annals of Internal Medicine* in December 1964.[6] Dr. Kirsner said, "João, this is going to be a success, let's order 400 reprints." The estimate turned out to be low, since they received more than 700 requests for reprints. (This was before copying machines, and physicians regularly mailed preprinted postcards to authors requesting articles from journals.)

In 1964 Dr. Prolla's first child, Gabriel, was born during a very hot August. In a measure of Dr. Kirsner's concern for the personal difficulties of his fellows, he helped defer the cost of the cesarean section that the delivery had required.

Dr. Prolla fondly remembers the summer picnics that the section organized and the opportunities to get to know the senior faculty members and their families. He made a strong and lasting friendship with Dr. Gerald Bowen and his wife, Norma, of Worcester, Massachusetts, who introduced Dr. Prolla and his wife to the "sacred North American ritual of Thanksgiving dinner."

When Dr. Prolla returned to Brazil, the cytology lab was turned over to Dr. Duane Taebel, who maintained the high standards of the laboratory until he left the University of Chicago to join a prominent clinical group in northern Wisconsin.

* * *

The experiences of Dr. Anderson (Andy) C. Hedberg, who joined the gastroenterology section in 1965 for a two-year fellowship, are fairly typical of physicians who trained to become gastroenterologists during this era in the United States.[7] Dr. Hedberg was a native of Chicago and the son of a well-known internist on the North Side of the city, Collie Hedberg. Andy had gone to Harvard for his undergraduate education and to Cornell Medical School, where he earned his M.D. degree. He remained at Cornell for his internship and residency in internal medicine. During his residency training he was inspired by Dr. Marvin Schlesinger to enter the field of gastroenterology. Dr. Schlesinger highly recommended Dr. Kirsner and the gastroenterology fellowship program at the University of Chicago. Dr. Hedberg was already well aware of Dr. Kirsner and the program at Chicago. His father was acquainted with Dr. Kirsner and Dr. Walter Palmer, both from their membership in the Chicago Society of Internal Medicine and from the many patients he had regularly referred to them over the years. Dr. Schlesinger gave Dr. Hedberg a strong letter of recommendation, and he flew to Chicago for an interview with Dr. Kirsner in his office on the M corridor on the fourth floor of Billings. There followed a tour of the facilities, and some weeks later he was accepted for the fellowship program to start in July 1965.

Dr. Hedberg was due to finish the last day of his residency at Cornell on June 31, and he asked Dr. Thomas Killup, the chief of the program and a well-known cardiologist, if he could be excused from rounds that morning as he was going to have to drive all day to Chicago to start his fellowship program the next day. The residency program was quite strict on this issue, and residents could be denied their final paycheck for leaving early. When he arrived at Billings on July 1 he was actually a few days late, because he had been confused about the exact day the fellowship was to begin, and he found that the other first-year fellows had already begun working. He remembers being assigned to perform proctoscopies, which were supervised by Dr. Prolla. The proctoscopic examinations were a major activity of the GI section. They were performed in the Medicine 6 clinic two full mornings a week and were an important clinical service. Dr. Hedberg's impression of Dr. Prolla was that he was one of the warmest and most helpful of physicians.

Gastroscopy training and gastroscopies were being done at the time by Dr. Richard Braucher. They were performed with the Schindler gastroscope, and Dr. Hedberg remembers being frightened by the use of the instrument and the possibility of causing a perforation. During Dr. Hedberg's two-year fellowship, Dr. Braucher obtained the use of a prototype of the fiberoptic gastroscope (made by the American Cystoscopic Corporation), but Andy's recollection is that the visual image was far inferior to that of the Schindler gastroscope.

Since he was interested in small-bowel physiology, Dr. Hedberg was assigned to work with Dr. Richard Reilly. This was an opportunity to determine whether he had a flair for bench research, although Andy knew he was destined to go into clinical medicine and join his father in practice at Augustana Hospital.

Andy's recollections of Dr. Kirsner match those of almost everyone who trained in the GI section. Dr. Kirsner was at his office at six o'clock each morning. He knew where everyone had their desk, and one pictures him quietly making his rounds in the half-lighted corridors of the section, placing messages written on yellow legal paper in his distinctive blue fountain-pen script. These messages frequently greeted the fellows when they arrived at work in the morning, ensuring that they would receive their immediate attention. The messages, often only a single sentence in length, ranged in content. Some called attention to an article that had appeared in a journal or that had come to his attention in an area he knew the fellow was studying. There were also questions about specific patients: had a patient's test result been reviewed and the patient contacted, or had the referring doctor been sent a follow-up letter? He would want to know how an article the fellow was developing was progressing and when it would be ready. All this conveyed that the "Chief" was aware of what everyone was doing. Dr. Kirsner often told the group how much he enjoyed coming to the hospital so early in the morning, since he could get the elevators without waiting. Dr. Hedberg was impressed with his style of clinically oriented bedside teaching, which was readily apparent at conferences and on rounds. Equally impressive was Dr. Kirsner's tremendous recall of the details of the literature on any subject relating to gastroenterology.

Dr. Kirsner also managed an enormous clinical load. Saturday morning clinics were especially famous and certainly remembered by every fellow who received his training in the section. At six o'clock in the morning, Dr. Kirsner was already in the clinic seeing patients he had agreed to add to his schedule. This was well before the time the clinic was officially scheduled to begin, at eight o'clock. Dr. Kirsner's list of patients was written in a column on the blackboard in the clinic conference room, where the fellows who had taken the initial histories and physical examinations wrote up the cases, reviewed the x-rays and clinical records, and formulated their thoughts on the appropriate clinical approach. The list of Dr. Kirsner's patients dwarfed all the other doctors', but he patiently heard each new case and reviewed the x-rays before going in with the fellow to see the patient and introduce himself, ask a few questions or examine the patient's abdomen, and then summarize their recommendations. He also saw most of the patients who returned for follow-up visits. In spite of the number of patients waiting to be seen, he was never rushed and gave the impression that time was never a consideration. The clinic frequently went into the early hours of the afternoon, and it was common for Dr. Kirsner to proceed from the clinic to the Medicine 4 GI service in the hospital for a family conference with a patient who was being discharged or for follow-up visits with patients he was treating in the hospital.

All the fellowships in gastroenterology included the opportunity to rotate with Dr. Kirsner for at least a three-month period, to make rounds with him in the hospital, and to work with him on the inpatient consultation service. Typical of this experience was a call Dr. Hedberg received late on a Saturday afternoon when Dr. Kirsner had just returned home from the annual meetings of the American

Society for Clinical Investigation in Atlantic City. "Andy, could you meet me in the hospital this evening and go over a few patients?" "A few patients" turned out to be the entire service, and they saw them all, working well past nine in the evening. Dr. Hedberg, who had observed how his father practiced medicine, recognized that this was how doctors practiced in this era. Regardless of the academic distinction he achieved, Dr. Kirsner never lost the touch of a personal doctor. Dr. Hedberg, a devoted sports fan, recognized that Dr. Kirsner was, as many others had commented, the last of the "triple threats" in medicine. In football, this referred to a skilled player who excelled at running, kicking, and passing—a player like Jay Berwanger, the famous University of Chicago quarterback who was the first winner of the Heisman Trophy. By the same token, Dr. Kirsner was a great clinician, teacher, and investigator.

In contrast to Dr. Hedberg's experience at Cornell, where there had been an atmosphere of competition in the Department of Medicine, and attending were highly critical of the residents' performance and would openly disparage their presentations and care, the atmosphere at Chicago was one of collegiality, and there was never an undercurrent of discontent or backbiting.

Another well-remembered trademark of the Dr. Kirsner style was the thick stack of pink telephone messages he kept in a message holder on his desk or carried with him during the day, folded in his wallet. The day's work was not done until all the calls of the day had been returned. In addition, his home phone number was listed in the Chicago telephone directory, and he accepted calls from patients day and night, seven days a week.

Many distinguished gastroenterologists visited the section each year, and it was traditional that a fellow be assigned to escort the visitor around the hospital for prearranged conferences, meetings with the fellows, and lunch. Dr. Hedberg remembers a visit by the distinguished clinician and hepatologist Dr. Hugh Butt, from the Mayo Clinic, a friend and respected colleague of Dr. Kirsner's. At the end of a long day of meetings and discussions, they returned to Dr. Kirsner's office. After talking a while, Dr. Kirsner held up a thick stack of pink telephone slips and suggested that a visibly tired Dr. Butt and Dr. Hedberg go get their dinner, since he still had some calls to return.

Dr. Hedberg, who went on to become president of the American College of Physicians in 2005-6, always marveled at Dr. Kirsner's ability to keep track of the activities of the fellows who had completed his training program. Dr. Hedberg, who frequently published comments in the communications from the American College of Physicians during his presidency, would receive notes or even a telephone call from Dr. Kirsner commenting or congratulating him on what he was doing and calling his attention to articles that had appeared in print.

* * *

Dr. David A. Morowitz, who practices gastroenterology in the Washington, D.C., area, is another of the fellows whose career and life were profoundly influenced by his tenure as a fellow in the gastroenterology section at the University of Chicago.[8] David grew up in Chicago and went to the University of Illinois Medical School, where he also took his internship and residency. He was drawn into the field of gastroenterology in part because his mother developed Crohn's disease a few years after he was born, giving him firsthand knowledge of the debilitating effects of the disease. He remembers that at one point, during a hospitalization at Mount Sinai Hospital on the near West Side of Chicago, his mother's doctor arranged for Walter Lincoln Palmer to see her. This was around 1962, and Dr. Palmer had probably just retired and begun his practice at Woodlawn Hospital. In the process of applying for training programs after his residency, Dr. Morowitz met with Dr. Kirsner in his office and on a subsequent visit made rounds with him in the Medicine 4 inpatient service. That experience clinched his decision, and when he received a phone call offering him a place in the fellowship program, he gladly accepted, withdrawing his applications to training programs on the East Coast.

Perhaps a word is appropriate here about Dr. Kirsner's habit of calling the applicant directly to offer him or her the fellowship. This was before computerized matching programs for fellowships, and applicants would be notified by mail or called on the phone—in the case of Dr. Kirsner, directly. Former fellows of the GI program can well remember being called into their residency programs and the secretary telling them that Dr. Kirsner was coming to the telephone.

Having the "Boss," as Dr. Morowitz likes to call Dr. Kirsner, say, "Dave, I would like to offer you a place in our fellowship program in July 1966," made it very hard to say, "Thank you very much, I would like to think about it and call you back." Anything but an enthusiastic acceptance would certainly be remembered.

Dr. Morowitz and his wife, Barbara, looked for an apartment in the Hyde Park area. His wife spotted the Cloisters and asked the doorman, Roosevelt, whom they long remembered, whether any apartments were available. As luck would have it, one had just been vacated, and seizing the opportunity, they leased an apartment on the fourth floor. With the Kirsners living on the top floor, David and Barbara had many opportunities to visit with and get to know both Dr. Kirsner and Minnie during David's fellowship.

Living in the Cloisters below Dr. Kirsner led to a memorable day in late February 1968. On a Friday afternoon and evening, Chicago experienced its largest snowfall on record, 27 inches. The city was shut down. On Saturday morning at six o'clock, Dr. Kirsner was on the phone asking whether Dave would like to walk with him to the hospital, some eight blocks away, for the Saturday morning clinic. In the stillness of that morning they walked along 57th Street to the hospital and experienced with delight the beauty of the snowfall and the quiet of the city. The Saturday clinic, normally bustling with activity, was empty, and Dave and Dr. Kirsner were the only physicians for the single patient who made it in that morning.

* * *

Joel D. Levinson, a fellow in the Section of Gastroenterology from 1968 to 1970, has devoted his career to establishing a group practice in gastroenterology in New Jersey. His remembrances of his time at Chicago illustrate some important points about the program at the university under Dr. Kirsner's leadership.

Dr. Levinson was a highly qualified candidate when he applied to the fellowship program in 1965. He had done his undergraduate training at Cornell University and was a graduate of Georgetown University Medical School. His medical residency training had been at Georgetown University Hospital and at Vanderbilt University.

Through a colleague also interested in gastroenterology, he came into possession of what he and his friends referred to as "Ingelfinger's list." This list contained the names of training programs in the country that Dr. Franz Ingelfinger, head of the training program in gastroenterology at Boston City Hospital, recommended to talented medical residents interested in going into the field. The list, arranged from east to west, contained the following programs: Dr. Ingelfinger's own program at Boston City Hospital and Kurt Isselbacher's program at Mass General, Howard Spiro's program at Yale University, Marvin Schleisenger's at Cornell University at New York Hospital, Joseph Kirsner's program at the University of Chicago, John Fortram's at Parkview Hospital in Dallas, Texas, Martin Prossman's at the University of California Medical Center in Los Angeles, and Wade Volwiler and Cyrus Rubin's at the University of Washington in Seattle. Dr. Ingelfinger was also enthusiastic about the programs of Henry Janowitz at Mount Sinai, Malcolm Tyor at Duke University, John Sessions at the University of North Carolina, Chapel Hill, and Fred Kern at the University of Colorado in Denver.

Joel systematically visited six of these programs and found them all to be excellent training programs with "charismatic chiefs." He had many friends who had trained at these programs and were pleased with their education. Chicago was the last program he visited, and he was "blown away" by the entire experience. He had the good fortune to check into the Palmer House on a beautiful cloudless day and to see the city and lakefront at their best. Equally impressive was the visual impression made by the University of Chicago, the Midway, and Billings Hospital.

In his interview he found Dr. Kirsner to be warm and open, with a real interest in him as a person; after their conversation, he had the feeling that Dr. Kirsner knew all about him. He was also impressed that Dr. Kirsner expressed considerable interest in his father, who had been a major in the army during World War II. After the interview he made rounds with Dr. Kirsner and several fellows on the inpatient GI ward. Compared with the other programs he had visited, the facilities at University of Chicago were spectacular, including a 45-bed inpatient service, an outpatient clinic that operated five and a half days a week, an endoscopy suite (the first he'd seen), a proctoscopy facility with several examination tables, a fluoroscopic unit for tube placement and esophageal dilations, and a laboratory performing gastric analysis and pancreatic secretion studies. These facilities, which would be taken for granted today, were far beyond what he had seen at the other training programs.

At that time the practice of gastroenterology was still dependent on high-quality barium contrast x-ray studies of the gastrointestinal tract. During rounds that morning with Dr. Kirsner, they visited the radiology department at Billings. Particularly impressive was the large viewing room with rotational viewing consoles that displayed all the films recently taken on the inpatient services. During their visit, the attending radiologist, Dr. John Fennessy, reviewed the films of Dr. Kirsner's patients in a careful manner, and the ensuing discussion of the relevant findings was an outstanding educational experience for Dr. Levinson.

Dr. Levinson remembers, during his fellowship years, the steady stream of prominent leaders in the field of gastroenterology, as well as promising young investigators, who regularly visited the section. Throughout his time at Chicago, he was impressed with Dr. Kirsner as a tireless investigator and clinician. He came to appreciate, too, that Dr. Kirsner was a superb administrator and that the "interaction and cooperation that he created between the Division of Gastroenterology and the departments of Medicine, Surgery, Pathology and Radiology was truly unique."[9]

Collaborative Work with Fellows

During the 1960s Dr. Kirsner published many papers on inflammatory bowel diseases that have made a lasting contribution to our understanding of the history of these diseases and their therapy. These studies were done through his close collaboration with a number of talented fellows who received their training in the section during this era, and Dr. Kirsner was always active in encouraging and aiding the fellows in the writing and publication of their papers. The following is a sampling of some of these physicians.

Marshall Sparberg began his fellowship in 1963 after graduating from Northwestern University Medical School and doing his internal medicine training at Barnes University, in St. Louis. His mother's favorite brother, Dr. Daniel Haffron, a psychiatrist, suffered from Crohn's disease and was a patient of Dr. Kirsner's. It was in this context that Dr. Sparberg first met Dr. Kirsner and began to understand the seriousness of gastrointestinal disease. He was inspired to enter the field and made a promise to his mother to dedicate himself to the medical problem that afflicted her brother. Today, Dr. Sparberg is still in clinical practice, a full professor on the clinical faculty of Northwestern University Medical School, and a highly respected consultant in the field of inflammatory bowel disease. Besides his notable contributions to patient care, he has been a leader in the local community and the Carol Fischer Chapter of the Crohn's and Colitis Foundation. During his fellowship he coauthored many clinical papers with members of the section. Perhaps the most important was a publication in the prestigious journal *Medicine* documenting the clinical picture and natural history of ulcerative proctitis (ulcerative colitis confined to the rectum), which may be regarded as a classic in the medical literature.[10] An anecdote that Dr. Sparberg likes to relate dates from 1965, the year Dr. Kirsner was president of the AGA. Chairing a session during the annual meetings, held that year at the Drake Hotel, Dr. Kirsner received an urgent call that took him away from the meeting. After the session ended, Dr. Sparberg asked Dr. Kirsner what had called him away. Showing no sign of irritation, Dr. Kirsner replied that one of his patients was not happy with the room she had been assigned in the hospital.

Richard Breuer was born in Brooklyn, New York, in 1933. He received his undergraduate education at Harvard and graduated from Yale University School of Medicine. Before coming to the University of Chicago he received training in internal medicine in a two-year program at Duke University under Dr. Eugene Stead, a year of residency in psychiatry at Johns Hopkins, and a year of training in endocrinology in Cleveland. As a fellow during this era, he participated in the publication of a number of important papers, most notably a large series of cases documenting the clinical picture of nephrolithiasis (kidney stones) in inflammatory bowel disease.[11] Dr. Breuer was the director of the gastroenterology program at the Northwestern-affiliated Evanston Hospital, in Evanston, Illinois.

Howard Schachter was truly a product of the University of Chicago. In addition to being gastroenterology fellow, he received his undergraduate degree, medical degree, and residency training at the university. He has recently retired from Northwestern University Medical School, where he was a highly respected consultant in gastroenterology. Early in his training, he worked with a distinguished member of the pathology department at Billings Hospital, Dr. Henry Rappaport. An outgrowth of this work was a "classic" paper on the pathology of ulcerative colitis, Crohn's disease, and the identification of a category of "indeterminate" colitis that defied categorization.[12] The importance of this paper hinged upon the necessity of properly distinguishing between ulcerative colitis and Crohn's disease, since surgical removal of the colon and rectum, a proctocolectomy, was a cure for ulcerative colitis, but the same procedure in a patient suffering with Crohn's disease involving the colon did not prevent the possible recurrence of the disease. During Dr. Schachter's fellowship, he and his wife had the misfortune of having their apartment on Hyde Park Boulevard destroyed by fire. In a typical gesture of concern, Dr. Kirsner asked his laboratory assistant Leroy Cockerham to assist Dr. Schachter in salvaging his belongings.

Dr. Eugene A. Gelzayd began regularly attending GI conferences at the Boston VA hospital in 1964. Through his participation, he got to know Dr. Robert Donaldson and Dr. Franz Ingelfinger, both of whom encouraged him to consider going into gastroenterology. Early in 1965, Dr. Donaldson not only called Dr. Kirsner to see if he had an opening in his fellowship program but also paid the airfare for Dr. Gelzayd's trip to Chicago (Dr. Gelzayd recalls that Dr. Kirsner paid for his return trip). During his fellowship in 1965-67, Dr. Gelzayd worked in Dr. Sumner Kraft's immunology laboratory, and under Dr. Kraft's mentorship published a number of important papers on the immunology of the gastrointestinal tract in inflammatory bowel disease that appeared in *Gastroenterology* and *Science*.[13] As a result of this work, Dr. Gelzayd was invited to become a member of the scientific research society of Sigma Xi. One important extracurricular duty he remembers during his fellowship involved fabricating and painting a kiln-baked clay hamantaschen to aid Dr. Kirsner when he participated in the university's annual debate on the merits of the hamantaschen versus the latke at Hillel House.[14] Currently an associate clinical professor at Wayne State University School of Medicine and a practicing gastroenterologist in Berkley, Michigan, Dr. Gelzayd recently wrote Dr. Kirsner a letter, after reading an article in the *University of Chicago Magazine,* thanking him for two wonderful years of fellowship training and congratulating him on his 98th birthday.[15]

Several additional publications on inflammatory bowel disease, particularly on important clinical problems involved in patient care, appeared in this decade thanks to the efforts of fellows. A paper noting that toxic dilation of the colon (toxic megacolon) might complicate Crohn's disease as well as ulcerative colitis was published in 1967 by Dr. Schachter and Dr. Melvin J. Goldstein (another outstanding Chicago gastroenterologist still in active practice on the staff of Northwestern University Medical School).[16] Dr. David Morowitz documented the occurrence of thrombocytosis (an elevated platelet count) in inflammatory bowel disease, and Thomas D. McCaffery published an important paper in the journal *Pediatrics* on severe growth retardation in children with inflammatory bowel disease.[17] In 1969 Dr. Charles C. Norland and Dr. Kirsner published a landmark study in *Medicine* reviewing the clinical features, treatment, and outcome of 42 patients with toxic megacolon.[18]

The Ileoptomists

In 1958 Dr. Kirsner and nurses and physicians at Billings Hospital founded a patients' support group, which they named the Ileoptomists, with six ileostomy patients.[19] The group represented Dr. Kirsner's interest in providing patients with the most-informed care. On October 26, 1966, the group held its first panel presentation at the university. Dr. Kirsner introduced the panel and emphasized how valuable the organization was in helping to increase knowledge and improve the care of the ileostomy patient. At the meeting the president of the group, Maurice Ettleson, outlined the services of the organization. One of the its most important functions was to arrange pre- and postoperative visits to patients at the request of the patient's attending physician. Visits were carefully planned to be helpful and relevant for the patient, and ileoptomists were matched to patients by age, sex, and marital status. The group developed educational slides for patients, nurses, and physicians and worked with the affiliated national organization, the United Ostomy Association, to address issues of insurance and employment. The group produced a monthly publication, *The Ileoptomists,* which won the Best Publication Award of the United Ostomy Association. Chicago physicians who contributed to the publication included Dr. Marshall Sparberg, who wrote a series of articles; Dr. Jean Spencer, who addressed the problem of postileostomy diarrhea; and Dr. Paul Lazar of Northwestern, who contributed articles on skin care. The Ileoptomists later disbanded, and their role was assumed by surgical nurses who specialized in stomal care—"stomal therapists" or "stomal therapy nurses"—and local chapters of the Crohn's and Colitis Foundation of America, which maintains rosters of members willing to visit patients facing surgery.

The Japanese Contribution to Endoscopy

In September 1966 Dr. and Mrs. Kirsner attended the Third World Congress of Gastroenterologists, in Tokyo. Dr. Kirsner was invited to read four papers at the meeting and to chair a program. The trip was part of the Kirsners' month-long trip to the Pacific, which included visits to Kobe, Kyoto, Osaka, Nagoya, and Tokyo in Japan, followed by Hong Kong and Honolulu on the way home. While in Nagoya, Dr. Kirsner counseled Minnie not to refer to his wartime experience with the 229th General Hospital, fearing that it might upset their hosts. His concern proved to be unnecessary, since the Japanese made it clear that they knew all about his wartime service.

One of the papers he delivered in Nagoya was on gastric cytology. He was a little chagrined when one of the faculty of the Aichi Cancer Center in Nagoya presented similar material, but with far more impressive data and microphotographs of cytologic material. Gastric cancer occurred at a much higher rate in Japan and was a widely recognized problem there.

This visit led to an important association between the University of Chicago and the Aichi Cancer Center in Nagoya. In 1967 the Gastro-Intestinal Research Foundation (GIRF) board donated $10,000 to Dr. Kirsner to help him bring Seibi Kobayashi, a 31-year-old physician affiliated with Nagoya University and an expert in the use of the Olympus gastrocamera, to Billings. Dr. Kobayashi was a fortunate choice. During his three-year stay he was very effective in training fellows in the art of endoscopy and the use of the equipment. Collaborations with the GI fellows and other faculty members led to the publication of a number of important observations in the relatively new journal *Gastrointestinal Endoscopy*. Dr. Kobayashi would be followed by his colleagues Dr. Chaseri Hattori and Dr. Kei Matsueda, whose participation in the section was equally effective.

To appreciate the significance of these events it is important to remember that until about 1964 gastroscopy was performed with the Schindler semirigid gastroscope. The esophagus was examined by a rigid open tube, an esophagoscope. This instrument featured a tiny incandescent bulb that illuminated the mucosa and a lens on the distal tip of the instrument. This instrument made the examination of the esophagus and stomach a formidable challenge for both the patient and the physician. In 1958 Dr. Basil Hirschowitz, while he was at the University of Michigan, had succeeded in developing the prototype of the first in a generation of flexible fiber-optic endoscopes that would revolutionize the field of gastroenterology.[20] The Japanese, who had struggled for years with a high incidence of gastric cancer, were in a strategic position to take advantage of this new innovation. They had already developed an effective tool, the gastrocamera, as a screening device for gastric cancer. This instrument was blindly positioned in the empty stomach and a series of photographs were taken in a sequence of standardized positions. It was not until 1963 that the Olympus Corporation commercially produced the Olympus GIF flexible endoscopes that allowed both visualization of the stomach and photographic documentation of the findings. Concomitantly with Dr. Kobayashi's arrival, the Chicago businessman and philanthropist, and a friend of Dr. Kirsner's, Maurice Goldblatt contributed $5,000 to the Section of Gastroenterology for the purchase of an Olympus gastrocamera.

In 1968, at Dr. Kirsner's invitation, Dr. Prolla returned to the University of Chicago to run the GI cytology laboratory and to assist in endoscopy. By this time, blind gastric lavage was no longer required to obtain upper gastrointestinal material for cytology, and with direct visualization, endoscopically guided cytology brushings and biopsies were feasible. Dr. Prolla worked closely with Dr. Kobayashi, and over the three years they produced numerous papers that established cytology and biopsy as a standard part of endoscopic practice. Several additional Japanese endoscopists and Brazilian fellows also rotated through the section and contributed to teaching and the study of patients.

At Dr. Kirsner's suggestion, the culmination of this work was the writing of a definitive handbook of gastrointestinal exfoliative cytology. In 1972 Dr. Prolla and Dr. Kirsner published the *Handbook and Atlas of Gastrointestinal Exfoliative Cytology,* published by the University of Chicago Press. Because of the large number of magnificent colored prints, the cost of publication was subsidized by a donation from Maurice Goldblatt, to whom the book was dedicated. The *Atlas* received many extremely favorable reviews, including in *JAMA* and the *New England Journal of Medicine.* Although now out of print, the *Atlas* remains a marvelous reference for those wishing to compare current microscopic findings with the medical literature.

An Important New Faculty Member: Dr. Charles Winans

In 1968 at the Atlantic City meetings, Dr. Charles Winans, on the recommendation of his chief, Dr. Franz Ingelfinger of Boston, met for breakfast with Dr. Kirsner and Dr. Ingelfinger.[21] The purpose of the meeting was to discuss a possible job in the Section of Gastroenterology at the University of Chicago.

"Chuck," as he was known to all the fellows and his colleagues, was just finishing his two-year military obligation as chief of gastroenterology at the U.S. Naval Hospital in Portsmouth, Virginia. He had been very busy there, and felt that he had received broad and valuable clinical experience. Originally from the East Coast, Chuck had been raised as a Quaker and had attended Haverford College as an undergraduate. He went to Case Western Reserve University Medical School in Cleveland, where he also did his internship and residency. The chairman of the Department of Medicine there was Robert Ebert, who in 1964 advised him not to go to Chicago for a fellowship, since he felt that the program there was too heavily oriented toward clinical medicine; he advised him instead to go work with either Kurt Isselbacher at Harvard or Franz Ingelfinger at Boston University.

Before their breakfast meeting in Atlantic City in 1968, Chuck had already met Dr. Kirsner in Chicago when he presented a paper at the AGA meeting in 1965, and he admired him as a leader in the field. By 1968, although he had learned the investigative tools needed to pursue his research on esophageal motility, he recognized that clinical medicine was his real love and that the program at the University of Chicago suited him very well. Chuck's wife was not entirely happy about the decision—perhaps it was the South Side of Chicago, perhaps it was the modest salary—but Chuck was so impressed with Dr. Kirsner that he felt confident about his choice. He viewed Dr. Kirsner as being exactly as people said he was: "calm, collected, serious, knowledgeable and very warm personally." Once he'd joined the section, Chuck found Dr. Kirsner to be everything he thought he would be. He was magnanimous in dealing with the faculty, and if you approached him with a legitimate request he would do everything he could to see that you got it.

It was a happy choice for both men. Chuck would become a full professor in the Department of Medicine and the Sara and Harold Lincoln Thompson Professor until he retired in 2004. Besides his expertise in esophageal disease, Chuck was an outstanding clinician, for which he received national recognition. He was regarded as an outstanding teacher by all the fellows that received their training in the section.

The AGA

During the 1950s, through his activities with the Gastroenterologic Research Group and his publications and presentations at national meetings, Dr. Kirsner's involvement in the AGA was gradually increasing. In 1960, at the AGA meeting in New Orleans, Dwight Wilbur, a past president of the association, asked Dr. Kirsner if he would assume the office of treasurer of the AGA. Dr. Kirsner accepted, telling Dr. Wilbur that he felt greatly honored. On April 11, 1960, Dr. Kirsner received a formal letter from Wade Volwiler, secretary of the AGA, informing him that the executive committee of the association had elected him treasurer and offering his congratulations.[22]

One Saturday afternoon that summer, Dr. G. Gordon McHardy of New Orleans, who had been the long-term treasurer of the association, came to his office with a $50,000 check, which represented the total assets of the AGA. Dr. Kirsner placed the money in deposit at the very conservative Harris Bank of Chicago. He remembers his feelings of responsibility to the organization, and that he required two signatures with explanation before authorizing any expenditure. He was more than happy when his term as treasurer came to an end.

It is interesting to look at the treasurer's report from December 31, 1962, prepared by Dr. Kirsner. Investments at the time were held in savings accounts, since the yield of U.S. government bonds did not exceed the 4 percent paid on savings accounts. The Research and Education Fund had a value of $96,000, and the association retained residual funds from the 1958 World Congress of $15,000 and a similar amount for the journal *Gastroenterology*. A sum of $300 was listed for foreign correspondents, and the Julius Friedenwald Medal Fund had spent $121.12 for the purchase of four medals. The association garnered $7,747.82 as its share of the profits for the year from the publication of *Gastroenterology*. The treasurer noted that the margin between income and expense was quite narrow, and that large increases in the financial position of the AGA in recent years were due to residual income from the 1958 World Congress, the 1962 Pan American Congress, and the New Orleans postgraduate course. Administration costs for the AGA were quite small, since there were no professional personnel employed. It was felt that the increasing complexity of the organization would eventually require a restructuring of the dues. At the time of the report there were 92 senior members, 268 active members, 79 associate members, and 21 life members. Fourteen members had failed to submit their dues.

Dr. Kirsner's term as treasurer lasted from 1960 until 1963; he then served as vice president from 1963 to 1964, president-elect from 1964 to 1965, and president from 1965 to 1966.

It is the tradition of the AGA to publish in *Gastroenterology* a brief biography of each new president as he assumes the responsibilities of that office. In the July 1965 issue of *Gastroenterology*, Dr. Walter Lincoln Palmer published a biographical sketch of Dr. Kirsner.[23] Dr.

Palmer expressed his gratitude for the opportunity to record an appreciation of his longtime associate and friend. He noted that "there is scarcely any area in the entire field of gastroenterology which has escaped his attention and on which some light has not been shed by him." He noted that if younger men in the section felt pushed, "they realized gratefully that he was working harder than any of them." Dr. Palmer praised his skill and service as a clinician, quoting Francis Peabody, "The secret in the care of the patient is in caring for the patient."[24] Ending on a personal note, Dr. Palmer told his readers a little about Dr. Kirsner's wife, Minnie, and the supportive role she played in his life, and also about their son, Bob, who was currently enrolled in the linguistics program at Columbia University.

National AGA Meeting in Chicago, 1966

It was perhaps fitting that the 68th Annual Meeting of the AGA, in 1966, was held in Chicago at the Drake Hotel. On May 27, Dr. Kirsner gave his Presidential Address, a highlight of the plenary session that formally opens the AGA meeting each year.[25] The plenary session features the outstanding research in the field of gastroenterology and an important state-of-the-art lecture in a selected field.

Dr. Kirsner took great care in crafting his address, and there is much to be learned from it about his thinking on the state of gastroenterology at that time. Reflecting his early exposure to the classics, he reminded the audience of one of Aesop's fables: the members of the body, thinking that they do all the work while the belly gets all the food, go on strike and refuse to take in food, only to find that, without the belly, the body itself starts to collapse. He saw it as an allegory of the situation of gastroenterology: the importance of AGA (the belly) to the interdependence of the limbs (the clinician, the investigator, and the teacher). His talk also highlighted the need for gastroenterologists to keep abreast of the increasingly sophisticated biomedical techniques in multiple disciplines—important information for gastroenterologists seeking to advance medical knowledge in their field. He chided his listeners for not having addressed the deeper issues in the causation of such diseases as peptic ulcers and inflammatory bowel disease. Current knowledge about the microflora of the gut and the colon was too limited, and further investigation was needed. He pointed out that "the ultimate goal of all biomedical research, even in this scientific age, still depends upon the well-trained and, may I add, dedicated physician." He sought to promote the status of the "inquiring physician," quoting the endocrinologist Fuller Albright: "The ultimate goal of most investigation is to find something of benefit to the human race; where other than at the bedside of sick patients, could one find so many suggestions of things to be investigated?" He stressed the importance of inspiring teachers to attract larger numbers of superior students to careers in gastroenterology. He viewed the future of gastroenterology with optimism, saying, in a paraphrase of T. S. Eliot's *Four Quartets*, that "we seem almost to be at the end of a beginning." With high expectations, he exhorted his colleagues, be they "belly" or "limbs," to work together so that the whole entity of gastroenterology might flourish.

Part of the festivities of the annual meeting that May was a memorable "Evening at the Art Institute," organized by Dr. Kirsner's wife, Minnie. The event included a dinner at the Art Institute from five thirty to seven, fortunately on the only night in the entire week that it did not rain. This was followed by an hour lecture on the featured holdings of the museum and a docent-led gallery tour. About 400 persons attended, and the cost for the three activities came to $5.50 per person ($4.50 for the dinner and $1.00 for the lecture). The event was a tremendous success. Mrs. Kirsner, who made all the arrangements herself, was later asked by the presidents of three other medical societies to repeat the event for their groups—but once was enough.

The AGA Presidential Commission

In 1973 the current AGA president Henry Janowitz appointed a presidential commission, to be chaired by Dr. Kirsner, to assess the overall future of the AGA. In the commission's 1975 report,[26] Dr. Kirsner and Dr. Winans listed the five major questions that the commission needed to address:

1. How could the association achieve the transition from an honor society to a service society, yet retain its rigorous standard of excellence?
2. How could it become one force for gastroenterology, given the wide range of interests in the field and existing groups within it?

3. How could the complexity of the internal organization of the AGA and the multiple types of membership be simplified?
4. What should be the overall financial objectives?
5. How could the association's diverse public policy activities be unified?

The commission studied these issues for two years before releasing their report. Their recommendations, which were accepted in full, would prove to have a lasting impact on the future of the organization. The commission felt that if the AGA were to speak for gastroenterology it would have to include most gastroenterologists. Membership should and would be cited as a measure of competence and qualification, therefore board certification would be a universal standard for membership. The commission also recommended that the AGA discontinue its "associate member" category and instead encourage added membership from basic scientists in the academic community. Consideration was given to ways of bringing the membership into better communication with the organization, including the possibility of local or regional chapters. The report highlighted the need to push for the expansion of funds for research and education through the National Institute of Arthritis, Metabolism and Digestive Diseases.

The Louis Block Professorship

On August 9, 1968, Dr. Kirsner received the following letter from Dr. George Beadle, the chancellor of the university.[27]

> Dear Dr. Kirsner:
> I have the honor and pleasure of inviting you to accept the Louis Block Professorship in Medicine as of October 1, 1968. The offer of this chair, made on the recommendation of Provost Levi, is both an indication of the high esteem in which you are held by your colleagues and a recognition of your many contributions to the University.
> Best Regards,
> Sincerely,
> George Beadle

Back in early 1955 Dr. Coggeshall had reported that he had been told by the nephrologist Alf Alving that his good friend Louis Block was considering making changes in his will that would leave substantial funds to the University of Chicago for medical research. Louis Block was at the time a "fifty-six-year-old bachelor" who had recently sold his chemical company in Joliet, Illinois, to Olin Mathieson. Mr. Block had been a patient at the university on several occasions and was grateful for the good care he had received during his illnesses. In October 1955 a meeting took place in Coggeshall's office to review a draft of the will. Mr. Block appeared satisfied with the will and expressed a wish to sign it. His lawyers recommended that he think it over for a few days first. He was due to travel to South Dakota to purchase some breeding stock, and he said that he would sign it shortly after returning. Unfortunately, Mr. Block died of a heart attack while in South Dakota. But Dr. Coggeshall learned that the new will, with a few minor changes, had in fact been signed by Mr. Block before he left for South Dakota. As a result, the university received $14 million, which was set up as the Louis Block Fund for Basic Research and Advanced Study.[28]

On September 26, 1968, the Office of Public Information of the University of Chicago issued the following announcement: "Two professorships honoring the late Louis Block have been established at The University of Chicago. To fill the chairs, Dr. Joseph B. Kirsner has been named the Louis Block Professor of Medicine in the Division of Biological Sciences and The Pritzker School of Medicine, and Clemens C. J. Roothaan has been named the Louis Block Professor of Physics and Chemistry."

Today the Block Fund provides small initial grants to newly appointed young faculty members, and is extremely valuable in helping recipients begin a research program.

The Section of Gastroenterology and Dr. Irwin Rosenberg

In September 1970 Dr. Irwin H. Rosenberg joined the Section of Gastroenterology, having been recruited by Dr. Kirsner.[29] Dr. Rosenberg had broad contacts in the academic community and was well liked by all who met him. Irv, as he was known to his colleagues, was born in Madison, Wisconsin. He received his bachelor's degree from the University of Wisconsin and went on to Harvard Medical School, where he graduated cum laude. He was a member of Phi Beta Kappa and Alpha Omega Alpha. He had taken his residence training at Massachusetts General Hospital. While still in medical school he studied the effects of intestinal inflammation in Puerto Rico. A commission in the U.S. Public Health Service from 1961 to 1964 had entailed two years of clinical research on malnutrition and cholera in East Pakistan (now Bangladesh). He had been a research fellow at the Thorndike Memorial Laboratory of Boston City Hospital and was a visiting scientist in the Department of Biophysics at the Weitzman Institute of Science in Israel. He had been the recipient of a National Institutes of Health Career Development Award while at Harvard. He was also active in the Medical Committee for Human Rights and a consultant to the nutritional program of the National Center for Chronic Disease Control. He was a member of the National Academy of Sciences Committee on International Nutrition. His research interests were in small-intestine function, nutritional diseases, and the absorption and metabolism of folic acid as a marker of intestinal disease. On coming to Chicago, he quickly established a laboratory to investigate intestinal function, and one of his first projects was the study of folic acid absorption in inflammatory bowel diseases.[30]

Irv brought to the section a renewed interest in research and was a thoughtful, dedicated academic who quickly made an impact on the activities of the section. In 1971 Dr. Kirsner announced that he would be assuming the position of deputy dean for medical affairs of the medical school and chief of staff of Billings Hospital. It was not surprising that although Dr. Irv Rosenberg had only been with the section less than a year, Dr. Kirsner chose him to fill his position as chief of the Section of Gastroenterology. During his tenure as chief, from 1971 to 1985, Dr. Rosenberg would reconfigure the gastroenterology section by establishing a section of hepatology, for which he recruited Dr. James L. Boyer from Yale, where he had trained under the distinguished hepatologist Dr. Gerald Klatskin. Dr. Rosenberg also formed a section of nutrition and recruited Dr. Michael D. Sitrin, a graduate of Harvard Medical School, to head the new program.

Notes

1. Joseph B. Kirsner, guest ed., foreword to *Diagnosis of Incipient Disease*, Medical Clinics of North America, Chicago number, vol. 44, no. 1, January (Philadelphia: W. B. Saunders, 1960); and "Early Manifestations of the Malabsorption Syndrome," ibid., 171-82.

2. Dale C. Smith, *The American Gastroenterological Association: 1897-1907* (Bethesda: AGA, 1999), 51-55.

3. Scheele GA and Kitzes G, Analysis of academic training programs in gastroenterology for the 10-year period 1957 to 1967, *Gastroenterology* 57:2:203-13, 1969.

4. Dr. João Carlos Prolla, now professor of internal medicine at the Federal University of Rio Grande do Sul in Brazil, kindly furnished the author with written reflections on his experiences at the University of Chicago.

5. For a review of the life and career of Cyrus E. Rubin, see *Masters in Gastroenterology*, vol. 4, no. 1 (Greenwich, CT: Cliggott Communications, in cooperation with the AGA, 2001).

6. Prolla JC and Kirsner JB, The gastrointestinal lesions and complications of the leukemias, *Ann Int Med* 61:6:1084-1103, December 1964.

7. From an interview with Dr. Anderson C. Hedberg, on May 15, 2006, during his presidency of the American College of Physicians.

8. In April 2006 Dr. David A. Morowitz generously supplied the author with personal interviews and written anecdotes recalling his fellowship in the Section of Gastroenterology.

9. Letter to the author from Joel D. Levinson, July 12, 2008.

10. Sparberg MS, Fennessy JJ, and Kirsner JB, Ulcerative proctitis and mild ulcerative colitis: A study of 200 patients, *Medicine* 45:5:391-412, September 1966.

11. Gelzayd EA, Breuer RI, and Kirsner JB, Nephrolithiasis in inflammatory bowel disease, *Amer J Dig Dis,* new ser., 13:12:1027-34, December 1968.

12. Schachter H, Goldstein MJ, and Kirsner JB, Ulcerative colitis and "granulomatous" colitis—validity of differential diagnostic criteria, a study of 100 patients treated by total colectomy, *Ann Int Med* 72:841-51, June 1970.

13. Gelzayd EA, Kraft SC, and Kirsner JB, Distribution of immunoglobulins in human rectal mucosa. Part I, Normal control subjects. Part II, Ulcerative colitis and abnormal mucosal control subjects, *Gastroenterology* 53:3:334-40 and 341-47, March 1968.

14. This humorous debate is a longtime tradition at the University of Chicago and has also spread to other campuses. At Chicago, participants have in-

cluded such academic luminaries as Hanna Holborn Gray, Martha Nussbaum, Milton Friedman, and Allan Bloom.

15. Letter from Eugene A. Gelzayd to JBK, December 17, 2007; in JBK's personal papers.

16. Schachter H, Goldstein MJ, and Kirsner JB, Toxic dilation complicating Crohn's disease of the colon, *Gastroenterology* 53:1:136-42, July 1967. Toxic megacolon is a dramatic and life-threatening complication of severe inflammatory bowel disease that requires emergency surgical intervention in the absence of a prompt response to intensive medical management.

17. Morowitz DA, Allen LW, and Kirsner JB, Thrombocytosis in chronic inflammatory bowel disease, *Ann Int Med* 68:5:1013-21, May 1968; McCaffery TD, Nasr K, Kirsner JB, et al., Severe growth retardation in children with inflammatory bowel disease, *Pediatrics* 45:386-93, March 1970.

18. Norland CC and Kirsner JB, Toxic dilation of the colon (toxic megacolon): Etiology, treatment and prognosis, *Medicine* 48:3:229-50, May 1969.

19. Breuer, RI, The Ileoptomists of Chicago, *Illinois Medical Journal,* March 1967.

20. Hirschowitz, BI, A personal history of the fiberscope, *Gastroenterology* 76:804-69, 1979.

21. This material was generously provided to the author by Dr. Charles Winans during an interview on March 9, 2006.

22. A copy of this correspondence between Dr. Volwiler and Dr. Kirsner, as well as treasurer reports and other documents cited below, is available in the AGA archives. These materials were kindly provided to the author by Stacie D. Gallice, director of Information and Planning Services, AGA.

23. Palmer WL and Kirsner JB, The new president, *Gastroenterology* 49:1:3-5, July 1965.

24. Francis W. Peabody's "The Care of the Patient," an address given to Harvard medical students on October 21, 1925, and printed in *JAMA* 88:877-82, 1927.

25. Kirsner JB, Time present and time past are both perhaps present in time future (Presidential Address), *Gastroenterology* 51:2:133-37, August 1966.

26. Joseph B Kirsner and Charles S. Winans, Final Report to the Governing Board by the Presidential Commission on the Future of the American Gastroenterological Association, May 22, 1974. Courtesy of the archives of the AGA.

27. Letter from Dr. Kirsner's personal papers; a copy is in the author's possession.

28. The history of the Louis Block Fund is outlined by C. W. Vermeulen in his 50-year history of the Medical Center, *For the Greatest Good to the Largest*

Number: A History of the Medical Center, The University of Chicago, 1927-1977 (Chicago: University of Chicago, 1977).

29. Biographical information on Dr. Rosenberg was taken from the GIRF *Newsletter,* Winter and Summer 1971, on file in the GIRF offices.

30. Franklin JL and Rosenberg IH, Impaired folic acid absorption in inflammatory bowel disease: Effects of Sulfasalazosulfapyridine (Azulfidine), *Gastroenterology* 64:517-25, 1973.

8 ✳ The Gastro–Intestinal Research Foundation

The story of the Gastro-Intestinal Research Foundation represents a major accomplishment in Dr. Kirsner's career.[1] From its conception in the early 1960s, GIRF was a partnership between Dr. Kirsner, the Section of Gastroenterology, and the University of Chicago on the one hand; and a community of citizens dedicated to the support of research in digestive diseases on the other. Their combined efforts led to the improved clinical care of patients and to major research efforts in the study of these diseases. This heartening story illustrates how the basic instincts of individuals to help their fellow citizens can be galvanized to address important needs in the society. The dedication of the members of GIRF inspired the clinicians and investigators of the Section of Gastroenterology to devote even more time and effort to conquering these debilitating diseases.

✳ ✳ ✳

Dr. Kirsner was frequently questioned by patients or their relatives on the current state of knowledge about inflammatory bowel disease and what research was underway to understand its causes. Dr. Kirsner would truthfully answer that, in truth, not much was known or being done, and then direct the conversation toward the need for community help. This was how Joseph E. Valenti Sr. (1916-2007) first became important in Dr. Kirsner's professional life. Around 1960, a business associate of his recommended Dr. Kirsner to Mr. Valenti, who was then becoming prominent in real estate development in the city. He had been born in Chicago and had attended Loyola and DePaul universities. He was founder of the Home Builders Association of Chicagoland, director of Catholic Charities, and director of the American Illinois Life Insurance Company. Having observed Dr. Kirsner over several visits, he made an appointment to see him in his office, where he offered him a check for $5,000 to help support his research. Dr. Kirsner suggested that he get together with another group of interested individuals who had recently started to meet to have lunch and talk over similar issues. This group included Martin Sandler and Bernice Goldblatt.

The inspiration for the Sandler group stemmed from an event that took place in the summer of 1961. Mr. Sandler and his wife, Lorraine, were driving Minnie and Dr. Kirsner to Ravinia, north of Chicago, for an evening concert. When Dr. Kirsner fell asleep in the backseat on the way to the concert, Martin asked Minnie, "What's the matter with Joe?" She told him about the enormous workload Joe was handling at the university and the shortage of assistance in the section.

Martin Sandler was born in Minneapolis. His father was from Des Moines, Iowa, and his family was distantly related to Minnie Schneider and her family. He attended the University of Minnesota and graduated from the School of Business Administration. With the outbreak of World War II, he enlisted in the navy and served in both the Pacific and the Caribbean. By the 1960s he had formed and was the president of several companies: Products of Tomorrow, Peau Seche Cosmetics, and Special Situations Company. He was very involved in the support of the new State of Israel and was chairman of the Board of Hotel Corporations of Israel.

A few weeks after the evening at Ravinia, Martin Sandler assembled a few families, who began to meet in each other's living rooms in the evening. They listened to Dr. Kirsner describe his research programs and the need for unrestricted funds to continue to tackle the investigational problems he wanted to focus on. Some of the men involved were Nathan Cohn, Sidney Port, Bernard Mitchell, Jerry Poncher, Tony Pogofsky, and Joe Antonow.

Joseph Valenti and the organization he had been developing had several meetings with Sandler and his group. In October 1962, recognizing their common goals, the two groups agreed to merge and work together. They coined the name Gastro-Intestinal Research Foundation, or GIRF, and formally incorporated the organization. Sandler recalls with a smile that not all the ladies approved or liked the sound of the acronym, but they went ahead with it anyway. Sandler and Valenti guided the foundation through its early development until the first annual dinner in January 1963. This inaugural dinner was held in the Tropical Room of the Sheraton-Chicago Hotel at $5 a seat. The event was attended by some 150 individuals, an encouraging start.

In the spring of 1964, GIRF published its first *Newsletter* from its offices on W. Madison Street.[2] The issue featured an announcement of the annual dinner, to be held on April 29 of that year. Dr. Kirsner would present an award to Dr. Charles W. Mayo for his work in gastroenterology. The chairman of the meeting would be Dr. Karl Meyer, the chief of surgery and director of Cook County Hospital, and Philip Klutznik, a prominent Chicago businessman, would be co-chairman. Dr. Morris Fishbein, who would serve as master of ceremonies at the annual dinner, had accepted the chairmanship of the board of directors of GIRF. The issue also announced that the NIH had agreed to match funds given to the Section of Gastroenterology dollar for dollar to a maximum of $75,000.

The *Newsletter* reported that by November 1, 1963, GIRF had 250 members, and an additional 77 had joined by spring 1964. There was a listing of the new board members, which reads like a "Who's Who" of distinguished Chicagoans. A few whose names would be recognizable today are Dr. H. Stanley Bennett, dean of the Division of Biological Sciences of the University of Chicago; the Hon. Richard J. Daley, mayor of the city; George S. Halas, president of the Chicago Bears football team; Sid Luckman, of the Chicago Bears and vice president of Cellu-Craft Products Corporation; Arthur Rubloff, chairman of the board of Arthur Rubloff & Company; and Dr. Theodore R. Van Dellen, medical editor of the *Chicago Tribune*.

The *Newsletter* printed a financial statement detailing the foundation's activities from September 30, 1961, through the first five months of its third year. GIRF had turned over $30,000 to the Section of Gastroenterology and still had over $4,000 in the bank; the operating expenses were $2,025.

A regular feature of the *Newsletter* has been a report on individual members of the Section of Gastroenterology and their research activities. These reports have grown to include introductions of new faculty members and new fellows who joined the section each year, as well as news about departing fellows and the positions they had assumed in various parts of the country. For example, this first *Newsletter* mentioned that Dr. Kenneth Barton was directing the exfoliative cytology program, Dr. Peter Ivan Reed was at the time in England studying genetics, and the biochemist Dr. Babette Stern had recently joined the section and would be studying the metabolism of the epithelial cells lining the gastrointestinal tract.

In August 1964 GIRF launched a Women's Division. A steering committee was formed with temporary officers: Mrs. Bea Levy (chairman), Mrs. Nathan Cohn (secretary), Mrs. Herbert Jacobs (treasurer), and vice chairmen Mrs. Eli Fisher, Mrs. Lester Winternitz, Mrs. Harry Zelzer, and Mrs. William Frishman, representing the North Side, north suburban, South Side, and near North Side of Chicago, respectively. The Women's Division, later renamed the Women's Board, would play an important role in ensuring the long-term success of the foundation. The agreed-upon annual membership dues for the Women's Division were a modest $6.00, and the get-acquainted luncheon, scheduled for September 17, 1964, was modestly priced at $2.50. Dr. Kirsner and Dr. Fishbein were guest speakers at the luncheon, where they outlined the projects and plans of the section and stressed the importance of research in digestive diseases.

Further perusal of the *Newsletter*s that GIRF published during its first decade reveals some of the creative methods that the organization devised to raise funds. The annual award dinners were initially quite formal and reflected the serious purpose of the organization. Speakers were leaders in gastroenterology and the medical community at large and included such names as Dr. Charles W. Mayo, Dr. Walter C. Alvarez, Dr. Lester R. Dragstedt, Dr. H. Stanley Bennett, Dr. Thomas Doxiades (a distinguished gastroenterologist in Athens), Dr. Karl Menninger, George W. Beadle, Dr. Dwight L. Wilbur (a past president of the AGA and the AMA), the sociologist Philip M. Hauser, Theodore Van Dellen, and Dr. Morris Fishbein. Dr. Kirsner's leadership in the activities of GIRF is apparent in the selection of the speakers and the informative program of the annual award dinner meetings. Other important fund-raising events were selling GIRF tribute and greeting cards, and the annual spring fashion show, organized by the Women's Division. Perhaps unique to GIRF would be the compiling, by Mrs. Howard Peltz, and publication of a GIRF cookbook, which was designed to help brighten the dull dietary routine of patients on a lengthy program of recovery. The project had been "whole-heartedly" approved by Dr. Kirsner and Jean Wilson, dietitian at Billings Hospital. Members were solicited for their favorite recipes, and the book was published under the title *Grand but Bland*. It proved to be a popular and successful venture. The book was published in 1970 and in the first two months sold 5,550 copies and went into a second printing.

GIRF also initiated an "equipment program." The *Newsletter* for winter 1965 lists 27 important pieces of medical research equipment that could be purchased by individual members. Examples include a Beckman DU Spectrophotometer with Flame Attachment and Atomizer Burner listed for $3,715, and a Tri Carb Liquid Scintillation Counter Model 3203 for $9,000. Appeals such as these brought results, and a list of equipment purchased for the section and the names of the people who contributed was soon published as well.

The fund-raising success of GIRF during its first decade was notable and a harbinger of the future success of the organization. One outstanding achievement during this period was the establishment of the Center for the Study of Digestive Diseases at the University of Chicago. The project, first announced in August 1968, required a pledge to the university of $320,000. By January 1969 GIRF had raised $225,000. As part of this project, an immunology laboratory was established in honor of retiring chancellor George Beadle. Dr. Beadle, himself a geneticist, spoke to the annual GIRF meeting that year on the importance of new discoveries in genetics and their implications for medical advancement. The funds for the Center for the Study of Digestive Diseases were turned over at ceremonies attended by the new chancellor, Edward H. Levi. On November 10, 1971, the president of GIRF, Jerry Poncher, and more than 200 members and guests celebrated the formal dedication and opening of the Center for the Study of Digestive Diseases. The dedication ceremonies and dinner were attended by Dean Leon O. Jacobson and Chancellor Levi.

During the 1970s and 1980s, GIRF's successful fund-raising programs continued. The activities of the Woman's Board, including the fashion show and Christmas card program, raised $150,000 to $250,000 annually.

In the 1980s the members of the gastroenterology section were scattered in diverse and cramped locations throughout the Medical Center. The need to develop a geographically unified section was a project undertaken by GIRF. The foundation's $2 million, together with $3 million raised by the university, led to the construction of the Joseph B. Kirsner Center at the University of Chicago.

In the mid-1980s GIRF accepted another major challenge. Over a three-year period, GIRF contributed $500,000 to develop a new research program on the biology of the intestinal epithelium. The program, the Cell-Tech Research Program, was under the direction of Drs. Thomas Brasitus, Eugene Chang, and Nick Davidson. GIRF's critical support served as seed money that allowed the section to develop "the best Digestive Disease Center grant application" received at the NIH at that time and resulted in the section's being awarded a five-year grant totaling $4.5 million. Additional support related to this project included individual grants from the NIH to Dr. Chang, Dr. Averil Ma, and Dr. Judy Cho. There were also important funds to support the work of Dr. Bernard Davis of the Liver Unit.

In the 1990s GIRF took on a new challenge, to establish a basic research facility to investigate the scientific aspects of Crohn's disease and ulcerative colitis. This facility required the development of 5,000 additional square feet of space on the seventh floor of the Medical Center. Major contributions came not only from the GIRF membership but also from major contributors, such as Leona Raue, Emma Getz, and Meta Gross. This five-year campaign, successfully completed in 1997, raised over $3 million, which was matched by the Medical Center to create the Biological and Molecular Inflammatory Bowel Research Center. At the same time, Martin Boyer contributed over $1 million to endow a named professorship in the Section of Gastroenterology. In 1996 Dr. Chang was honored as its first recipient.

Another of GIRF's remarkable achievements during this decade was raising $1.5 million to establish a named professorship in honor of Dr. Kirsner. This academic honor was formalized on September 21,

1999, in honor of Dr. Kirsner's 90th birthday. In 2000 Dr. Stephen B. Hanauer became the initial recipient of the Kirsner Professorship.

Research into the genetics of inflammatory bowel disease had a long history in the Section of Gastroenterology. As early as 1948, Dr. Kirsner published his observations on a family with more than one member with Crohn's disease. The gastroenterology clinic's history of publication on this topic, and its ability to carefully and systematically follow a large number of patients, put it in an excellent position to conduct important research into the genetics of these disorders.

In the fall of 1996 the GIRF's Men's Board accepted the challenge of developing a research program on the genetics of inflammatory bowel disease. The principal investigators would be Drs. Chang, Ma, and Cho. The Men's Board awarded $600,000 over a period of three years to support Dr. Cho's research in the area of the genetics of inflammatory bowel disease.

Dr. Ma received additional critical support from Miles Fiterman and Marian Edelstein for laboratory equipment to support research in transgenic animal science to investigate the genetic and immunologic basis of inflammatory bowel disease. Dr. Ma was one of the few scientists at that time capable of this type of research. The major genetics unit was developed through access to the 5th floor of the Billings Research Pavilion and the efforts of Dean Glenn Steele and Dr. Kirsner. Another $3 million raised by GIRF led to the establishment of the first gastroenterology DNA research laboratory. The project was also supported by the national Crohn's and Colitis Foundation of America. Individual donors who contributed generously to this program included William Getz of Colorado, Angelica Biasco of Virginia, and Marian Edelstein, Mrs. William Weisz, Harriet Katz, and Mr. and Mrs. Martin Boyer, all of Chicago. These efforts to support genetic research have already contributed to important developments in the field, and Dr. Judy Cho was responsible for studies that led to the discovery of the first gene known to be responsible for Crohn's disease, the *NOD2* genetic locus.

In 1998 the GIRF Women's Board sponsored a first-of-its-kind citywide conference on women's gastrointestinal health, "Gender Matters: Issues in Women's Gastrointestinal Health." GIRF also developed an Associates' Board, which has raised money to be directed to younger investigators in the GI section, and sponsored an annual fellowship competition, which began in 1991.

Dr. Kirsner's dedication to the activities of GIRF continues to the present day. He attends each monthly board meeting and serves as an adviser to the leaders of the organization and a bridge between the faculty of the Section of Gastroenterology and the membership of GIRF. He is present at all major fund-raising activities, including the annual GIRF ball. As he works to ensure the continued success of the organization, GIRF continues to honor him, never failing to mark and help celebrate milestones in his life and career, recently including his 60 years of service on the faculty of the University of Chicago, his 95th birthday, and his retirement from active clinical practice at the age of 95. Scanning any recent issues of the quarterly GIRF *Newsletter* makes it clear how important his active presence is to the organization. To the members of GIRF, he is affectionately and respectfully known as "Dr. Joe."

Notes

1. Materials used in the preparation of this chapter come from tape-recorded interviews conducted by the author with Dr. Kirsner. Interviews were also given to the author by founding members of GIRF Martin Sandler (April 24, 2006) and Joseph Valenti (March 1, 2006).
2. The collected GIRF *Newsletter*s from 1964 to 1979 were kindly made available to the author by the GIRF offices in Chicago. I especially thank Marge Dowling for her help in providing this material.

9 ✳ Chief of Staff and Deputy Dean, 1971–1976

The decade of the 1970s witnessed an accumulation of problems in the health care system in the United States—including at the University of Chicago Hospital and Clinics. These problems had been slowly increasing in magnitude over several decades. Regrettably, they remain with us today and are still unaddressed. Significant financial pressures related to the rising cost of health care were aggravated by wage and price controls that had been instituted by the Nixon administration, which led to increased unemployment and rising energy costs. In medicine, the ongoing demand for new technologies continued to drive the costs of hospital care upward. In addition, the increasing reliance on technology and the complexity of medical care continued to widen the gulf between patients and their physicians. This weakening in the doctor-patient relationship was reflected in a spiraling increase in medical malpractice lawsuits and the resulting higher costs of malpractice insurance for both hospitals and physicians. The problem was nationwide, and articles appeared with such titles as "Where Are the Doctors?" Senator Edward Kennedy of Massachusetts gave a spirited talk before the U.S. Congress titled "Who Speaks for the Patient?"

At the University of Chicago Medical School and at Billings Hospital, these factors all contributed to declining morale among the members of the staff. The loyalty of the hospital staff was further eroded by the university's tenure system, which emphasized outstanding research but failed to reward clinicians for their care of patients and for their teaching activities. Young investigators were made to feel that the time they devoted to clinical care and teaching would detract

from their chances of achieving tenure. A faculty member had to get tenure to remain on the staff, and an individual entering the system had to achieve the rank of full professor within a seven-year period. Since advancement was based on a system that valued the candidate's research achievements, highly talented clinicians were forced to leave the university. This lead to a high turnover of the faculty, and a resulting decline in morale and loyalty to the university.

In the face of these difficulties, Dean Leon Jacobson decided in 1971 to activate the position of chief of staff and deputy dean for clinical affairs. He asked Dr. Kirsner to take the position for a two-year period, which eventually was extended to five years. Dr. Kirsner accepted the position with the understanding that he would continue his highly regarded Saturday morning clinic and also continue to make rounds as the attending gastroenterologist on the GI service for two months each year, August and December (which he hoped might be quieter months). Dr. Charles Winans remembers that Dr. Kirsner called together a meeting of the GI section at which he announced that he was undertaking the new position and that Irwin Rosenberg would become the new chief of the Section of Gastroenterology.

The vigor and dedication with which Dr. Kirsner entered into his new assignment were reminiscent of a military campaign. His initial approach involved meeting at length with numerous members of the clinical faculty, the hospital administration, the nursing staff, food services, cleaning employees, and chairmen of all the clinical departments. After six weeks spent gathering information on the functioning of the Medical Center, he was ready to address the faculty. On June 16, 1971, Dr. Kirsner met with the entire faculty of the medical school and delivered a carefully worded address entitled "Problems, Policies, and Plans: The University of Chicago Medical Center." Given the difficulties besetting the Medical Center, one senses the atmosphere of anticipation and interest that must have attended this address, even for a group that had perhaps become somewhat apathetic.[1]

Dr. Kirsner first welcomed the clinical staff as their new chief of staff and pledged his dedication to the development of first-class clinical activities at the University of Chicago. He repeatedly emphasized that clinical excellence was a worthy academic activity—and worthy of recognition. He announced that his first-floor deputy dean's office was open for problems or questions from six thirty to eight o'clock on weekday mornings, and from one to four o'clock on Saturday afternoons. Perhaps with a sly wink, he noted that if those hours were not appealing, he could make special arrangements, and he welcomed written comments as well. He reviewed the history of the full-time faculty and the mission of the Medical Center from the opening of the medical school in 1927. He asked his audience, "Where have we failed?" The answer, he said, lay in the rapid growth of the Medical Center, the decreased administrative interest in medical affairs, and the erosion of the concept of service, including follow-up patient care, which he cited as vital to the medical profession. He pointed to the "crescendo" of new tests and procedures that neither the staff at the hospital nor anyone else could have adequately prepared for. There were also poorly understood fiscal practices stemming from the fact that Billings was not an independent hospital but rather a property of the University of Chicago. He pointed further to administrative limitations and employee incompetence. Many of the problems arose from a system that rewarded the investigator and failed to recognize the efforts of the clinician. He called on the group to discard their apparent air of indifference and to dedicate themselves once again to becoming a great medical center.

Discussing the issue of clinical excellence, he pointed out that it required efficient administration, a superb medical records department, and quality laboratory services. But above all, excellence begins with sincere physicians and nursing staff committed to patient care. Continuing in the manner of a "Dutch uncle," he pointed out that clinical excellence meant

> a willingness to see patients regularly; a humaneness in not turning away a feeble patient who arrives on the wrong day; seeing patients at the bedside and not as a unit number in the conference room; it involves instructive and authoritative supervision of interns and residents, even on Sundays, so as not to condone incomplete workups or sloppy medical care; prompt efficient scheduling of necessary tests to reduce excessive duration of hospital stays; and it includes the readiness of a surgeon to postpone a laboratory experiment to operate on an acute surgical emergency.

Clinical excellence meant an unwillingness to settle for the average, the ordinary: "a rejection of the present tendency to overlook mistakes, the omissions and the deaths that result occasionally from inadequate or misguided medical attention."

If there was any doubt about where the new chief of staff stood, he continued, "For those of you who feel comfortable with these remarks, I warmly renew my welcome. For those of you who may be uncomfortable or even unhappy, for the 'don't give a damn' faculty or premature retirees, I suggest that you would do well to seek employment elsewhere." Those in the audience even only recently acquainted with Dr. Kirsner's personal dedication to clinical excellence in patient care could not doubt the authority with which he spoke. He signaled that all departmental chairmen would be required to document annually in writing the clinical activities of each faculty member as a condition for budgetary consideration. He stressed a new determination to ensure that all peer-review mechanisms to establish accreditation and improve the quality of care would be implemented. He further emphasized his concern that permanent chairmen for the departments of Surgery, Anesthesiology, and Radiology be found as soon as possible (and within three months of his address, these positions were indeed filled). He discussed the debate between continuing a full-time faculty versus implementation of part-time or geographic full-time faculty and emphasized his personal preference that the full-time system be preserved.

Dr. Kirsner also called for the reexamination of the administration of the Medical Center. He felt that hospital administrators needed to be properly empowered to act decisively. The nonavailability of records had to be corrected, and the problem of missing laboratory reports addressed immediately. Incompetence would not be tolerated, and those who did not meet the standards of an outstanding medical center would be replaced. Some of the center's difficulties were related to an employee pool that was poorly educated and poorly trained. He saw this as part of "a national pattern of declining service performance for increasing salaries in an inflationary economy." He affirmed his complete confidence in the ability of Regis Kenna, the chief hospital administrator, to address the administrative problems of the institution.

He told the audience that he did not feel that the outpatient department was being properly utilized; he reviewed the volume of referrals to the institution versus the actual number of visits to the various departments and questioned whether the faculty was working hard enough. A similar hard analysis of the statistics on bed occupancy revealed inadequate bed utilization. He pointed to mystical fiscal policies for charges and soaring free care costs. He noted that for a 600-bed hospital to have 57 administrators, 258 house staff, 302 clinical faculty, and 2,118 nonmedical personnel seemed excessive. He warned, in language that had its origins in his military experience in World War II, that they had developed their own form of "boondoggling" and that reductions might be forced upon them by hospital rate-review boards. Further, he addressed the issue of the inadequacy of the emergency rooms for Billings and Wyler Children's Hospital to meet the needs of total number of visits, which had gone from 12,348 in 1961 to over 80,000 in 1970. The hospital would have to respond to these needs, and he announced the appointment of Dr. Peter Rosen, of Denver University, as the first medical director of the emergency room.

He closed his address on a literary note, crediting Dr. Frank Newell, who was chief of the Section of Ophthalmology, for pointing out a quotation from Samuel Beckett's *Waiting for Godot:*

> Let us not waste time in idle discourse! Let us do something, while we have a chance! It is not every day we are needed. Not indeed that we personally are needed. Others would meet the case equally well if not better. To all mankind they were addressed, those cries for help still ringing in our ears! But at this place, at this moment of time, all mankind is us, whether we like it or not. Let us make the most of it, before it is too late!

Since the Medical Center had not previously had a chief of staff, there existed no formal job description. Dr. Kirsner viewed his main mission as the strengthening "of clinical medicine as a worthy academic enterprise and to help the proper functioning of the clinical departments and patient care programs." He served as the chairman of the executive committee, which comprised the heads of the hospital's clinical departments. The committee met every Monday for lunch to discuss current issues and problems. His approach to administrative problems was to establish select committees that included house staff, clinical faculty members, and representatives from the administration, as appropriate to the issue at hand. There were meetings at breakfast, lunch, and dinner, and also on weekends. It was a very demanding job. Dr. Kirsner estimated that at one point there may have been some 25 committees representing 125 faculty members organized through the office of the chief of staff. He also scheduled monthly breakfast meetings with the house staff to give them a chance to bring to the administration's attention any issues at the hospital that were of concern to them. To further unite the faculty in a common effort, Dr. Kirsner reintroduced the quarterly staff meetings. To attract as many members of the faculty as possible, the administrative meetings were followed by a dinner held in the main dinning room. These proved to be highly popular events, and Dr. Kirsner felt they did much to increase the degree of cooperation between the various departments.

Early in his tenure as chief of staff, Dr. Kirsner encountered a problem emblematic of the difficulties the Medical Center was facing.[2] The incident occurred on a Saturday afternoon, always a precarious time for patient care at almost any hospital. Dr. Kirsner was consulting on a child with Crohn's disease on the pediatric service in Wyler Children's Hospital. The child's medical condition had worsened, and there was a marked increase in abdominal tenderness and signs of peritonitis. Dr. Kirsner requested that the pediatric surgeon who had previously operated on the patient be called back to reevaluate the child's condition. But he was told that the surgeon was signed out and had an unlisted telephone number. Dr. Kirsner was irate and contacted the local police department to locate the surgeon's home and have him return to the hospital immediately. When the surgeon appeared, Dr. Kirsner angrily demanded to know how he could pretend to be rendering patient care while insulating himself from his responsibilities with an unlisted telephone number. He told the surgeon that this conduct would not be tolerated and that if he could not abide by the Medical Center's standards, he would do well to find employment elsewhere. The child did indeed require emergency surgical intervention, which the surgeon performed. Dr. Kirsner adds that the surgeon subsequently left the University of Chicago.

Throughout his medical career, Dr. Kirsner's home telephone was always listed, both in the telephone book and with the hospital operators, and he accepted calls from patients seven days a week, both during the day and at night.

Another problem that came to his attention fairly early on illustrates the type of personnel problems the institution faced. A nurse had given a patient the wrong unit of blood, and although fortunately the incident did not result in any lasting injury, a review of the nurse's record indicated a number of other careless incidents. Dr. Kirsner decided that she was less than qualified and potentially dangerous to patients. He told Mr. Kenna that he felt the nurse should be dismissed. A few days later, Kenna reported to him, "The union says you cannot fire this lady!" Dr. Kirsner requested that he and Regis Kenna meet with two of the union leaders. At the meeting Dr. Kirsner told them, "Look, fellows, I don't know how you feel about it, but I wouldn't want to come to a hospital with the knowledge that nurses would give the wrong medicine and the wrong blood to patients. I don't understand your position in this regard. It's positively dangerous." It was perhaps not widely known how tough Dr. Kirsner could be when the need arose. He went on, "Furthermore, I know every health-care editor in this city, and I'm going to have a story published on the front page of the *Chicago Tribune* and the *Sun Times* with your names in it as opposing the dismissal of a nurse who is incapable of proper care." The result of this meeting was that Mr. Kenna was able to dismiss the nurse.

In his drive to monitor and improve patient care, Dr. Kirsner was aided by the efforts of the chief hospital administrator, Regis Kenna. Mr. Kenna was a quiet, personable, and capable individual, well liked by both the medical staff and hospital personnel. A hospital is a complex organism that prospers or falters, not on the basis of an elegant organizational diagram, but through the loyal and dedicated individuals at many levels throughout the institution. Regis Kenna was such a person, as was Dr. Kirsner himself. Throughout the years that he was chief of staff, Dr. Kirsner and Mr. Kenna were situated in offices across from each other and met on a daily basis to review problems arising in the hospital. Together they instituted a practice of unexpected visits to individual hospital units. These visits would be made at odd hours, including evenings and weekends. They were meant not to embarrass individuals but to gather an accurate picture of how the hospital was functioning. (Again, one cannot help but wonder whether this practice might be traced back to Dr. Kirsner's years in the military.) They would observe how food trays were delivered to patients, whether cleaning personnel would enter rooms without knocking, and if nurse call lights were not properly answered. They talked with patients to learn what difficulties they were experiencing in their care and even asked such basic questions as whether the patients knew their doctor's name.

As chief of staff, Dr. Kirsner instituted a practice of periodically sending out memos to the clinical faculty.[3] Reading through these documents, one sees that Dr. Kirsner addressed a wide range of issues over the years: problems arising from the use of particular intravenous catheters, failure of clinical faculty to maintain the status of their narcotic licenses, or setting down guidelines for good patient care.

For example, on April 4, 1972, he sent a memorandum to the clinical faculty and house staff titled "Patient Consultation." The memo eloquently spelled out the roles and responsibilities of both the consultant and the consulting service. He pointed out that a consultation does not imply nor should it be regarded as a transfer of the primary care role of the service sending the consult. The consultant is not expected to initiate a comprehensive discussion of the clinical problem with the patient or the patient's family until after reviewing the situation with the referring physician. He emphasized the importance of communicating personally and in writing with the referring physician. The consult should not be regarded as a substitute on the part of the referring physician or service for their responsibility to do a thorough study of a patient's problem. The consultant should be prompt and regard the consult as recognition of his knowledge and experience, and it should be fulfilled in a timely manner, within 24 hours. The consultation should serve a teaching function, and communication with the house staff and medical students should be regarded as part of the consultation.

Some of his memoranda concerned fiscal issues, such as the transferring of patients who had exhausted their insurance resources and were thus taxing the hospital's budget, which in 1973 allowed $2.5

million for bad debts. There was the overutilization of the laboratory. In one instance, he identified a patient who had 95 sets of individual normal electrolytes in 82 days! This type of oversight was not an uncommon problem in teaching hospitals, where house staff were fond of using "standing orders." Calling this to the attention of the staff was not simply an economic issue but a matter of proper and thoughtful patient care. The hospital also had to address an energy crisis and reduce the use of heating and lighting in certain non-patient-care areas of the hospital. Some of the memoranda alerted the clinical directors of departments to the fiscal shortages that limited the replacement of equipment and called on department heads to assess their anticipated needs. There were the needs of the blood bank and its source of donated blood. The use of paid professional donors had been abandoned in the wake of an alarming incidence of post-transfusion-related hepatitis, which at the time could not be excluded by routine screening of donors. The scheduling of elective surgical procedures required the patient's donation of blood for autologous transfusion at the time of surgery, and attending were urged to encourage family members to donate blood to help replace blood that was being used for their relatives.

Through his memoranda he also sought to educate the staff in areas of patient care. In January 1975 he called to the attention of the clinical and house staff the problem of Clindamycin colitis. The relatively new drug was being recognized as a cause of a serious colitis that resulted from a change in the bacterial flora of the large intestine. His memorandum includes a review of the pertinent literature at the time. Later it would be understood that, in addition to Clindamycin, there were a number of antibiotics capable of suppressing the normal bacterial flora such that an overgrowth of *Clostridium difficile* might occur, and that this organism was capable of producing a toxin that could cause pathologic changes in the lining of the colon. This clinical problem remains a concern in hospitals to this day, where the age-old lessons of regular hand washing and sanitation measures aimed at reducing cross-contamination of patients by hospital personnel must be continually relearned. Witness the current nosocomial (hospital-acquired) infections with multi-drug-resistant *Staphylococcus aureus*.

A yearly tradition during his tenure as chief of staff was Dr.

Kirsner's welcome to the clinical faculty and the house staff at the start of the "new year," which, he pointed out, was traditionally timed at university medical centers to the arrival of the new house staff. He wished them all a successful year marked by personal satisfaction and compassionate patient care. Dr. George V. Le Roy had called to his attention a poem, "The Care of the Patient," by Sir Robert Hutchinson, that he liked to quote.

THE CARE OF THE PATIENT
From inability to let well alone;
From too much zeal for what is new and
    contempt for what is old;
From putting knowledge before wisdom,
    science before art, and cleverness before
    common sense;
From treating patients as cases; and from
    making the cure of the disease more
grievous than its endurance;
God Lord deliver us!

Dr. Kirsner was appalled at the smoking by hospital staff in the main corridors of the hospital, and on one occasion counted over 100 cigarette butts scattered along the first-floor corridor. He decried the wanton disregard by visitors, staff, and hospital employees of their responsibility to keep the hospital environment clean. In 1975 Dr. Kirsner pointed out that smoking had become a serious problem affecting the safety and health of the patients. Cigarettes had caused fires on a number of units, and a check with the Chicago Fire Department revealed that the Medical Center had one of the poorest ratings among the hospitals in the city. He felt compelled to take drastic measures in restricting smoking by patients, visitors, staff, and employees throughout the Medical Center. He did not escape the ire of some staff members, including the chairman of the Department of Psychiatry, a smoker, who felt that Dr. Kirsner was treading on an issue of personal liberty. Dr. John Fennessy recalls that the issue was contentiously debated at faculty meetings, and when he first put the matter to a vote among the department chairmen, Dr. Kirsner was voted down. He had to persuade them by reviewing the medical literature and especially the studies of the British epidemiologist Dr. Richard Doll. The issue was so emotionally charged that on one occasion the above-mentioned chairman of the Department of Psychiatry called him at home and called him an SOB. Dr. Kirsner advised him that he would hang up if he persisted in using profanity. At this point the caller demonstrated the extent of his colorful vocabulary, and Dr. Kirsner was forced to hang up the telephone. (It is hard to imagine anyone speaking to Dr. Kirsner in that manner!) Ironically, Dr. Kirsner notes, this individual left the institution and ultimately succumbed to lung cancer.

Another major problem that the Medical Center had to confront was a rising tide of medical malpractice claims. Dr. Kirsner remembers sitting next to a prominent attorney at a meeting he attended in the Loop on an unrelated matter, and being informed by the attorney that the quality of the medical records at the Medical Center at the University of Chicago was the worst in the city. When Dr. Kirsner assumed his role as chief of staff, Dr. Charles Winans remembers, the Medical Center employed only a single attorney in its Office of Legal Affairs. Suits against the Medical Center were not contested and simply settled out of court. Dr. Winans relates that he was sued because of a perforation that occurred after a pneumatic dilation of the esophagus for a condition called achalasia. The risks of the treatment and technique were well recognized and had been fully explained to the patient. Dr. Winans refused to allow the matter simply to be settled out of court, and it was probably the first instance when the Medical Center and its insurance carrier fought a lawsuit. The suit went to a jury trial, and Dr. Winans was gratified when the jury found that there was no evidence of malpractice.

In 1973 the Office of Legal Affairs and Policies was established to receive all subpoenas and handle the verification of attorneys' requests for records. It was necessary to point out to the medical staff the hazards of imprudent remarks made to patients and their families. One example was a surgeon who came out of the operating room and informed the family that "he had done everything he could for the patient with the instruments they had to work with." Not surprisingly, that remark proved costly to the hospital. In a memo titled "On the Need for Sensitivity in Our Communications with Patients,"

Dr. Kirsner warned that physicians had been rightfully charged with both the "curse of non-communication (*Analogia Pox*)" and the "curse of over-communication (*Polylogia Pox*)." And there was also the problem of "insensitive, thoughtless communication (*Malologia Pox*)." In his memo, Dr. Kirsner listed several examples of these failures of communication. One involved a patient whose blood pressure fell to hypotensive levels after the administration of Thorazine. "We gave you more than the usual dose because you were nervous," he was told. Although the dose was not in fact excessive, the patient and his family were convinced from the remark that he had erroneously received an overdose. To the distraught patient worried that he might have a serious illness, "Your problem is in your head; we will do a few tests but I doubt that we can help you" was among the cruelest of remarks. Even worse, a patient worried about a medication that he was given and the safety of the drug was told: "Don't bother me with such questions; you must do as I say or find another doctor." Dr. Kirsner reminded the staff of the observation of Philip A. Tumulty of Johns Hopkins University: "A clinician is one whose prime function is to manage a sick person with the purpose of alleviating the total effect of his illness . . . the ability to listen and to talk so that valid clinical evidence is gathered, anxieties are dissipated and understanding and motivation are instilled."[4]

In April of 1976 Dr. Kirsner invited the clinical faculty, house staff, and hospital administration to the general clinical staff dinner meeting on Tuesday, April 20. He told them that this would be the last general staff meeting that he would arrange, and that he would be introducing the new chief of staff, Dr. Henry Russe, who would assume the position on June 1, 1976. He thanked those who had attended meetings over the past five years and said he looked forward to seeing them at the April 20 meeting.

In May, shortly before stepping down, Dr. Kirsner wrote down some of his reflections on his tenure as chief of staff and deputy dean and summarized his thoughts about the Medical Center. He viewed some of the experiences as being like those of the "legendary King of Corinth who was condemned to roll a heavy stone up a steep hill in Hades only to have it roll back down again for eternity." (Here again we see the influence of his exposure to the classics while a student at

Boston English High School.) He meant, of course, that some problems were continuously recurring and seemed never to be solved.
Further reflection led him to acknowledge that considerable progress had been made in the quality of and sensitivity toward patient
care. He continued to regret the "man-made untidiness" of the hospital hallways. He felt that fiscal problems at the institution would
continue, but expressed confidence in the way Regis Kenna was addressing them. He continued to worry about the medical malpractice
crisis. In the two years prior to 1976 he noted that malpractice claims
settled against the University of Chicago exceeded $2.1 million. He
also noted that, as of May 1976, the Medical Center had 75 malpractice claims pending against it with claims totaling $27 million dollars.
He commended the staff for its improved communications with referring physicians and noted that excellent patient care was leading
to increased recognition of the institution as a tertiary referral center.
He was also gratified by increased involvement of the clinical faculty
and house staff in patient care–related affairs. He noted that he had
developed 24 clinical committees involving 110 faculty members, 24
house staff, 18 nursing staff, and 39 hospital administrators.

During the years that Dr. Kirsner was chief of staff and deputy
dean he took steps to develop a clinical pathway that would lead to
tenure. He presented his thoughts on this issue at meetings of the
deans and in discussions with the chairmen of departments. The
nature of academic medicine during his career at the University of
Chicago had undergone an evolution that placed greater demands
on the clinical investigator to conduct well-designed clinical studies
of the highest quality. It was necessary to have proper controls and
strict criteria for the patient populations to be studied; random allocation of patients to treatment regimens and control groups had to
be set up by an unbiased method (so-called randomized double-blind
controlled studies), and data analyzed by appropriate, validated sta-
tistical tools. All this meant that the clinician doing clinical research
had to be as rigorously schooled in these methods as a bench laboratory investigator. Teaching activities in the medical school were also
changing, and rigorous evaluation of the curriculum and systematic
analysis of the outcomes of teaching methods were demanded. The
delivery of health care itself was steadily becoming more specialized

and complex. Individual techniques—for example, cardiac and coronary artery catheterization or, in gastroenterology, therapeutic endoscopic retrograde pancreatic cholangiography—required that physicians performing these procedures devote full-time clinical effort to achieving the best possible results. In view of these developments, and in part through Dr. Kirsner's efforts, the university changed its promotion policies and recognized the achievements of individuals in teaching and clinical work as being worthy of promotion and tenure.

Each holiday season, Dr. Kirsner sent a greeting to the entire medical staff that offered his "Best Wishes for Peace, Service to Mankind and a Happy Hospital Season." The cards were set in tasteful typography and carried a meaningful quotation. It is fitting to end a chapter on this phase of Dr. Kirsner's career with a sampling of these quotations:

> Medicine is an art, not a trade; a calling, not a business; a calling in which the Heart will be ever exercised equally with the Head.
>
> WILLIAM OSLER

> In no other way does man approach so near the gods as when he is restoring the sick to the blessings of health.
>
> MARCUS TULLIUS CICERO

> Man is here for the sake of other men—above all, for those upon whose smile and well-being our own happiness depends, and also for the countless unknown souls with whose fate we are connected by a bond of sympathy. Many times a day I realize how much my own outer and inner life is built upon the labors of my fellow-men, both living and dead, and how earnestly I must exert myself in order to give in return as much as I have received.
>
> ALBERT EINSTEIN

Notes

1. The full text of this address is in the collected papers of Dr. Joseph B. Kirsner, and a copy is held by the author.
2. This and other anecdotes were related to the author by Dr. Kirsner in a

184 : Chapter Nine

series of taped interviews. Dr. Kirsner has also described his experiences as
chief of staff and deputy dean of the Medical School in a typed manuscript
that is part of his personal papers.

3. The collection of memos sent to the clinical faculty and house staff are part
of the collected papers of Joseph B. Kirsner.

4. Tumulty, PA, What is a clinician and what does he do? *New Eng J Med*
282:20-24, 1970.

10 ✳ The Morocco Story, 1976–1998

In February 1976, shortly after Dr. Kirsner resigned his position as deputy dean at the University of Chicago Medical Center, he received a telephone call from Ambassador Abdeslam Jaidi, the ambassador-at-large of Morocco, asking if he would come to Morocco to see His Majesty the King, King Hassan II.[1] Dr. Kirsner was astonished and asked how they had gotten his name. It turned out that Dr. Donald Fredrickson, the director of the NIH, had given Dr. Kirsner's name to the ambassador and the physicians caring for the king as the best gastroenterologist in the United States. Dr. Fredrickson, a noted authority on lipid disorders, was involved in the king's medical care as an adviser on the treatment of an elevated serum cholesterol level, and he had gotten to know Dr. Kirsner as a result of their collaboration on the medical advisory board of the NIH's Institute of Arthritis and Metabolic Diseases. Dr. Kirsner was quick to tell the ambassador that he was Jewish but was told, "We know all about you. And we want you." Cautioning Ambassador Jaidi that he would have to check with the "boss," by whom he meant his wife, and provided she approved, he agreed to come. He also consulted with the dean of the medical school, Dan Tosteson, who urged him to go. Thus began Dr. Kirsner's association with the kingdom of Morocco, which continued from 1976 until 1998, the year King Hassan II died. Even after the king's death, however, Dr. Kirsner has maintained a connection with the country, and a delegation of physicians from Morocco were present at his 95th birthday celebration.

In 1957 Morocco gained its independence from France, and Muhammad V assumed the title of king. On his death in 1961, he was suc-

ceeded by his son, King Hassan II, who had been educated in France as a lawyer. The king was highly respected in the West and stood out among other leaders in the Middle East for his openness to establishing a dialogue with Israel. As king, he faced enormous pressures, and at the time Dr. Kirsner was asked to see him, he had already survived two violent but failed coups. The first was in 1971, when a military faction attacked his seaside palace of Skhirat near Rabat, and the second in 1972, when his private jet was attacked by fighter planes from the Royal Moroccan Air Force.

Dr. Kirsner's first trip to Morocco began on February 10, 1976. He was met by Ambassador Jaidi and Dr. Tuhani, the minister of health, in New York, where they boarded an Iberian plane for Madrid. During the flight he learned something of the king's symptoms and began to develop some preliminary thoughts about an appropriate diagnostic and therapeutic approach. Arriving in Madrid, they were met by one of the king's private jets and flown to the oldest city in Morocco, Fez.

Chauffeured cars drove the party to a hotel located a few minutes from the palace. There Dr. Kirsner waited and organized his thoughts while awaiting further instructions. For Dr. Kirsner, this first trip to a Muslim country on the continent of Africa, with camels in the streets and veiled women, was a major culture shock. Several hours later he was called to have lunch with the ambassador and a few of his friends. Lunch was in a small town, a short distance from Fez, where he first became acquainted with dining while seated on pillows, eating with one's fingers, and the separation of men and women during meals.

After lunch, he returned to the hotel and was told he would meet His Majesty that evening in the palace. At seven o'clock he was taken in a chauffeured car to the palace to await the king. His Majesty arrived dressed in traditional Moroccan robes. They were then joined by a number of his physicians: Dr. Berbiche, Dr. Arani, and Dr. Metkall, the king's immediate personal physician. His physicians had all been educated in France, and Dr. Kirsner felt that they were committed to the best in medicine. The group proceeded to a conference room, where Dr. Kirsner reviewed some of the king's x-rays and began to take a medical history. A young French Canadian employed by the NIH had accompanied them on the trip to facilitate communication with the king in French. In the event, Dr. Kirsner knew enough French and the king knew enough English that they managed to communicate quite well with each other. Obtaining the king's history took about an hour and fifteen minutes. Dr. Kirsner found that the king's gastrointestinal problem did not appear to be serious but was consistent with a highly irritable bowel syndrome that was both annoying and inconvenient. The king had been seen by numerous physicians, including several Americans, in the past, but the recommended treatment had failed to control his bowel function or relieve his symptoms.

Dr. Kirsner proceeded to the physical examination, which was performed in the presence of the king's physicians. Then he came to that moment in the physical examination requiring a rectal examination, which he considered important, since the king had previously had ano-rectal surgery in France. His Majesty declined to proceed with the examination. Without carefully considering his response, Dr. Kirsner said, "Your Majesty, I did not travel 5,000 miles to do an incomplete physical examination, and if I am not allowed to complete this examination, I will be honored to find you another doctor." Dr. Kirsner thought he heard a gasp from the medical people assembled. However, the king smiled and agreed to the examination, which was done in an adjoining room. Afterward, they returned to the conference room and resumed their discussion. Dr. Kirsner, emboldened by his earlier experience, said, "Your Majesty, during the history I have taken you have smoked nine cigarettes, and I must tell you that smoking is very bad for your health, for your heart, your lungs and for your bowel, and it is important that you discontinue smoking." Again there was an audible gasp from the assembled physicians, and Dr. Kirsner realized that he had broached a sensitive topic. However, the king again smiled and said, "Would you like me to sign a contract to stop smoking?" Dr. Kirsner responded, "No, Your Majesty, I never sign contracts with any patient, but if you believe this is a good idea why don't we shake hands, man to man." The king's remark gave Dr. Kirsner the sense that he was progressing well with his noble patient, having negotiated two vital issues at the first visit. The examination was scheduled to resume the next morning, when Dr. Claude Betournet, dean of the medical sciences at the University of Paris and the physician in charge of the king's medical care, was scheduled to arrive from Paris. At that time, Dr. Kirsner would summarize his impressions and recommendations for treatment.

Just when Dr. Kirsner was ready to "call it a day," he found himself escorted to a Moroccan nightclub and treated to a late-night dinner and a typical Moroccan dance performance. Finally, at around one in the morning, he was able to return to his hotel to rest in preparation for the events of the coming day.

The next morning Dr. Kirsner again met with the king. Dr. Kirsner quickly realized that his "so-called victory" of the previous evening had not materialized, since the king was still smoking. Dr. Kirsner said nothing about it, although he was later to bring up the issue on numerous occasions. Dr. Kirsner told Dr. Betournet that his evaluation of the situation was that the king suffered from an irritable bowel syndrome brought on by a variety of factors including a demanding schedule, stress, the use of cigarettes, and numerous antibiotics that had been prescribed for suspected bowel infections including yeast infections. The physicians present agreed that Dr. Kirsner would recommend a medical program of diet modification and the use of phenobarbital and belladonna tablets, and if the situation did not improve, they could then proceed to selected x-ray studies. The use of a combination of phenobarbital and belladonna in a single tablet was, in that era, a mainstay in Dr. Kirsner's approach to the treatment of irritable bowel syndrome.

When Dr. Kirsner returned to the University of Chicago, his visit was a lively topic of discussion among the hospital staff. Over the next 20 years he would end up making about 55 visits to Morocco.

Dr. Kirsner was later accompanied by his colleague Dr. John Fennessy, chairman of the Department of Radiology, who performed x-rays studies on the king.[2] Dr. Kirsner had reviewed the king's earlier barium x-ray studies and felt that better examinations were needed. He therefore asked Dr. Fennessy, whom he relied upon for gastrointestinal radiology at the university, to accompany him on a return visit to Morocco. Dr. Fennessy gathered the materials he would need for these studies--laxatives for cleansing the gastrointestinal tract, and barium and the equipment for administering it as part of the radiologic study of the colon or "lower GI." A native of Ireland, Dr. Fennessy likened himself to the executioners that the English imported to Ireland who came bearing the tools of their trade for public executions.

The medical clinic area of the palace at Rabat had its own self-contained radiology suite, whose equipment Dr. Fennessy describes as "passable." Once in Morocco, Dr. Fennessy described to the king the details of the examinations he would perform. The king listened to his presentation and turned and looked at one of his aides, a cousin, who immediately volunteered to undergo a "trial run" of the procedure. So the king's cousin became the first Moroccan that Dr. Fennessy would study, and when the cousin reported back that the examination was not that difficult, the king agreed to undergo it himself. Performing the study on the king was not quite the same as a standard examination. The king would not simply roll over and lay face down on the examining table, but would insist on getting off the table and having it repositioned so that he could again get back on the table in the desired position. Dr. Fennessy felt that in spite of the limitations imposed upon him, he obtained reasonable studies of the large intestine and the stomach and small intestine. Communication was through a French translator, but the king clearly knew the English language far better than he let on. Dr. Fennessy recalls seeing a televised meeting of King Hassan II and President Ronald Reagan when the king visited the United States. During the meeting the French translator was rendering an answer that the king had given in French when the king interrupted to correct the translator with the English response he preferred.

During that first year, Dr. Kirsner made five trips to Morocco, confirming his initial diagnosis of irritable bowel syndrome and following the approach he had been using successfully for many years at the University of Chicago. In July 1976 he was invited to celebrate the king's birthday. Mrs. Kirsner was able to accompany him on this trip, and on another visit at the end of the year to celebrate the New Year with the king and his friends and family.

As Dr. Kirsner became further acquainted with the king, he came to appreciate his abilities as a wise and intelligent leader. He learned that he was highly informed about world events and Islamic culture. He had been a good athlete and a better than average golfer. Dr.

Kirsner would walk with him on the golf course adjoining the Rabat palace on numerous occasions. When the king wished to discuss something with Dr. Kirsner in private, the fairways of the palace golf course or a ride in his limousine provided an excellent opportunity.

Professor Mohamed Binbine, a good friend of the king and his family, composed a poem in Arabic to honor Dr. Kirsner--an indication of how successful he had been in helping the king that year. The original manuscript in Arabic, supplemented with an English translation, remains among Dr. Kirsner's personal memorabilia of his Moroccan experiences. The translation reads as follows:

> Have you known another physician like Dr. Kirsner
> Who deserves our gratitude and our praise
> In whose chest Allah deposited the Aya (signs) of knowledge.
> And through his hands He ran the art of grace
> In his ten fingers lies the secret of recovery
> The miracle which perplexed doctors and Saints
> His character may doctor you before his medical enigma
> When he spreads upon you his smiles and his charisma
> Among physicians he shines like a star which lightens
> our galaxy, near and far
> My thanks all go to him and my gratitude
> With my best wishes and grandest attitude.
>
> PROFESSOR MOHAMED BINBINE

Over the next several years Dr. Kirsner would continue to average five trips a year to Morocco to check on the details of the king's health care, and Dr. Fredrickson would frequently accompany him. He was also consulted by Ambassador Jaidi for advice on the management of other medical problems, both among the king's friends and family and his own. Often these were problems outside the field of gastroenterology, and then Dr. Kirsner would find two or three American physicians in that particular area, be it nephrology, dermatology, or endocrinology. One of the most important of the physicians selected by Dr. Kirsner and Dr. Fredrickson was Dr. Roman De Sanctis, an outstanding cardiologist from Massachusetts General Hospital and Harvard Medical School. Dr. De Sanctis proved to be a key person on the team of physicians caring for His Majesty.

Mrs. Kirsner was able to accompany Dr. Kirsner twice a year, to celebrate the king's birthday and the New Year, until her own medical problems interfered with travel. The king was very fond of Minnie, and he appreciated her vivacity and charm. Over the years the king gave Mrs. Kirsner a number of fine pieces of jewelry and Moroccan carpets, which would eventually adorn almost every room of their apartment in the Cloisters. In later years, most of the jewelry would be donated by Dr. Kirsner to GIRF, to be auctioned off at the annual GIRF ball to benefit the research activities of the Section of Gastroenterology.

In the fall of 1979 Dr. and Mrs. Kirsner were just preparing to go to the temple for Yom Kippur services when he received an urgent telephone call from Ambassador Jaidi. The king's younger brother Prince Moulay Abdallah was seriously ill, and the family needed Dr. Kirsner's help. Since calls of this nature had become a fairly regular occurrence, Dr. Kirsner kept a traveling suitcase packed at home, and after discussing it with Minnie, he agreed to make the trip. The trip to Morocco through New York was quickly arranged. Dr. Kirsner flew first to Casablanca, where he was met by a Moroccan military jet and flown to the king's summer palace in the Atlas Mountains region. There was no time to check into a hotel. Entering a room in the palace, Dr. Kirsner was confronted with an unimaginable scene. The king's brother was lying on a mattress in the center of a large room, surrounded by members of his family and a number of French and Moroccan physicians. Disheveled and confused, the prince was deeply jaundiced, and his abdomen was distended, presumably as a result of the accumulation of intra-abdominal fluid, a condition called ascites.

After an initial examination, Dr. Kirsner asked to speak with His Majesty, who was in another area of the palace. He told the king that his brother was gravely ill, and if he was not transferred to a major medical center, he would probably die. He made several suggestions, including hospital contacts in Paris, at the Royal Free Hospital in London, and Hans Popper at Mount Sinai Hospital in New York. Smiling, the king told Dr. Kirsner that he and the prince's doctors had already decided that he should go to the University of Chicago. The king later confided to Dr. Kirsner that the French physicians were convinced that the prince was going to die, and they did not wish to

1. The Kirsner children, 1920-21. *From left:* Joe (age 11–12) and Ethel, *standing;* Morris and Lena (Lea), *on the pony.*

2. Burton Resnic's
bar mitzvah, 1920s.
Burton is standing with
Ida and Harris Kirsner.

3. Medical school graduation photo,
Tufts University, 1933

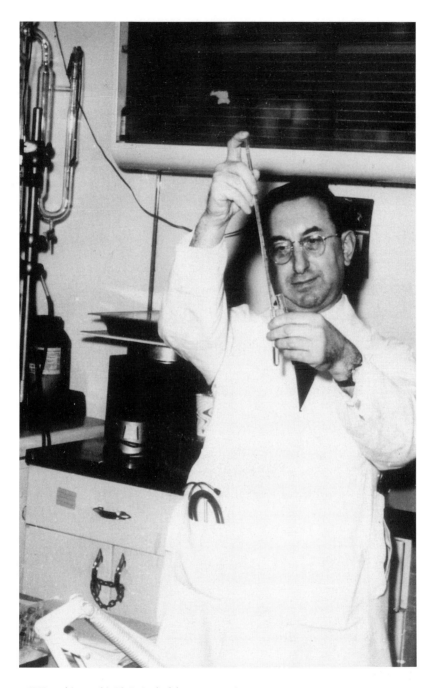

7. JBK working on his Ph.D. in the laboratory, 1936

8. Graduation 1942. JBK and his proud mother, Ida

9. Battle ready. World War II, 1944.

10. Nagoya, Japan, 1945. JBK (*right*) with Dr. Herb Ensworth

11. Minnie Kirsner and son Bob on the Midway, 1945.

12. Section of Gastroenenterology, University of Chicago, ca. 1947. *From left, standing:* Gracen Dashille, Alfred Kline, William Ricketts, Walter Palmer, JBK; *seated:* Marian Dakens, Samuel Maman.

13. Autographed photograph of the Section of Gastroenterology, June 1956

Dr. Franz J. Ingelfinger

Dr. Julian Ruffin

Dr. Stewart Wolf

Dr. Thomas P. Almy

Dr. Joseph B. Kirsner

Dr. Wade Volwiler

14. Gastroenterology members of the first General Medicine Study Section (NIH), 1950s. Reproduced by permission from Dale C. Smith, *The American Gastroenterological Association: 1897-1997* (Bethesda: AGA, 1999).

16. (FACING, BOTTOM) Advisory Council of the National Institute of Arthritis and Metabolic Diseases, 1968-74. *From left, back row:* Laurent Harris, Lui Welt, Bill Valentine, Bill Herbst, Miles Fiterman, Grant Liddle; *front row:* Bill McElroy, Abe Gutman, Dave Whedon, JBK, Sid Anderson.

15. Visit to the Vatican and Pope Pius XX, 1956. JBK is in the upper right-hand corner of the photograph.

17. Dr. Sumner Kraft, director of the Section of Gastroenterology's immunology research laboratory, 1960s

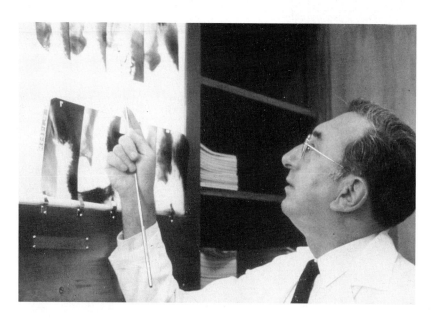

18. JBK reviewing a case of inflammatory bowel disease, 1968

19. JBK at the front desk of the GI clinic, 1971

20. First GIRF banquet, 1963. *From left:* Nathan Cohn, Martin Sandler, Joseph Valenti, JBK, Dr. H. Stanley Bennett, and Charles Goulet.

21. Early GIRF luncheon speakers, including JBK (*second from left*), the surgeon Dr. Lester
Dragstedt (*second from right*), and Dr. Morris Fishbein, the third president of GIRF (*far right*).

22. Maurice Goldblatt, one
of the founders of GIRF
and of the Cancer Research
Foundation, 1950s

23. Joseph Valenti (*left of JBK*) and Martin Sandler (*right*) being presented with Founders
Awards at the GIRF ball, 1978

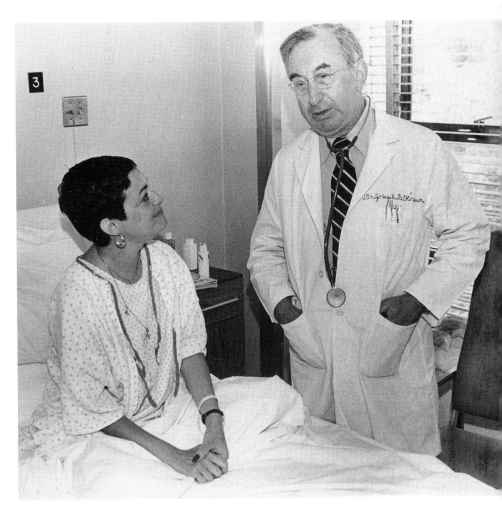

24. JBK, then chief of staff, at a patient's bedside, 1975

25. JBK on teaching rounds, 1975

26. JBK in his office, 1975

27. King Hassan II of Morocco

28. JBK celebrating his 80th birthday in Morocco, 1989. Seated are Ambassador Jaidi and his wife.

29. Dr. Donald S. Fredrickson, of the NIH, and JBK standing before the birthday cake,
Morocco, 1989

30. Robert Kirsner addressing a celebratory dinner as part of the dedication ceremonies for the new Center for the Study of Digestive Disease, 1987

31. Minnie and Joe at home, 1980s

32. JBK addressing the members of the Greek Gastroenterology Association at the temple of Asclepius in Greece, April 1989

33. Dr. Kirsner being congratulated by Mayor Harold Washington on Thursday, May 21, 1987 in the Council Chambers of City Hall, Chicago, on his induction into the Senior Citizens Hall of Fame, an award given by the city's Department on Aging and Disability.

34. Illinois Alliance for the Aging (IAA), in the council chambers of the mayor of Chicago, October 30, 1993. *From left:* Joseph L.Gidwitz, Helen Heyrman, President of the Illinois Alliance on Aging, Bernice Neugarten, Dr. Joseph B. Kirsner, Mayor Richard J. Daley, Mildred Johnson, and Dr. Charles W. Nolen.

35. JBK receiving the Lincoln Laureate Award from Illinois governor James Edgar, 1995

36. JBK receiving the Horatio Alger Award, presented by
Rev. Norman Vincent Peale, 1979

37. Dr. Kirsner in his office, M-226, 1998

38. Ceremony renaming part of Maryland Avenue the Honorary Dr. Joseph B. Kirsner Drive, 1999. *From left:* JBK, Harriet Katz, Mrs. Jerry Poncher, Marci and Joseph Valenti, Norman Frankel.

39. JBK in his office, 2004

40. JBK in conversation with Dr. Eugene Chang, 2004

41. Dr. Kirsner and Dr. Stephen Hanauer, Chief, Section of Gastroenterology, Hepatology and Nutrition, University of Chicago, 2008.

42. JBK celebrating with some of his favorite guests at the GIRF ball, June 2008. *From left:* Hortense Singer, Paul and Nancy Weiss, and Dr. B. H. Gerald Rodgers and his wife, Mae.

have the death on their hands, as had happened with the king's father, who had died while under general anesthesia in a French hospital.

Dr. Kirsner agreed but indicated that he himself would have to return to Chicago as quickly as possible to make arrangements for appropriate bed space and staff at the hospital. Since no flight was available for several days, the king called the president of France, Valéry Giscarde d'Estaing, on the phone, and a flight on the Concorde to Washington, D.C., was arranged for that same Sunday evening, making use of the seat that was regularly held open for the diplomatic service. These arrangements having been made, Dr. Kirsner was taken by limousine with a motorcycle escort to a private airfield for the flight to De Gaulle International Airport in time to board the Concorde. At Dulles Airport, a limousine was waiting to take him to Washington International for the flight to Chicago. The limousine was surrounded by police, since it was parked in the "wrong place," but a $20 bill settled the matter, and Dr. Kirsner reached Washington International in time to board his flight.

Although it was a Sunday, Dr. Kirsner contacted the hospital administrator, Ralph Muller, and arrangements were made to accommodate the prince and his wife, as well as the Moroccan security service and U.S. secret service agents, in the G3 medical unit on the third floor of the hospital. On Tuesday, however, a far larger party than was anticipated arrived with the prince, including some 32 individuals for whom accommodations had to be arranged in suitable hotels on the North Side of Chicago.

Shortly after arrival, the prince suffered an upper gastrointestinal hemorrhage. Dr. Kirsner feared this complication could prove fatal, but fortunately the prince's condition stabilized. Surgical consultants noted that since the patient had recently had a cholecystectomy in Paris for gallbladder stones, an exploratory operation for a possible common bile duct injury or common bile duct stone was indicated. The American Association for the Study of Liver Diseases just happened to be meeting in Chicago, and Dr. Kirsner contacted a friend, the distinguished British hepatologist Dame Sheila Sherlock, and asked her to consult on the prince.[3] She told Dr. Kirsner that he was "wasting his time" and the prince was going to die. (Dr. Kirsner somewhat ruefully noted that she submitted a substantial consultation fee for this negative advice.) Also attending the liver meetings was a former colleague, Dr. Fenton Schaffner, who was now on the staff of New York's Mount Sinai Hospital. Dr. Schaffner was similarly pessimistic about the chances for recovery.[4] Dr. Kirsner was not convinced by these gloomy prospects, vowing, "He will not die on my service."

A week later he received from Paris the records and x-rays from the prince's cholecystectomy. Dr. Kirsner suspected that the common bile duct might have been severely traumatized and become swollen as a consequence of the rather large clamps used by the French surgeons during the cholangiogram.[5] Dr. Kirsner decided to wait to allow the swelling of the injured common bile duct to subside and the level of jaundice to improve. Slowly over the next several weeks this did indeed occur, and the prince's condition improved. Early in his hospital stay, the prince decided that he did not like the hospital furniture, and new furnishings were ordered. In time, a portion of the hospital kitchen was turned over to his own chef, although the dietary program remained under Dr. Kirsner's careful supervision.

During the several months the prince remained a patient at the University of Chicago hospital, Dr. Kirsner continued to make rounds three times a day, seven days a week. Toward the end of what was a demanding experience for Dr. Kirsner, both as a clinician and as an administrator of a complex cultural situation, the prince and his wife, on a Sunday before they were scheduled to return to Morocco, invited Dr. and Mrs. Kirsner to his hospital area for tea. There he presented Mrs. Kirsner with a beautiful double-stranded gold necklace adorned with a golden ram's head as its centerpiece. Mrs. Kirsner asked the prince about the significance of the ram's head. The prince told the Kirsners that since God had sent a lamb to Abraham that he might spare his only son, Isaac, the ram was a symbol of Abraham and the Jewish people. He added that since both the Jews and the Muslims shared this common ancestry, the gift was a symbol of this kinship. For Dr. Kirsner and his wife, it was a precious moment. Throughout the prince's hospitalization, Dr. Kirsner had received frequent calls from his brother, King Hassan II, inquiring about his brother's progress. As a reflection of the appreciation he felt for the care that his brother had received at the University of Chicago, the king sent a shipment of 40 to 50 handwoven Moroccan carpets to be distributed to members of the staff who had cared for the prince.

In July of the next year, Dr. Kirsner and his wife traveled to Morocco to see the king and his brother. The whole country seemed to know about his success in the care of the prince, and the Kirsners were treated like heroes. There was a special dinner at the prince's hunting lodge, where the prince would not let them get their own food but insisted on serving them personally; he was particularly attentive to Minnie. The prince's recovery went so well that he was able to father a son. Mrs. Kirsner would remark that he might have named him Joseph, but he was named Ibriham. Dr. Kirsner later saw this youngster as a patient during one of his trips to Morocco.

This dramatic success in the management of the prince's critical illness created an aura of medical infallibility, and Dr. Kirsner found himself frequently called upon by Ambassador Jaidi and His Majesty's medical staff to see patients both in Chicago and on his trips to Morocco. Consultations were arranged for prominent government officials and their families in the suite at the hotel where the Kirsners stayed. Dr. Kirsner could identify with the role played by the famous Jewish physician Moses Maimonides, who was frequently consulted by Arab leaders throughout the Middle East.

On one occasion, when Dr. Fredrickson and Dr. Kirsner traveled together to Morocco for the king's annual physical examination, they were informed by the king that they would be flying at midnight to London to see the sister of the king of Saudi Arabia. In London, the two doctors were registered at the Dorchester Hotel and went the next day to see the sister in her home. Her problem turned out to be renal failure, and referrals were made initially to a nephrologist at Peter Bent Brigham Hospital. Ultimately Dr. Kirsner learned that she underwent a successful renal transplantation under the care of Dr. Thomas Starzl of the University of Pittsburgh.

Several years later the prince was seen at the University of Chicago and discovered to have a carcinoma in the lung; a CAT scan of the brain also revealed cerebral metastasis. Dr. Fennessy recalls that the king himself in effect made the diagnosis. The king and his brother were on a hunting trip to shoot wild boar, but the prince, who was normally an excellent marksman, missed several times. The king said that he thought his brother ought to have a CAT scan of his brain, and this led to the discovery of the tumor. Arrangements were made with Dr. Fennessy and Dr. Harvey Golumb, a University of Chicago oncologist, to supervise a program of radiation therapy for the prince. The radiotherapy was to start at the University of Chicago and be continued in Rabat, at a cancer hospital that was in the process of being built. The work was rapidly completed so that a cobalt unit could be installed, and the prince became the hospital's first patient.

Dr. Fennessy, Dr. Golumb, and Dr. Kirsner made many trips to Morocco to oversee the treatment. The exact nature of the prince's condition was not disclosed to the patient and his immediate family. Dr. Fennessy describes a "charade" that took place during the radiation therapy whereby a "sham" treatment of the liver preceeded the actual treatment of the lung and central nervous system. (Although this practice seems unthinkable in our era of full patient disclosure, it was a common practice in France and therefore in the tradition of medical practice that the Moroccans had learned from the French.) Initially the prince responded to the treatment, and his medical condition improved to such an extent that he was able to make a discreet trip to Chicago, where he visited Dr. and Mrs. Kirsner in their home. On that occasion he presented Dr. Kirsner with a beautiful watch, later also donated to GIRF. In December 1983 Dr. Kirsner received a telephone call requesting that he return urgently to Morocco. The prince was dying, and the royal family wanted him in attendance to support the public's perception that he was dying of liver disease, as had been reported in the press. Both Dr. Kirsner and Dr. Fennessy attended the state funeral for the prince and walked in a procession through the streets of Rabat to the mausoleum and the Great Mosque of Morocco, where the prince was buried and where eventually King Hassan II would be laid to rest.

In 1990 Dr. Kirsner, in consultation with the king's physicians in Morocco, decided that the king should have a colonoscopy. This would be done in the palace in Rabat. To do the procedure, Dr. Kirsner called on his colleague Dr. B. H. Gerald Rodgers, who had earlier performed a colonoscopy at the University of Chicago on one of the king's physicians, a procedure that had gone well.[6]

Dr. Rodgers was a graduate of the University of Chicago's medical school. He had then completed his residency at Northwestern University Medical School's Wesley Memorial Hospital. Here he was first exposed to gastroscopy while rounding with George Cummings, the hospital's chief of gastroenterology, and Ivan Sippy, a brother of the famous Bertram Sippy. For Dr. Rodgers, this experience inspired him to specialize in gastroenterology. In the fall of 1969 Dr. Kirsner accepted him as a fellow in the Section of Gastroenterology. At the time fiberoptic colonoscopy was in its earliest stage of development and was not yet being performed at the University of Chicago. Dr. Rodgers's first exposure to colonoscopy came when a salesman from the Olympus Corporation brought a 70-cm instrument to the gastro-enterology section to demonstrate the equipment and allow a faculty member to try it. He was later able to study several patients with an instrument provided by the American Cystoscopic Corporation. Dr. Rodgers was inspired to invest in a colonoscope and powerpack out of his own resources. He trained briefly with Dr. Bergen Overholt in Nashville, Tennessee, who was a pioneer in the field of colonoscopy, and he traveled to New York to observe Dr. Hiromi Shinya, another surgeon who was a forerunner in this new technique. Performing his 10th colonoscopy at the University of Chicago, he found a previously undiagnosed sigmoid cancer in a Chicago-area surgeon with rectal bleeding who had been diagnosed with ulcerative colitis. Dr. Rodgers remembers that when he showed him the results of the examination, Dr. Kirsner said, "I think you are onto something."

After completing his fellowship, Dr. Rodgers went into practice on the North Side of Chicago and traveled to local community hospitals performing colonoscopies for physicians and their patients. His prompt and expert examinations gave him a citywide reputation as an expert in the relatively new procedure. Dr. Kirsner began referring patients to Dr. Rodgers and was impressed with his expertise. Within a few years Dr. Rodgers was invited back to the University of Chicago as a member of the clinical faculty, and he taught colonoscopy techniques to the gastroenterology fellows.

Having been invited to perform a colonoscopy on King Hassan II, Dr. Rodgers first had to equip an endoscopic facility in the medical clinic area of the palace. This included purchasing the latest video endoscopic equipment, installing resuscitative equipment and the means to administer anesthesia, and providing a system for chemically sterilizing the endoscopic equipment. Dr. Rodgers was an advocate of using CO_2 as an insufflating gas during colonoscopy, since he felt that CO_2 caused less abdominal distention during the examination and was more rapidly reabsorbed from the intestinal tract afterward. Obtaining the hardware to fit the CO_2 tanks and delivering them to Morocco proved to be one of the more challenging aspects of the preparations for the king's examination. For a number of years Dr. Rodgers's wife, Mae, had served as his nurse assistant, and she traveled with him to Morocco to serve as his assistant during the examination.

On his first visit, Dr. Rodgers set up the equipment. However, the king then decided he did not need the examination, and they packed up and returned to Chicago. On a second visit, the same sequence of events occurred, but this time Dr. Rodgers and his wife performed several successful examinations on other members of the royal family. Finally, on a third visit the king agreed to proceed with the examination. Before actually performing the colonoscopy, though, Dr. Rodgers had to travel to a farm of the king's in the country outside Rabat. Here he met the king for the first time and explained the nature of the examination and the preparations. Dr. Kirsner and Dr. Fennessy accompanied him on all three of these trips to Morocco.

The colonoscopy finally took place in the fully equipped endoscopy suite that had been set up in the Rabat palace. The king's physicians, a Moroccan anesthesiologist, and Dr. Kirsner were in attendance. Outside the procedure room waited the prince (the king's son and successor to the throne) and security agents. Dr. Rodgers was told he would have to complete the examination in 20 minutes and that "no biopsies could be taken." Dr. Kirsner recalls being somewhat apprehensive about the examination and its outcome. Mae remembers feeling a sense of anxiety that the procedure might prove difficult or uncomfortable for the king. Dr. Rodgers was confident of his skills and performed a complete and normal examination in the allotted time. After the examination was over, the king and all the physicians involved in his care met around a large conference table. Dr. Rodgers was seated next to the king, who at one point took Dr. Rodgers by the hands and complemented him, saying that he had "golden hands." The king, his physicians, and Dr. Kirsner conducted a discussion in English about the implications of the examination for the king's gastrointestinal symptoms. Dr. Rodgers was impressed with Dr. Kirsner's careful style at these conferences. He would allow everyone in the room to voice their opinions before carefully summing up his recommendations, and he never conveyed haste in the formulation of his thoughts. As Dr. Rodgers would comment, "Dr. Kirsner was a very wise man."

Dr. Rodgers recalls that the whole party went into town the next morning, and he remembers selecting three high-quality Italian suits that were fitted by the king's tailor. That year he and his wife and daughter were invited to the king's New Year's party in Marrakech. The king was so charmed by his daughter that he asked if he might give her a kiss. Dr. Rodgers and Mae say that their daughter has never forgotten the thrill of this visit. Dr. Fennessy relates a similar experience when one of his daughters, then in her teens, accompanied him on a visit to Morocco. Both Dr. Fennessy and Dr. Rodgers were regularly invited to the parties for the king's birthday and the New Year's celebration. Dr. Fennessy's wife accompanied him several times, and on other occasions all seven of his children were able to come along. Once his daughter Imer, a teenager, was invited to attend a reception arranged for the women guests to meet the king. Dr. Fennessy can still picture the rather frightened wisp of a girl being driven off from the hotel in a limousine. She returned wide-eyed and related how, on seeing her, the king said, "Ah, you must be Miss Fennessy" and personally took her on a tour of the palace.

It was the custom at dinners held in the king's presence that he would sit on the first floor of the banquet room with the female guests, with special dignitaries seated on a platform. The male guests at these banquets sat in a balcony overlooking the scene. It was also customary that when the king had completed his meal, all the guests ceased to eat as well, and the dishes were cleared. Traditional Moroccan dancing was a regular part of the entertainment at these banquets, in addition to entertainment imported from all over the world.

On Dr. Kirsner's regularly scheduled visits to Morocco in July and December, he would fly to New York and then on to Casablanca, where either a helicopter would take him to the palace in Rabat or a military plane would take him to the summer palace in the foothills of the Atlas Mountains. But many of the visits were arranged on an emergency basis. One of the more memorable trips occurred in midwinter when he received an urgent call from Ambassador Jaidi. By this time the calls would begin, "Uncle Joe, we need you." On this occasion the patient was the king's personal physician, Dr. Berbiche, who was seriously ill. They wanted Dr. Kirsner to come immediately to consult on his condition. Dr. Berbiche had been attending a state dinner with the king in Zaire, where he had acquired an amoebic infection of the intestine. His illness had been complicated by multiple pulmonary emboli, which eventually necessitated the emergency placement of an umbrella-like device in the inferior vena cava to prevent further embolization of blood clots to the lungs.

That evening Dr. Kirsner had an important meeting with the president of the university, so he arranged to make the trip the next day. He flew to New York, where he was to meet a plane scheduled to arrive from Montreal. A midwinter storm resulted in the plane being stuck in Montreal, so Dr. Kirsner had to spend the night in the airport, and the ambassador's staff sent bedding out to him. The next morning he took the Concorde to Heathrow, where he was met by a representative of the Moroccan embassy. A private jet flew him to Morocco, where he arrived at nine o'clock at night. He was met by physicians who drove him directly to the hospital. As it turned out, Dr. Berbiche was receiving good medical care, and he was feeling considerably better. But Dr. Kirsner's work was not yet finished. He was placed on a jet to Marrakech to report to the king. The king frequently worked late into the night, and Dr. Kirsner found himself being treated to a remarkable dinner in the early hours of the morning. He was brought back to his hotel at three thirty in the morning. He had just enough time to ready himself for a flight on a military jet to Charles De Gaulle Airport and a flight on the Concorde to Kennedy, followed by a drive to LaGuardia and a flight back to Chicago--completing his "whirlwind consultation."

Dr. Kirsner was not alone in being asked to accommodate the royal family on an emergency basis. Dr. John Fennessy relates an incident that occurred while he was a visiting professor in Taiwan. Ambassador Jaidi contacted his home in Chicago, and with his wife's help was able to reach Dr. Fennessy in Taipei. He agreed to come to

Morocco to perform an upper gastrointestinal x-ray on the "Mother of the King's Children," which was her official title. All his travel arrangements were quickly made. He traveled back to his apartment in Chicago to pick up fresh clothes and then back to the airport and the trip on to Morocco. Arriving in Rabat in a somewhat "bedraggled" state, he gathered with the physicians for the royal family at the radiologic suite in the palace the next morning. Word came down that the lady was not going to have the examination that day. The doctors sent word back that they would be happy to perform the examination the next day or thereafter. The word came back down that the "Mother of the King's Children" was not going to be having the examination in the foreseeable future.

On one occasion, Dr. Kirsner received an urgent call from the ambassador that the king would like Dr. Kirsner to go to Paris to see Dr. Betournet, who was a heavy smoker and had been hospitalized with a cancer of the bladder that had invaded his intestine. Dr. Kirsner flew to Paris and saw Dr. Betournet in the hospital the next morning. Unfortunately, the tumor had advanced to such a degree that no therapy was possible. Dr. Kirsner reported these findings to the king, who was greatly saddened. Later, Dr. Betournet was replaced as leader of the French medical support team by Dr. Pierre Godeau, a well-known internist in Paris. Dr. Fredrickson continued to supervise the king's nutritional and blood lipid status.

On one of his visits to Morocco, Dr. Kirsner was handed a laboratory report that contained an analysis of food samples from the king's farm which revealed excessively high bacterial counts. He was asked if he could find someone to advise them on how to eliminate the source of this bacterial contamination. Upon returning to Chicago, Dr. Kirsner called the dean of the University of Illinois School of Agriculture. He was given the name of three senior faculty members, and the first person he contacted proved to be an excellent choice. The consultant traveled several times to Morocco and helped improve the standards of hygiene at the farm. Sometime after these events, President Richard Nixon traveled to Morocco and met with the king. The king told the president that he must try the yogurt that was produced on his farm. Nixon responded, "I don't like yogurt." A supply was nevertheless sent to Nixon at his hotel, and he later remarked to

His Majesty that he had really liked it. Dr. Kirsner felt the story was an acknowledgment that the consultant had properly done his job in improving the conditions on the farm. On a subsequent visit to Morocco Dr. Kirsner brought a certificate of honorary citizenship of the city of Chicago from Mayor Richard J. Daley.

Dr. Kirsner found the king to be a generous and caring person, and he was particularly attentive and kind to his wife, Minnie. He remembers an incident when they had traveled by plane from Rabat to Fez and stayed in a hotel where they had lunch. The manager brought out the entire menu for them to choose from, and lunch proved to be a very lavish meal. That evening they were taken to a nightclub that featured exotic dancers and snake charmers and, once again, lavish quantities of food. That evening Minnie became acutely ill from food poisoning, and they quickly returned to Rabat. The following day at a function, as they passed through the receiving line to greet His Majesty, the king said to Minnie, "I hear that you had a problem at the hotel in Fez." Minnie quickly responded, "Your Majesty, the food was so wonderful that I had to eat all of it." The king was struck by her ready wit and became quite friendly with her over the years. He never failed to ask Dr. Kirsner about his wife on every visit he made to Morocco. He kept abreast of Minnie's illness as it advanced and she could no longer travel to Morocco, but continued to ask Dr. Kirsner about her health and to express his concern. He sent his personal condolences to Dr. Kirsner when his wife passed away in 1998.

Dr. Kirsner noted that the Moroccan people truly loved and respected King Hassan II. He felt they recognized his leadership and devotion to his people. King Hassan II was also a friend to the country of Egypt. The king had played an important role in persuading Anwar Sadat to travel to Jerusalem and initiate diplomatic relations between Egypt and Israel, the first steps in what was hoped would be a true peace process in the Middle East. The king was highly respected by the Israelis, and Dr. and Mrs. Kirsner remembered that they met Moshe Dayan at the palace in Rabat.

Dr. Kirsner's connection with Morocco and his relationship with the king enhanced the reputation of the University of Chicago throughout the world, an association that was publicized especially in French newspapers. Over the years he saw approximately 200 patients with gastrointestinal complaints referred from Morocco to the university. Dr. Kirsner attended to or advised on the health of the king's wife and all his children, including the current king, Sidi Mohamed. On several trips to Morocco, Dr. Kirsner was accompanied by Dr. Stephen Hanauer, the current head of the Section of Gastroenterology, and by Dr. Barbara Kirschner, the head of the Section of Pediatric Gastroenterology, who came to Morocco to see one of the king's grandchildren. His Majesty made several generous contributions to the Section of Gastroenterology, to funding the Joseph B. Kirsner Center for Digestive Diseases on the 4th floor of Billings Hospital, and to the University of Chicago to help create the Joseph B. Kirsner Professorship in Medicine.

After King Hassan II died of a massive myocardial thrombosis in June of 1998,[7] Dr. Kirsner's direct involvement in medical affairs in the kingdom of Morocco came to an end, although his relationship with Ambassador Jaidi continued. For Dr. Kirsner, his friendship with Ambassador Jaidi was a major part of his experience with Morocco and its people. Dr. Kirsner found him to be a remarkable and capable person who had a tremendous knack for managing events across international borders. Telephone calls from Morocco to Dr. Kirsner continued after the king's death, seeking his advice on the best place for the ambassador's friends and influential Moroccan citizens to find medical care in the United States. Dr. and Mrs. Kirsner developed a long and warm friendship with the ambassador and his wife, Malu. Dr. Kirsner viewed him as a genuine friend, and the ambassador came to Chicago to see Minnie when she was recovering in the hospital after having undergone a gastric ulcer operation.

On Saturday, October 9, 2004, Ambassador Jaidi attended the 95th birthday dinner for Dr. Kirsner held in conjunction with the 3rd Annual Conference on Inflammatory Bowel Disease held by the Section of Gastroenterology. Also in attendance were a contingent of Moroccan physicians, including Dr. Ben Omar, an outstanding cardiologist at the Cleveland Clinic; Dr. Arshane, a military physician to the king; Dr. Metkall, who had served as a general internist to the king; and Dr. Berbiche, whom Dr. Kirsner referred to as one of the most outstanding renal physicians he had ever known.[8]

Notes

1. Dr. Kirsner has prepared a written summary of his experiences in Morocco. This and information gathered during a series of interviews with Dr. Kirsner furnished much of the material used in this chapter.
2. The author wishes to thank Dr. John Fennessy for participating in a recorded interview in his home on April 6, 2006.
3. See the obituary for Dr. Sheila Sherlock (1918-2002), *New York Times,* January 10, 2002.
4. Fenton Schaffner, M.D., In Memoriam: December 8, 1920–January 24, 2000, *Mount Sinai J Med* 68:1:2-3, 2001.
5. A cholangiogram is an examination done with contrast material injected into the bile ducts during the course of a surgical procedure on the gallbladder to exclude the presence of a stone in the bile ducts.
6. The author recorded and interview with B. H. Gerald Rodgers, M.D., on February 25, 2006.
7. Joseph R. Gregory, "Hassan II of Morocco Dies at 70: A Monarch Oriented to the West," *New York Times,* July 24, 1999.
8. From Dr. Kirsner's 95th birthday celebration address, given on Saturday, October 9, 2004, at the Fairmont Hotel in Chicago entitled "Highlights of a 69-Year Career at the University of Chicago."

11 ✳ Medical Research: Inflammatory Bowel Disease

While Dr. Kirsner was a medical student at Tufts in Boston, he rarely heard the word "research"; research was limited to the physiology laboratory. This was understandable, since the six-year program under the Bigelow Fund was oriented toward developing general practitioners to meet the needs of Massachusetts and the New England area. The situation changed dramatically when he arrived at the University of Chicago, as reflected in Dr. Dick's admonition that if he did not do credible research, he shouldn't expect to stick around. As discussed in chapter 3, from the beginning there was an emphasis at the University of Chicago on fostering research. It was a motivating theme supported by Frederick Gates and John D. Rockefeller and fully accepted by the first president, William Rainey Harper.

His initial assignment in the Department of Medicine in the Section of Allergy gave Dr. Kirsner his first exposure to "benchtop" research through his collaboration with Dr. Clarence Bernstein Jr., which resulted in several publications on insulin allergy and anaphylaxis. It was his acceptance by Dr. Walter L. Palmer into the Section of Gastroenterology, and his decision to enter the Ph.D. program in biology, that afforded him the opportunity to fulfill his desire to pursue medical research. His early research was focused on gastric secretion and peptic ulcer. His Ph.D. work—on the complication of alkalosis observed in patients on the Sippy Program and the effect of alkalosis on renal function—led to a number of publications before his 1943 enlistment in the Army Medical Corps during World War II.[1]

His bibliography shows that his interest in these aspects of gas-

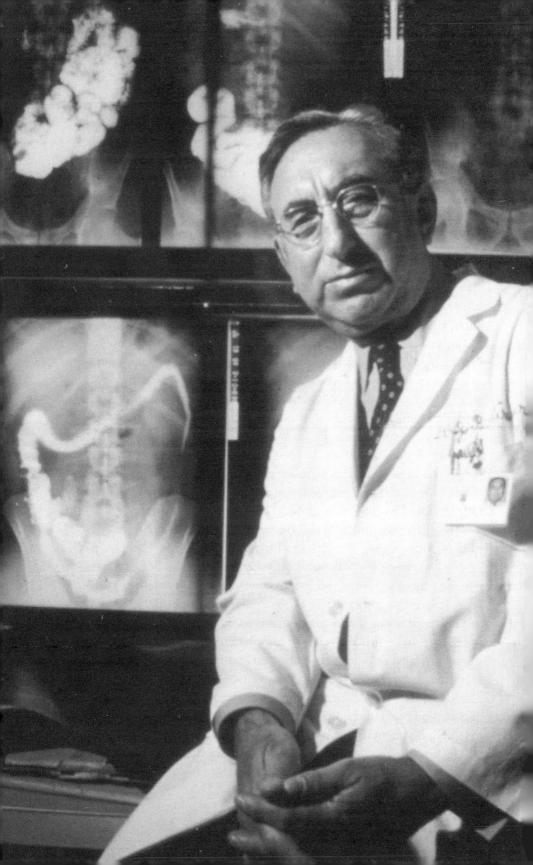

tric secretion and peptic ulcer disease continued when he returned to the University of Chicago in 1946. There was also a notable series of papers detailing the results of gastric irradiation in the treatment of peptic ulcer disease. For the decade following his return to civilian life, his bibliography lists more than 30 publications relating to these interests. These important papers continued into the early 1950s and reflected in part a useful collaboration with Dr. Erwin Levin, later of Cleveland, Ohio. Dr. Levin, who was first a gastroenterology fellow and then a section member, has related the important guidance and support he received from Dr. Kirsner in performing these studies and preparing the papers for publication.[2]

However, for Dr. Kirsner, the care of the patient with inflammatory bowel disease and his dedication to the study of these diseases have been the commitments that dominated his academic career. From 1935 to 1942 his bibliography reflects his growing interest in this topic. This was the period in which he first became aware of the problem and its clinical challenges, and his first publications explore possible infectious etiologies. As recounted in chapter 4, he performed microbiological and immunological studies of specific bacterial pathogens in patients with chronic ulcerative colitis, including therapeutic trials of the newly available sulfanilamide. Gail M. Dack, professor of microbiology in the Department of Bacteriology, thought that the anaerobic organism *Bacterium necrophorum*, a *Streptococcus*-related species, was associated with ulcerative colitis. In conjunction with Dr. Dack, Dr. Kirsner performed studies of *Bacterium necrophorum* and also looked for agglutinins to this organism in the serum of patients with chronic ulcerative colitis.[3] He also performed studies testing for serological evidence of *Lymphogranuloma venereum* in patients with chronic ulcerative colitis and regional enteritis. The resulting article, published in 1943, appeared in the first volume of the new journal *Gastroenterology*.[4] The effect of sulfanilamide on *Bacterium necrophorum* and on normal fecal flora were further areas of study on patients with inflammatory bowel disease.[5]

The years between 1946 and 1971 saw his most intensive period of investigation into the nature of inflammatory bowel disease. He and his colleagues were leaders in describing the multifaceted aspects of the natural history of inflammatory bowel disease: the numerous extraintestinal manifestations of the disease, salient epidemiologic factors, and the familial aspect of the disease, highlighting the need to explore its possible genetic basis. It is noteworthy that over half a century after these initial observations, genetic studies are a major focus of research in intestinal bowel disease. This fruitful area of research has led to the discovery of the first gene implicated in vulnerability to Crohn's disease, the *NOD2* (*CARD15*) gene.[6]

In the early years after Dr. Kirsner returned from his military service, the University of Chicago continued to study the effect of sulfonamides on the fecal flora. With the discovery of cortisone, university researchers were pioneers in reporting the effects of cortisone steroids and ACTH in inflammatory bowel disease, first in patients suffering from ulcerative colitis and then those afflicted with Crohn's disease.

Dr. Kirsner's interest in developing experimental models of ulcerative colitis and Crohn's disease as a means of understanding the etiology and pathogenesis of the disease and identifying and evaluating therapy date from this period in his career. Along with his colleague Dr. Hugo Moeller, he instilled filtrates of the fecal contents from patients with severe ulcerative colitis into surgically constructed ileocolonic pouches that Dr. Dack had prepared in dogs, but they ultimately failed to induce inflammatory intestinal disease. Studies done with Dr. Ralph Victor, a gastroenterology fellow at the time, involved injecting fecal filtrates from patients with severe active ulcerative colitis into the rectal mucosa of macaque monkeys, but this too failed to produce the characteristic lesions of inflammatory bowel disease.[7]

The search for an appropriate experimental model for the study of inflammatory bowel disease led Dr. Kirsner to investigate the role of immune mechanisms in the pathogenesis of these diseases. His first research interest in immunology had begun in 1936 with his work in the allergy section. During the 1940s and early 1950s, the role of immune mechanisms was being considered in the pathogenesis of a variety of diseases of unknown etiology.

Numerous clinical experiences strengthened Dr. Kirsner's interest in the role of the immune system in ulcerative colitis and Crohn's disease. These events included the abrupt onset of severe ulcerative colitis in several patients following episodes of food poisoning, and the frequent association of ulcerative colitis with a personal or family history of allergy, including hay fever and asthma as well as immune-mediated diseases such as autoimmune hemolytic anemia and systemic lupus erythematosus. The beneficial response of the disease to ACTH and adrenal steroids, as he and Dr. Palmer had documented, also influenced his thinking.[8] In 1920 John Auer had described experiments demonstrating that foreign protein—crystalline egg albumin—applied to the earlobe of rabbits would lead to autosensitization of the rabbit and an immune-mediated reaction.[9] Borrowing on this work, Dr. Kirsner demonstrated that rectal instillation of dilute noninflammatory solutions of formalin in rabbits led to an ulcerative colitis–like inflammatory response in these areas with subsequent exposure.[10] After publishing this important work—with the help of Dr. Moshe Goldgraber, a postgraduate fellow—Dr. Kirsner published further studies demonstrating the production of both the Schwartzman phenomenon and the Arthus phenomenon in experimental colitis. This experimental model for ulcerative colitis, which was duplicated by other investigators in two other laboratories in the country, became known as Auer-Kirsner colitis and served as a model for future studies of inflammatory bowel disease. Dr. Kirsner, along with the immunologist Dr. Frank Fitch and Dr. Sumner C. Kraft, then a fellow in gastroenterology, demonstrated the accumulation of immune complexes in the colonic mucosa of experimentally induced Auer-Kirsner colitis.

Dr. Moshe Goldgraber had come from Israel to the United States at great personal hardship, leaving his young family behind. He had initially assumed a position at Michael Reese Hospital in Chicago, where he hoped to study nephrology. But he was not happy with his position there, and with Dr. Kirsner's help he came to join the Section of Gastroenterology at the University of Chicago. After an initial period of study with Dr. Kirsner, he returned to Israel to bring his family back to Chicago. Over a 10-year period, working closely together in the laboratory, Dr. Goldgraber and Dr. Kirsner published many important studies on inflammatory bowel disease. He subsequently returned to Israel, where he lives today, in a leprosarium near Jerusalem where he serves as a physician. Dr. Goldgraber and his family have sponsored a series of visiting fellows in the Section of Gastroenterology.

Dr. Sumner C. Kraft and Dr. Richard Reilly also played an important part in helping Dr. Kirsner develop the research program in inflammatory bowel disease. Dr. Kraft, like Dr. Kirsner, was originally from the East Coast, from Lynn, Massachusetts. As a young man, he was an eagle scout (he is a life member of the National Eagle Scout Association), and perhaps this led to his participation in the Ready Reserve from 1958 to 1996, when he retired from the Medical Corps with the rank of colonel. For two weeks every year he participated in reserve activity and overseas duty in Belgium, Germany, Japan, and Panama. After graduating from Tufts University in 1948 with a B.S. degree, he completed his master's thesis, "The Relationship of the Endocrine System to Alimentary Motility and Secretion" at Boston University Graduate School. In 1949 he came to Michael Reese Hospital and worked with a gastroenterologist on the staff there, Dr. Heinrich Necheles. He then entered the University of Chicago School of Medicine and graduated in 1955.

During his medical school years, Dr. Kraft's bond with the Section of Gastroenterology was strengthened when he became ill with a gastrointestinal ailment. The illness required hospitalization, and Dr. Kirsner became his personal physician. Changes in his stomach were initially thought to be lymphoma, but surgical exploration and a biopsy proved him to have hypertrophic gastritis, which earned him a place in series of a published case studies.

Dr. Kraft was clearly destined to become a member of the section, and while still a medical resident he worked with Dr. Frank Fitch and Dr. William Wissler in the Department of Pathology. As a clinical and research trainee in gastroenterology from 1958 to 1960, he worked with Dr. Jane Elchlepp, who was working with Dr. Kirsner on the Auer model of colitis. Dr. Kraft remembers Dr. Kirsner being personally involved in these studies and frequently looking over their shoulder in the laboratory. Working with Dr. Fitch and Dr. Kirsner, Drs. Elchlepp and Kraft completed further studies on the histological and immune-histological features of the Auer-Kirsner colitis model. Dr. Elchlepp went on to become the president of Duke University.

During a site visit from the NIH by Dr. Richard Farr, it was suggested that the research program of the section as well as Dr. Kraft's own work might be strengthened by a period of postgraduate research at the Scripps Institute. Dr. Kirsner agreed to sponsor Dr. Kraft's further training, and from 1964 to 1966 Dr. Kraft was part of the Division of Allergy, Immunology and Rheumatology at the Scripps Clinic and Research Foundation in La Jolla, California. Returning to the University of Chicago, Dr. Kraft continued to do research in the immunology of the gastrointestinal tract and inflammatory bowel disease. Working with Julian J. Rimpila, a recent graduate of the medical school who had earned his master's degree working in Dr. Kraft's laboratory, and with Eugene Gelzayd, a fellow in gastroenterology, Dr. Kraft coauthored with Dr. Kirsner important papers on the immunology of the GI tract and the immunology of ulcerative colitis. In 1969 the section established and dedicated an immunology research laboratory in honor of university president George W. Beadle, and Dr. Sumner Kraft was named its first director.

Dr. Richard W. Reilly was another important member of the research team. After serving in World War II, he earned his undergraduate degree in science and an M.D. degree at the University of Chicago. For a two-year period, he practiced general medicine in a small town, Cedar Lake, Indiana. He returned to the University of Chicago for his residency in 1956. In 1958 he spent some time in Scotland, as a visiting fellow and honorary faculty member at the University of Edinburgh. His research interest was in the basic biology of epithelial cells of the small intestine.

Also part of the research team was Erl Dordal, whose area of interest was liver disease. Dr. Dordal, Dr. Kirsner, and Dr. Seymour (Sy) Glagov, of the Department of Pathology, performed one of the first studies that systematically documented the spectrum of liver disease in a large sample of patients with inflammatory bowel disease.[11]

From the 1950s to the 1970s, the Section of Gastroenterology received a research grant from the NIH to conduct fundamental studies of inflammatory bowel disease. A sample application from the late 1960s, submitted by Dr. Kirsner as principal investigator, shows the scope of the section's commitment to this area of research. Clinical aspects included studies on the genetic and epidemiologic features of the disease; studies of the radiographic features of inflammatory bowel disease (in collaboration with John Fennessy of the Department of Radiology); therapeutic aspects of the disease, included the initiation of protocols to evaluate the use of azathioprine (Imuran); and surgical aspects of treatment, including the recognition and characterization of nephrolithiasis as a complication of inflammatory bowel disease. The section was beginning to study the problem of colon cancer as a complication of ulcerative colitis, and also the extraintestinal manifestations of inflammatory bowel disease, such as pyoderma gangrenosum, liver disease (sclerosing cholangitis), growth retardation in children, and granulomatous inflammation of the colon. There was also basic research on the immunology of inflammatory bowel disease and the nature of injury and healing of the intestinal mucosa, and biochemical studies on mucopolysaccharides and the biology of individual epithelial cells.

With the formation of the General Medicine Study Section of the NIH in 1955, Dr. Kirsner had the exciting opportunity to help further medical research throughout the country. He shared with other distinguished scientists and physicians the task of reviewing and evaluating research grants in medicine at the national level. This group met three times a year, and members were assigned to review grants in their field of expertise. Dr. Kirsner looked forward to these meetings, since it put him in contact with outstanding and articulate scientists; he regarded every meeting as a wonderful learning experience. Larger grants on review often required site visits to make sure that the applicants had the facilities and personnel to properly carry out their proposed research. Members of the group would travel to the particular institution to meet with the investigators over several days, and then review their findings and make recommendations to the General Medicine Study Section. One of the largest studies that the NIH reviewed and approved during Dr. Kirsner's tenure was the National Cooperative Crohn's Disease Study, led by Dr. Fred Kern and the University of Colorado. This multiphase study notably established the validity of the Crohn's Disease Activity Index and also evaluated the efficacy of Azulfidine and steroids in a randomized controlled study of these drugs stratified on the basis of location of the disease in the gastrointestinal tract. The study, eventually published in *Gastroenterology*, represented the first truly controlled study of the efficacy of drugs in Crohn's disease performed in the United States.

The 1960s witnessed the formation of the Gastro-Intestinal Research Foundation (GIRF), a philanthropic support coalition of devoted patients and their families, leaders in the business community, and other concerned citizens interested in medical philanthropy, developed in Chicago under Dr. Kirsner's guidance. GIRF rapidly evolved to become a remarkable organization that has played a pivotal role in supporting the research activities of the Section of Gastroenterology. The history of this group and Dr. Kirsner's role in advising their activities have been recounted in chapter 8.

In 1965 Dr. Henry D. Janowitz, of Mount Sinai Hospital of New York, and Irwin Rosenthal, an attorney and the husband of a patient at Mount Sinai, established the Foundation for Research in Ileitis, Inc. Mr. Rosenthal served as the president, and Dr. Janowitz as the medical director. The need for citizen philanthropy aimed at the study of inflammatory bowel disease is underscored by the fact that in 1965 NIH-funded research in ileitis totaled only $25,000. The growth of this important organization is explored in detail by Suzanne Rosenthal in an article published in the *Mount Sinai Journal of Medicine* in March 2001.[12] Ms. Rosenthal describes a conference held at Mount Sinai in 1966 to design clinical trials and the research protocol for a double-blind study, proposed by Dr. Daniel Present and Dr. Burton Korelitz, on the therapeutic effect and side effects of 6-mercaptopurine in Crohn's disease. Among the eminent gastroenterologists invited to attend this conference were Dr. Kirsner, Dr. Fred Kern of the University of Colorado, and Dr. Thomas Chalmers, who was then serving on the NIH and in 1973 would become the president and dean of Mount Sinai Medical School. In 1967 the name of the foundation was changed to the National Foundation for Ileitis and Colitis; it was ultimately changed one more time, to the Crohn's and Colitis Foundation of America (CCFA).

By the mid-1970s the leadership of the organization sought to counter the perception that the group was primarily a project of Mount Sinai Hospital. Irwin Rosenthal recruited Dr. Kirsner to be the first National Scientific Advisory Board chairman. Dr. Kirsner's continued service to the CCFA was recognized by his receipt in 1974 and in 1978 of the foundation's distinguished achievement award, and in 1987 of its distinguished service award. In 1991 and 2002 the CCFA further recognized Dr. Kirsner with separate lifetime achievement awards.

In his remarks on the occasion of the second lifetime achievement award, September 27, 2002, Mr. Rosenthal emphasized that when he and Bill Modell, who joined the Ileitis Foundation as a cofounder (Dr. Janowitz had retired as medical director in 1975), sought to expand the organization's national image by rotating the medical chairmanship among leading clinicians and scientists, "there was only one obvious choice--Dr. Joseph B. Kirsner." Mr. Rosenthal told his audience how he flew to Chicago to urge Dr. Kirsner to accept the position. During that meeting, at Dr. Kirsner's suggestion, they discussed the wisdom of the foundation's placing the medical chairmanship and grants review chairmanship under two physicians so as to ensure independence and credibility. Dr. Kirsner proposed that Dr. Kurt Isselbacher, the chief of gastroenterology at Harvard and Massachusetts General Hospital, be appointed chairman of the National Scientific Advisory Board. As Mr. Rosenthal said, "Dr. Kirsner called Dr. Isselbacher right then," and Mr. Rosenthal flew to Boston to invite him to assume that role, which he immediately accepted. He ended his address by noting, "Joe, we still look forward to your leadership and wisdom and know you will be here to celebrate your 100th birthday."[13]

Beginning in the mid-1930s--during his first years at the University of Chicago, when he saw his first patients with inflammatory bowel disease and realized how little was known about it--to the first decade of the 21st century, Dr. Kirsner has continued to contribute to our understanding of these diseases. He is regarded as one of the pioneers in the field, which has grown in complexity to the extent that physicians completing their basic two-year fellowship in gastroenterology who wish to focus on the treatment of inflammatory bowel disease will elect to spend an additional year working at an institution and with a clinician devoted to the care of these patients. At the University of Chicago, the clinical and clinical research activities of the section are currently led by Dr. Stephen Hanauer, who is the director of the Section of Gastroenterology, and his codirector, Dr. Eugene Chang, who is in charge of the basic research program in inflammatory bowel diseases. Institutions in this country that have a similar tradition of expertise in inflammatory bowel disease are the Mount Sinai Medical Center and the Mayo Clinic. The Mount Sinai Medical Center traces its genealogy back to Burrill B. Crohn (and to

Leon Ginzberg and Gordon Oppenheimer, authors of a seminal 1932 publication on "regional enteritis") up through physicians such as Henry D. Janowitz, who trained the next generation of specialists in inflammatory bowel disease, including Daniel Present, David B. Sachar, and Burton I. Korelitz.[14] The Mayo Clinic traces its history from Dr. J. Arnold Bargen to the current era of physicians, including William J. Tramaine and William J. Sanborn.

Dr. Kirsner's contributions to the recognition of the importance of inflammatory bowel disease stem not just from his important clinical observations on all aspects of these diseases, his epidemiologic and family studies and his own basic research investigations. They also evolve from his tireless efforts on behalf of the NIH and the National Institute of Arthritis and Metabolic Diseases, which fostered public awareness of the problem and supported meaningful research. Over the years he has contributed to the field through his many insightful and timely reviews of the "state of the art," both in journals dedicated to gastroenterology and in journals with a wider distribution in the medical profession. His contributions to a historical perspective on the evolution of thinking in the field of inflammatory bowel disease are found in his textbooks and monographs, including his major textbook, *Kirsner's Inflammatory Bowel Disease,* now in its 6th edition. He has participated in many symposia both in the United States and in foreign countries, as an organizer and as a presenter. He has been invited to lecture and to serve as a visiting professor at many of the major medical centers in this country. And finally, one cannot begin to measure his contribution to the care of patients suffering with inflammatory bowel disease--through his own clinical career and the careers of generations of residents and fellows who have worked at the bedside with him.

Notes

1. A representative paper from this era, Kirsner JB and Palmer WL, The effect of various antacids on the hydrogen-ion concentration of the gastric contents, *Amer J Dig Dis* 7:3:85-93, January 1940, is of interest for the manner of presentation of the data.

2. From an interview with Dr. Levin and his wife, Ruth. Sadly, Dr. Levin has since died.

3. Dack GM, Kirsner JB, Dragstedt LR, et al., A study of Bacterium necrophorum in chronic ulcerative colitis and the effect of sulfanilamide in treatment, *Amer J Dig Dis* 6:5:305-8, July 1939; and Dack GM, Kirsner JB, Dragstedt LR, et al., Agglutinins for Bacterium necrophorum in the serum of patients with chronic ulcerative colitis, *Infec Dis* 65:200-205, September–October 1939.

4. Rodaniche EC, Kirsner JB, and Palmer WL, The relationship of Lymphogranuloma venereum and regional enteritis: An etiologic study of 4 cases with negative results, *Gastroenterology* 1:7:687-89, July 1943.

5. Rodaniche EC, Kirsner JB, and Palmer WL, Morphologic changes in effect of the oral administration of sulfonamide compounds on the fecal flora of patients with non-specific ulcerative colitis, *Gastroenterology* 1:2:133-39, February 1943; and Rodaniche EC, Palmer WL, and Kirsner JB, The streptococci present in the feces of patients with non-specific ulcerative colitis, and the effect of oral administration of sulfonamide compounds upon them, *J Infect Dis,* 72:222-27, May–June 1943.

6. Gaya, DR, et al., New genes in inflammatory bowel disease: Lesson for complex diseases? *Lancet* 367:1271-84, 2006; and Abraham C and Cho JH, Functional consequences of *NOD2* (*CARD 15*) mutations, *Inflamm Bowel Dis* 12:641-50, 2006.

7. Victor RG, Kirsner JB, and Palmer WL, Failure to induce ulcerative colitis experimentally with filtrates of feces and rectal mucosa (a preliminary report), *Gastroenterology* 14:3:398-400, March 1950.

8. Kirsner JB, The historical basis of the idiopathic inflammatory bowel diseases, *Inflamm Bowel Dis* 1:2-26, 1995.

9. Auer J, Local autoinoculation of the sensitized organism with foreign protein as a cause of abnormal reactions, *J Exp Med* 32:427-44, 1920. John Auer (1875-1948) was a physiologist and pharmacologist. A graduate of Johns Hopkins, he worked with his father-in-law, Samuel J. Meltzer, at the Rockefeller Institute for Medical Research. He was interested in immune-mediated disease and studied the physiologic consequences of anaphylaxis.

10. Kirsner JB and Elchlepp J, The production of an experimental ulcerative "colitis" in rabbits, *Trans Assn Amer Phys* 70:102-19, 1957.

11. Dordal E, Glagov S, and Kirsner JB, Hepatic lesions in chronic inflammatory bowel disease, part I: Clinical correlations with liver biopsy diagnosis in 103 patients, *Gastroenterology* 52:239-53, February 1967.

12. Rosenthal S, To make a difference: The founding of the Crohn's and Colitis Foundation of America, *Mount Sinai J Med* 68:2:113-16, March 2001.

13. As reported in his Annual Activity Report to the Department of Medicine, the University of Chicago School of Medicine, July 1, 2002, through June 30, 2003.
14. Sachar DB, Planting the seeds of knowledge about inflammatory bowel disease, *Mount Sinai J Med*, 68:2:79-86, March 2001.

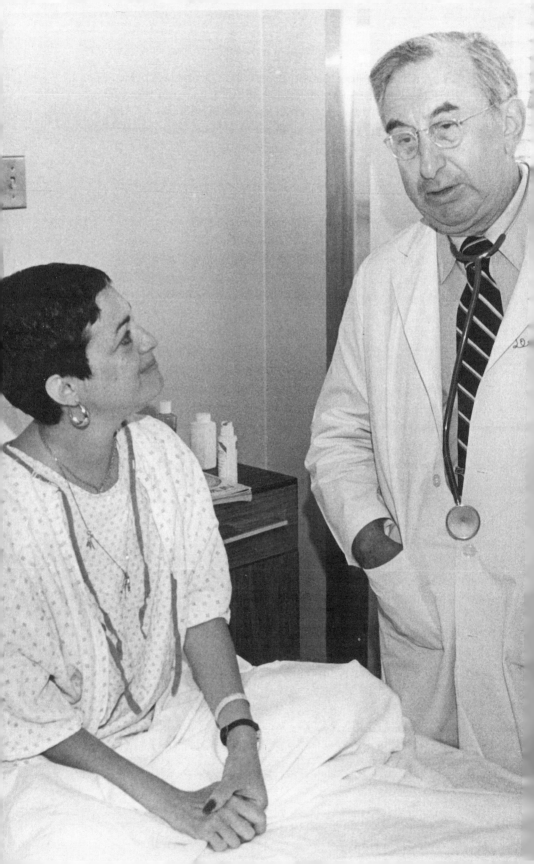

12 ✳ "The Care of the Patient"

By the time Dr. Kirsner assumed the role of chief of staff and deputy dean of medical affairs at the University of Chicago Hospitals and Clinics, he had practiced the art of medicine for 35 years. Most of his clinical activities had been devoted to the care of patients with gastrointestinal illnesses. He had established a reputation as one of the leading consultants in the country for gastrointestinal illnesses, and for inflammatory bowel disease in particular. He was recognized both locally and nationally for his successful and compassionate care of patients. The love and devotion his patients felt for him was celebrated and admired. If we are to understand how he achieved this outstanding reputation as a compassionate physician and consummate clinician, we must look at the man himself, the anecdotes that colleagues and students have remembered, and his own writings on the subject of patient care.

It is clear that during those 35 years it was not solely a matter of the countless number of hours he had spent in the care of patients. Nor would his having seen and managed innumerable challenging clinical problems alone have led to his becoming a master clinician. As in any endeavor, an individual can do his work in a routine manner with little thought, analysis, or self-criticism. For a physician, there must be the commitment to recognize and constantly learn from mistakes and to constantly improve one's clinical skills. Experience—the day-in and day-out care of significant numbers of patients with challenging medical problems over many years—is one of the first requisites that serves to establish a doctor as worthy of being an outstanding clinician. But without thoughtfulness and analysis, the number of patients and the hours of care cannot, in and of themselves, lead to the making of a Master of Gastroenterology, the status granted Dr. Kirsner by the American Gastroenterological Association and the American College of Physicians. The art of medicine must be learned at the bedside, and to study medicine without seeing patients is, as often noted, like trying to learn naval science and never going to sea.

Similarly, the physician must always refresh and update his or her knowledge of medicine so as to avail himself of the latest information that the science of medicine has to offer. Failing to do so, he or she would be like the captain of a ship trying to navigate dangerous waters without the benefit of updated navigational charts and equipment. Dr. Kirsner was fully aware of this, and throughout his career he has had the habit of carefully and extensively reading the latest literature, regularly attending local and national meetings, participating in clinical conferences, and exchanging ideas with his colleagues on clinical problems. He eagerly looked forward to receiving new issues of *Gastroenterology,* the *Journal of Clinical Investigation,* and a host of other journals, scanning their contents for articles that were of interest to him and his colleagues. Today, at the age of 99, though he has reluctantly stopped seeing patients, he regularly scans numerous journals to flag articles of interest. As recounted in an earlier chapter, his former fellows recall coming to work in the morning to find on their desks one of his famous yellow memos directing their attention to an article in the literature that might relate to a patient they were seeing. In the same spirit, he selects and forwards articles he considers important to the current editors of *Kirsner's Inflammatory Bowel Disease.*

It is appropriate to start with the patient in developing our understanding of Dr. Kirsner's approach to patient care before moving on to the broader principles that govern the doctor-patient relationship. The following account of one individual's experience is meant to illustrate the essentials of this relationship.

* * *

In 1959 Andrew Herskee and his family moved from Greenfield, Massachusetts, to Highland Park, Illinois.[1] Nine years of age at the time,

Andrew can remember the rural feeling of the community. Chickens, geese, and rabbits roamed freely in the courtyard of the elementary school that he attended, and near his home there were "vast woodland areas" that afforded him and his friends opportunities for outdoor adventures after school and during weekends. During the winter of 1961 he experienced an episode of what seemed to be the flu. His symptoms lingered, with recurrent cycles of high and low fevers, abdominal cramps, and loss of fluids that resulted in a complete loss of energy. He lost his appetite, and as soon as he attempted eating, he would often vomit and then avoid eating again for a long time. His parents took Andrew to numerous doctors, each of whom had different thoughts as to the diagnosis, and each physician insisted on his own series of tests. As Andrew got sicker, his parents' concern increased and was exacerbated by his lack of response to any of the proposed treatments.

His maternal grandparents were friends of a noted pathologist at Chicago's Michael Reese Hospital, Dr. Otto Saphir. Dr. Saphir urged Andrew's parents to take him to see Dr. Joseph Kirsner at the University of Chicago. His parents called the hospital, but because of Dr. Kirsner's demanding schedule, they were unable to secure an early appointment. Following a personal request from Dr. Saphir, though, Dr. Kirsner arranged an immediate appointment to see Andrew.

Andrew remembers his first visit and the long series of questions about his medical history, including his family history. He remembers that his medical history included many instances of allergic reactions, including eczema, dating back to infancy. This history was important in that his allergy to sulfonamides (sulfa drugs) prevented the use of an important first line of therapy for what seemed to be a case of colitis.

Dr. Kirsner recommended that Andrew be hospitalized. At this time, there were no pediatric gastroenterologists at Billings Hospital, and Dr. Kirsner hospitalized patients of Andrew's age on the Medicine 6 gastroenterology floor with adult patients. For a 10-year-old, the thought of not going home was overwhelming. The hospital was a frightening place. Sirens wailing outside the hospital as ambulances pulled up to the emergency entrances, beepers and buzzers, announcements over the public address system paging doctors--all contributed to his sense of disorientation. In his words, he was not a very "happy camper."

He was admitted to a hospital bed in a semiprivate room, sharing the room with an older man who was perturbed by the prospect of having a cranky child for a roommate. He was soon to learn about the unpleasantness of the "chalky" barium "upper and lower" GI x-ray studies, and the ordeal of having his arm strapped to a wooden plank and a stainless-steel needle inserted into a vein to give him the glucose/saline fluids he urgently needed. Besides the intravenous fluids and intravenous cortisone, there were the painful intramuscular injections of iron in the buttock that he had to endure. He encountered a confusing array of strangers in the form of hospital personnel, including nurses, medical students, residents, phlebotomists, and radiologists, but many of the hospital personnel could relate to the frightened child, and he sensed that the entire staff seemed to acknowledge his special status as one of Dr. Kirsner's patients.

His parents came from Highland Park every day and spent long hours with him, timing their visits so as to be present when Dr. Kirsner made his rounds. At least once a day Dr. Kirsner, always smiling and calm, came into the room to see him, often accompanied by what seemed to Andrew to be a "sea of white coats." He came to look forward to Dr. Kirsner's visits and the encouragement and reassurance they gave him. Dr. Kirsner would listen to his abdomen with his stethoscope and palpate it. He remembers that Dr. Kirsner always spoke to him as an adult and was genuinely interested in him and understood the challenges he was facing. Andrew felt that Dr. Kirsner was always attentive when he tried to explain how he was feeling, and he was grateful that Dr. Kirsner included him in discussions about his treatment plan so that he would understand his condition.

Six weeks was a long time in the hospital for an active youngster, but he gradually recovered his appetite and his energy; he gained weight, and the hydrocortisone made him "chubby" and his "cheeks puffy." After being discharged from the hospital, he would look forward to his follow-up visits with Dr. Kirsner in the gastroenterology clinic for reassurance that his recovery was progressing on schedule.

In 1963 his father's career required that the family move to a suburb of New Haven, Connecticut. Dr. Kirsner secured Andrew an appointment with Dr. Howard Spiro, an outstanding gastroenterologist at Yale University with whom Dr. Kirsner was personally acquainted. During his visits with Dr. Spiro, Andrew could tell that there was a feeling of mutual respect and cooperation between the two physicians. He came to appreciate that Dr. Kirsner's reputation extended to other cities and that there existed a special community of physicians dedicated to the study of inflammatory bowel disease and to providing the best available treatment. This was an experience that would be repeated later in his life when he lived in Colorado, New York, and California.

In 1963, while living in Connecticut, Andrew's symptoms recurred, and this time serious gastrointestinal bleeding required surgery and the removal of his entire colon in two stages. The procedure, known as a total colectomy and ileostomy, involved removal of his large intestine (the colon) and his rectum along with the creation of an opening for the small intestine through the abdominal wall (an ileostomy). This required that he learn how to empty and change a bag or ileostomy pouch, which became a way of life for this active preteenager. At 12 years of age, and after several difficult months spent overcoming postoperative complications, he was suddenly off all medications and feeling great. He began to gain weight again, and his growth, which had been arrested during his long illness, resumed.

Throughout these ordeals he would periodically receive notes from Dr. Kirsner wanting to know how he was doing. These notes continued into adulthood, and he remembers how great he felt to have this "famous physician as a pen pal." It is heartening to read through these letters, the first one written in 1963 to "Master Andrew Herskee" to acknowledge his nice letter and his contribution to the section's research fund. The letters that follow, addressed to "Mr. Andrew H." or "Dear Andy," include interest in the boy's newly acquired pet dog and comments on the success of the games that he and his parents had contributed to the Medicine 6 gastroenterology floor so that patients, particularly adolescents, might be able to relieve the stress of a long hospitalization. The letters, to both Andrew and his parents, continue throughout that decade, commenting on aspects of his clinical care and offering reassurance.

Andrew was an unusual young man whose positive outlook led to his becoming involved with both local and national ostomy organizations. He became a popular visitor for hospitalized patients facing similar ostomy surgery, and he accumulated information on different appliances that would help patients who had allergies to some of the products, as he himself did. He became a popular visitor to classes at the Yale School of Nursing, where he shared his thoughts and experiences with the nursing students.

When he was 17, his family returned to the Chicago area. About a year later he developed what again seemed to be a flulike illness, and when his symptoms persisted, he returned to the University of Chicago to see Dr. Kirsner. A small-bowel x-ray revealed changes consistent with a diagnosis of Crohn's disease. The physicians caring for Andrew in 1963, when he had his colectomy and ileostomy, were convinced that he was suffering from ulcerative colitis. However, when the microscopic slides of the specimen from the 1963 operation were reexamined in 1971, it was apparent that the real diagnosis was Crohn's disease of the colon. The distinction between ulcerative colitis and Crohn's disease of the colon was recognized only slowly, and it was not unusual for instances of inflammatory bowel disease confined to the colon to be classified as "indeterminate." It was only in 1959 that there was full recognition in the medical literature that Crohn's disease of the colon alone could occur as a distinct clinical entity.

Because of its capacity to affect any portion of the gastrointestinal tract, the new diagnosis of Crohn's disease signaled that Andrew would battle this illness for the rest of his life. Indeed, he would endure a further surgical resection of a portion of his small intestine as a result of complications of the disease. His history illustrates the lifelong struggle that some patients with inflammatory bowel disease face. In spite of these adversities, Andrew, like many other patients, successfully grew into adulthood, and he has prospered. He is currently a senior vice president of an international corporation. He recently celebrated his 30th wedding anniversary, and he is the proud father of three talented children, now young adults. We see in this story both the inspiring inner spirit of this young man and the role a confident, optimistic, and caring physician played in his recovery. His parents remember with gratitude the care and compassion they received in 1959 at the University of Chicago under the guidance of

Dr. Kirsner when they struggled with the mysterious illness that had afflicted their first-born child.

*　*　*

For Dr. Kirsner, the patient and the patient's illness came first in his medical thinking. In reviewing the direction of clinical and basic research in inflammatory bowel disease, he sought to focus on problems that were relevant to improving patient care and to understanding the nature of their diseases.

During the 1930s and early 1940s, the Section of Gastroenterology paid considerable attention to the psychosomatic basis of gastrointestinal disease and inflammatory bowel disease in particular. It was traditional then that a member of the Department of Psychiatry routinely made rounds with the gastrointestinal service. Some patients with active ulcerative colitis were even hospitalized for extended periods of time so that they would be separated from what were perceived as adverse family interactions. A few patients also underwent psychoanalysis. These trends reflected Dr. Palmer's keen interest in psychiatry and also the influence of the prominent program in psychoanalysis at the Medical Center. Dr. Kirsner always remembered one patient who was kept an entire year in the hospital for this purpose. Years later, while participating in an international symposium on inflammatory bowel disease, he felt compelled to publicly apologize for this approach to the patient's care. However well-intentioned it had been, it was now seen as clearly misguided.

In general, Dr. Kirsner sought to understand the causes of disease from what the course of his patient's illness seemed to be telling him. For example, he noted during his service in World War II that, despite all the trauma and stress of war, he had seen no new cases of inflammatory bowel disease, among either military personnel or civilians. This experience caused him to begin to rethink his ideas about the possible psychosomatic causes of the disease. Another example can be found in the papers he wrote on familial occurrences of the disease. As early as 1948, he published a report in *Gastroenterology* with F. M. Owens and Eleanor Humphreys on regional enteritis in a father and son.[2] His frequent observation that a family outbreak of infectious diarrhea would often precede and precipitate inflammatory bowel disease in one member of the family while other members would recover completely led to his recognition of the importance of genetic factors and individual susceptibility in the causation of the disease. Noting the frequent presence of allergic disorders in his patients with inflammatory bowel disease pointed his research toward the immunological aspects of the disease. He also observed changes in the intestinal bacterial flora as a consequence of enteric infection or the use of antibiotics prescribed in the treatment of the initial illness.

For Dr. Kirsner, an important tenet in patient care was the need to take a second medical history. He is fond of citing examples of individuals whose stories changed and became clear only after the patient had spent two or three days in the hospital, when it was his practice to return to take a second history. Sometimes even this measure would not be sufficient for patients to feel secure enough in their relationship with the physician to reveal the underlying sociological factors relevant to their illness. Dr. Kirsner delights in recalling instances when he felt somewhat smug about having found the psychologic basis of a very symptomatic patient with irritable bowel syndrome on subsequent histories taken in the hospital, only to find later that the "real" factors would only be revealed with time. He recalls the instance of a professional actress and entertainer who revealed in the hospital that she had been born in Italy during World War II and was the illegitimate child of a U.S. military officer. At the time Dr. Kirsner was seeing her, she had learned the identity of the man and where he was living. She told Dr. Kirsner that she was struggling with the dilemma of deciding whether she should contact him. She sought Dr. Kirsner's advice, but he counseled her that ultimately she would have to decide the issue herself. With these discussions, her symptoms seemed to improve, and she was discharged from the hospital. Dr. Kirsner felt that he had been successful in her care until some weeks later, when she contacted him from Fort Worth, Texas, to report that she was again in much distress and had to acknowledge that she had learned that her husband was having an affair with another woman.

The economic constraints on today's practice of medicine no longer allow doctors the luxury of lengthy hospitalizations and the careful evaluation of patients within a hospital setting. Of course, this does not mean that, during the course of outpatient visits, physicians cannot take the time to carefully revisit the patient's history instead of relying solely on initial impressions.

An important part of Dr. Kirsner's care of hospitalized patients included frequent visits to the bedside during the day. The frequency of these visits depended upon the severity of the patient's illness and the correspondent need for critical decision making and communication with family members. The location of his office and clinic near the inpatient floors facilitated this style of practice, and Dr. Kirsner took full advantage of this arrangement, visiting the gastroenterology floor both early in the morning and late at night to observe and supervise the care of his patients. This set the tone for care on the Medicine 6 Gastroenterology service. While attending physicians on other services in the Department of Medicine turned the care of their patients over to the house staff and assumed a supervisory role, the gastroenterology section was perhaps less popular with some medical residents and interns because the attending staff carefully monitored the day-to-day activities of the house staff. A standard practice established by Dr. Kirsner on his Thursday rounds included a staff conference (sometimes referred to by him as "Life Situational Rounds") that included the entire patient-care team. This included the house staff, the nurses, dietary services, representatives from the pharmacy department (at the time an innovation instituted by Dr. Kirsner and the GI section). Consulting services, including psychiatric and surgical specialty services, involved in the care of the patient were also encouraged to participate in these conferences. Dr. Kirsner provided coffee and doughnuts as an incentive.

Most important in his teaching on the care of patients was the discharge conference. This included the patient and the patient's immediate family along with the house-staff team. The format was to review the essentials of the patient's presenting illness, the results of tests that been completed in the hospital and pertinent x-ray findings that would help the patient understand his or her illness, and a careful review of the recommended therapy and arrangements for follow-up care. The discharge conference took time and energy on the part of the physicians. Dr. Kirsner's enthusiasm set an example for his fellows, and discharge conferences often took place on Thursday afternoons, when Dr. Kirsner held his schedule open to be free to guide these conferences without interruptions. These matters were not to be left to the intern or a nurse who might hand the patient a list of medications and tell them to call their doctor if they had questions. Dr. Kirsner's practice provided a model that his fellows would take with them and incorporate into their own practice habits. These activities yielded dividends for the patient in terms of increased understanding and compliance with their medical program, and thus an improved outcome with a decreased need for repeat hospitalizations. Most importantly, they fostered an improved doctor-patient relationship.

By what parameter or outcome analysis can one "scientifically" measure the impact of the discharge conference as practiced by Dr. Kirsner? In fact, thoughtful physicians are now at work designing studies to test the impact of patient-education programs. Patients suffering from a disease such as asthma are randomly assigned either to groups receiving additional patient education or to control groups receiving only "standardized care" in an attempt to document and quantify the impact of these measures on disease outcomes. One cannot help suspecting that the results of this evidence-based approach to medical care will document the wisdom that Dr. Kirsner empirically arrived at through his bedside observations.

An article written years later by a former patient of Dr. Kirsner's might be cited as an example of the lasting impact that his approach to patient care made on patients. "Memories of a Health Care System That Worked" was published in October 2006 and sent to Dr. Kirsner by the author, Diane Drell.[3] Drell writes in her article, "Once upon a time, many years ago, nearly all physicians were kind, compassionate and caring human beings that were very dedicated to the work that they did." She considers the negative impact that insurance and complicated reimbursement schemes have brought to the health care environment. She describes her own experience when, 32 years earlier, she was quite ill and made an appointment at a well-known research facility at the University of Chicago Hospital and Clinics, where she had the opportunity to be treated by "an extraordinary doctor and human being whose name was Dr. Joseph Kirsner." She describes her first visit with Dr. Kirsner as "a unique experience that I will remember as long as I live." Her recollection of Dr. Kirsner's words at the end of the visit ring so true that reading them summons up the sound of his voice. "Mrs. Drell, I know you are physically sick. We will find out what is wrong with you and you will get better." These positive and encouraging words contributed to her recovery.

In the covering letter she sent to Dr. Kirsner on October 3, 2006, along with the copy of the article, she recalls: "There was a conference held with about seven people in attendance the day I was discharged from Billings Hospital. You sat at the center of that conference table across from me. There was total silence, and every one's attention was completely focused on you as you spoke and discussed my diagnosis." In her letter she praises the team of doctors working on her behalf and specifically mentions her clinic doctor, "Giovani Benvenuti [Bemvenuti], a Brazilian doctor who was exceptional." Dr. Bemvenuti was a friend and colleague of Dr. Prolla's from Brazil who sought further training at the University of Chicago.

In speaking to the men and women who have been patients of Dr. Kirsner's, a theme that frequently emerges is his personal warmth and friendliness. Patients felt that he genuinely liked them as human beings and that he provided a constant source of hope, encouragement, and follow-up in their care. Many years ago, a writer in the Sunday New York Times Magazine described what happened when he inadvertently arrived at the office of his longtime psychiatrist on the wrong day. The door to the doctor's office had been left ajar, and the expression on the doctor's face in learning of the mistake made it clear to the man that the doctor didn't like him as a person, an event that led him to break off treatment.

An anecdote related by Dr. David Morowitz from an experience that occurred during his fellowship at the University of Chicago illustrates this point:

I was well into the first year of my fellowship when a particular, superficially inconspicuous event occurred on morning rounds, one that revealed much about the man I was working for, and working with. The year, 1966, was still in the seemingly blessed period when patients could be hospitalized for their evaluations, and the young woman I recall was admitted to JBK's service with a tearful history of abdominal cramping, the issue to the house staff being a "disease or no disease" evaluation. Apart from a sad demeanor, the patient was compiling a negative medical dossier, and Dr. Kirsner's bedside inquiries, scrutinized by the usual coterie of medical students and trainees, seemed confirmatory. As his white-coated platoon emerged onto the Medicine 6 corridor, one of the interns piped up, "What this patient needs is a psychiatrist." And almost immediately, he was corrected by Dr. Kirsner, responding, "No! What this patient needs is a friend."

And there it was: the fundamental declaration, the *credo* of what it meant to Dr. Kirsner to be a physician and to try to teach his conviction on the obligation of doctor to patient. That one unrehearsed line, stated simply, almost accidentally, as this little group proceeded to its next bedside evaluation, said it all. The science was set apart quietly, along with the usual dismissive attitude of doctors when dealing with "complainers," those patients who lack the good grace to demonstrate a mass, ulceration, or an abnormal biopsy to their overworked physician. This highly revered professor, it seemed to me then, was everyone's doctor, the very sick and the not so sick, the great and the small, and he was making it his job to show that commitment, and in doing so, to teach it. I thrilled in further realizing how lucky I was to have been allowed to study with him.[4]

Many patients can recall receiving telephone calls from Dr. Kirsner inquiring about their progress after being discharged or as a follow-up to a clinic visit. He often sent short letters for the same purpose. For a patient, his or her illness is the focus of concern, as is the doctor to whom they entrust their care. Patients understand that doctors have many patients and they must share the physician's attention. The telephone call or letter—an act of spontaneity—sends a message to the patient that their welfare is in the physician's thoughts and that this relationship extends beyond the few moments they are seen in the clinic, office, or hospital.

Dr. Kirsner's thoughts and practice on the interaction between attending physicians and the consultants asked to see their patients is another facet of his style of patient care. Dr. Kirsner believes strongly that, in asking a consultant to see a patient, the physician should never send a signal to the patient or the consultant that the patient's primary care has been abdicated. Similarly, calling a consultant or consulting service must never be a substitute for a complete evaluation of the patient by the primary physician. The primary or attending physician should speak personally with the consultant about the patient's medical problem to ensure that the medical facts in the case and his or her expectations of the consultant are properly communicated. Later in his career, as chief of staff of the University of Chicago Hospitals and Clinics, Dr. Kirsner used his position to communicate these values to the entire medical staff. Since Dr. Kirsner and the Section of Gastroenterology were dedicated to the training of physicians who would move out into the larger medical community where they would themselves serve as consultants, he stressed the importance of seeing consultations promptly and communicating with referring physicians both by direct and prompt communication and in writing. Fellows who trained in the Section of Gastroenterology quickly learned that Dr. Kirsner would be sending them a note in the morning to ensure that they followed through in calling a referring physician and sending a letter to that doctor.

The telephone was an important tool in the practice of medicine for Dr. Kirsner. The principles that he stressed and practiced included the importance of returning the call of every patient the same day, and of keeping patients informed of the results of important laboratory results and not compelling them to anxiously wait for a report at their next outpatient visit. He strongly believed in the practice of maintaining a home telephone number listed in the telephone directory and with the hospital operators, so that he could be reached when needed by colleagues and patients. This extended to evenings and weekends, a practice he continued throughout his career.

We live in a cynical age that regards concerns over etiquette and dress code as superfluous or irrelevant, and so-called casual Fridays are in vogue. Fellows in Dr. Kirsner's gastroenterology clinic learned the importance of greeting every patient with a friendly handshake. It was understood that fellows came to work, including the noted Saturday morning clinic, wearing a tie. Dr. Kirsner kept an envelope in the clinic with spare ties for the occasional "free spirit" who came without one. (This was an era when most, but not all, of the fellows were men.) The tie, the white coat, and a clean-shaven appearance were tokens of respect for the patient and an understanding of the trust they placed in the doctor. Of course, Dr. Kirsner knew and taught that it was not enough to "mean well" and "show the proper empathy." Those qualities alone would not "impede the logarithmic growth of bacteria or diminish the azotemia of renal insufficiency." He knew that "the highest compassion of the physician may be in establishing the correct diagnosis and applying the correct treatment to relieve suffering caused by disease." He also knew the importance of the doctor-patient relationship in relieving stress and recognized, as many have, that "psychological stress can have important consequences for both immune function and health." In the many articles that he wrote over the years addressing the state of medical care and education, a recurrent theme is the importance of the quality of the doctor-patient relationship and the importance of resisting the trends that would erode this relationship.

In June 1960 Dr. Kirsner published one of the first of many articles on what he saw as the broader principles of patient care. The article grew out of an invited "Oration in Medicine" presented to the Illinois State Medical Society at their annual meeting in Chicago on May 25, 1960. Titled "The Treatment of the 'Untreatable' Patient," the article reflects the energy and thoroughness of its author.[5] It is impressive in its length (some 15 printed pages) and thoroughness, and is unfortunately one of those gems in the medical literature that is obscured by the avalanche of medical publications. Dr. Kirsner acknowledges that "untreatable" is not a word in Webster's dictionary, and yet notes that it has been recognized since the time of Hippocrates that there are diseases for which no effective treatment exists. He proceeds to summarize 22 patients from his recent clinical experience who had been deemed "untreatable," and describes new approaches that either reversed the diagnosis and the course of their illness or relieved their suffering and provided hope.

The subject of the "Untreatable Patient" occupied his thoughts throughout his career and was a topic he would revisit in writing in 2003.[6] In an article in the *World Journal of Gastroenterology,* September 2003, he again pointed out that "untreatable" was not in the *Random House Dictionary* or in the *American Heritage Dictionary,* and that *Webster's Medical Desk Dictionary* simply defined untreatable as "not susceptible to medical treatment." Dr. Kirsner recounts his experience with two patients with severe ulcerative colitis who were considered "untreatable" and referred for colectomy. These patients responded to a program in the hospital of emotional support, nutritional support, correction of anemia by transfusion, and an optimistic atmosphere. The article describes other factors leading to the label of "untreatable," including the failure to establish the correct diagnosis, the failure to provide the correct medical program—or the patient's failure to cooperate with a medical program. He points out that there are individuals who, through their own determination to recover or through deep religious faith, are able to overcome what appeared to be an "untreatable" illness. He points to research documenting biologic and physiologic relationships between the mind and body that might operate in the natural history of disease. The importance of offering hope and yet providing realistic expectations was of great importance to Dr. Kirsner. It was an anathema to him that a doctor would tell a patient or their family that there was nothing that could be done for them.

The nature of the doctor-patient relationship and the manner in which it has been buffeted by changing societal and economic factors has long occupied Dr. Kirsner's thinking and writing. By reading a series of four important articles he wrote on this topic, it is possible to trace his reflections over the years. Although the articles vary in length and scope in keeping with the journals in which they were published, together they reflect his thinking on many of the same issues, updated in response to changes in the field of medicine, refined through his study of contemporary writings on similar issues, and expressed with increasing eloquence. The earliest article, "In Defense of Medicine and the Physician," appeared in 1979 under the summary heading "Good clinicians remain indispensable for good patient care—as well as for the effort to slow the relentless increase in the cost of medical care."[7] In 1986, in the scholarly journal *Perspectives in Biology and Medicine,* he published "The Changing Medical Scene (1929-1985): A Personal Perspective."[8] As a result of a talk he presented at Mount Sinai Hospital in Cleveland, on March 27, 1991, the *Archives of Internal Medicine* published his commentary, "Living with Hippocrates in a Changing World, with Particular Reference to the Patient-Physician Relationship."[9] In 2002 his thoughts on the patient-physician relationship, significantly titled "The Most Powerful Therapeutic Force," appeared in a series *JAMA* published under the general heading "A Piece of My Mind."[10]

These four articles contain Dr. Kirsner's reflections on medical care in the United States from 1929, when he entered Tufts Medical School, to the first decade of the 21st century. While it is customary to speak of the "doctor-patient" relationship, even in the 1979 paper Dr. Kirsner has changed the standard phrase to the "patient-physician" relationship. The meaning of this reordering is clear: first the patient, then the doctor. The dilemma addressed in each of these articles is that while the understanding of human illness is greater than ever, medicine has also changed in less desirable ways: commercialization of medical service, decreasing physician autonomy, proliferating bureaucracy, weakening of the patient-physician relationship, a diminished degree of caring by the physician, escalating malpractice suits, and "concern as to whether the clinical benefits of medical research are commensurate with its expense."

Of *medical students,* he notes that they are smarter and better prepared educationally today than they were in 1929 and that they enter medicine for the same humanitarian considerations. But a cynicism seems to envelop more students now than in the 1930s, and he attributes this to programs that over the four-year period emphasize science and provide fewer genuine faculty role models.

He describes the *physician* as having changed from a "superficially informed entrepreneur with limited resources to a knowledgeable, well-equipped, and resourceful professional." He recognizes the trend toward group practice as necessary to meet the comprehensive level of care required by a seriously ill patient, and does not see this change as necessarily limiting the patient's relationship to an individual physician in the group. He condemns physicians who exhibit diminished sensitivity to the needs of their patients, both emotional and physical, and worse, that small number of physicians whose loss of integrity has regrettably tarnished the time-honored eminence of the medical profession. Medical progress has provided today's physicians with "unusual powers over life and death and awesome clinical responsibilities."

Patients are better informed and more deliberate in their selection of medical care and rightly seek to participate in medical decisions. However, they are conditioned by media publicity to unrealistic expectations and have developed an unrealistic reliance on medicine to solve personal difficulties.

Hospitals have undergone a transition from disagreeable places to isolate patients with communicable diseases, early in the 20th century, to medical school–affiliated hospitals that serve as emergency-type facilities oriented toward the demanding care of seriously ill patients. They have responded to the competition for paying patients with aggressive advertisement programs and to the increasing administrative costs for employees and equipment by becoming business-oriented enterprises influenced by "commercialization" and "monetarization."

Dr. Kirsner is very concerned about *humanism in medicine.* He observes that historically writers have often expressed concern at the loss of this quality. Some degree of humanism must motivate candidates for the study of medicine, and this quality should already be present in freshman medical students, instilled by parents, relatives, the family doctor, or high school and college teachers. At the same time, he recognizes that empathy alone will not stop the progress of disease. "It is not enough for the physician to mean well: the physician must know enough to do well." The greatest form of humanism is in the fully informed, careful, and skillful diagnosis and delivery of the correct treatment. Specialization is a necessity for expert care, and he attributes the great advances in clinical care to the development of specialties in medicine. Specialization need not result in a fragmentation of medical care or a loss of those humanistic values.

He also explores the impact of today's *society* on medicine. He is concerned about the retreat from excellence, a decline in moral precepts, disruption of the family, escalating crime, the concept of more money for fewer services, and such disordered priorities as underpaid teachers versus grossly overpaid athletes. Spiraling health care costs he sees in part as related to a greater reliance upon technology versus careful patient evaluation coupled with accurate and careful planning of diagnostic testing and therapeutic intervention.

Looking ahead, Dr. Kirsner remains optimistic that solutions to the economic problems will be found and that society will recognize that personal health is not solely a government bequest but that it demands personal responsibility.

Of the importance of the patient-physician relationship he is ever confident. Quoting Norman Cousins's insightful observation "The will to live is not a theoretical abstraction but a physiologic reality with therapeutic characteristics,"[11] he reviews, in "The Most Powerful Therapeutic Force," some of the scientific observations that support this observation. He cites experimental studies undertaken on diseases such as rheumatoid arthritis and asthma that demonstrate that supplementing standard pharmacologic intervention with management of emotional stress leads to an improved outcome.

Progress in the therapy of inflammatory bowel disease from the 1990s into the first decade of the 21st century has been characterized by the discovery and application of powerful biological agents targeting specific molecules playing a critical role in the inflammatory process. Emblematic of these agents is infliximab or anti-tumor necrosis factor alpha. Similar strides are being made in the field of genetics with the discovery at the University of Chicago of the role of the *NOD2* (*CARD15*) gene in Crohn's disease. These advances in gastroenterology, as well as those in many other fields of medicine, have seemed to some to signify that human illness could be reduced to a "malady of molecules." This notion was perhaps furthered by the greater understanding of the molecular basis of emotions. These trends prompted Dr. Kirsner to write a leading editorial in the journal *Inflammatory Bowel Diseases* in 2002, "We Still Are More Than Molecules."[12] Here he does not discount the tremendous strides that have been made in the understanding, diagnosis, and treatment of disease, but says that in his observations of young physicians today he is often "left with a sense of incompleteness in their seemingly detached approach to the patient: the superficial history, the minimal physician-patient communication, and the discontinuity of patient care." He points to his belief that "scientific information, no matter how molecular, cannot encompass the wholeness of a sick person. . . . In the fullest sense, human illness encompasses much more than molecules. After all, 'We are living human beings, not things.'"

A visitor to Dr. Kirsner's office will note that among the many certificates of achievement and photographs of memorable events, family, and persons who have played an important part in his career, there are boldly typed quotations and aphorisms that reflect his philosophy about illness, patient care, the role of the physician, and basic humanistic values. At the end of this chapter on patient care, it is appropriate to reproduce two in particular that epitomize Dr. Kirsner's thinking.

Francis Weld Peabody is often quoted for his famous observation in 1927 that "the secret of the care of the patient is in caring for the patient." This simple truth is taken from a larger paragraph that deserves quoting in full:

> Disease in man is never exactly the same as disease in the experimental animal, for in man the disease at once affects, and is affected by what we call the emotional life. Thus, the physician who attempts to take care of a patient while he neglects this factor is as unscientific as the investigator who neglects to control all the conditions that may affect his experiment. The good physician knows his patients through and through, and his knowledge is bought dearly. Time, sympathy, and understanding must be lavishly dispensed, but reward is to be found in the personal touch which forms the greatest satisfaction in the practice of medicine. One of the essential qualities of the clinician is interest in humanity, for the secret of the care of the patient is in caring for the patient.[13]

The other quotation epitomizes the wisdom in the title of his article "We Still Are More Than Molecules":

> Medicine is not merely a Science but an Art. It does not consist in compounding pills and plasters and drugs of all kinds. But it deals with the processes of life which must be understood before they can be guided. PARACELSUS (1493-1541)

Notes

1. The author is very grateful to Andrew Herskee, of Teaneck, New Jersey, for providing a written narrative of the history of his experiences at the University of Chicago, for permitting the publication of the details of his

medical illness, and for providing copies of the letters written to him by Dr. Kirsner. The author also wishes to express his appreciation to Andrew's parents, Elinor and Bert Herskee, of Lake Forest, Illinois, for allowing him to record an interview on the history of their son's illness.

2. Kirsner JB, Owens FM, and Humphreys EM, Regional enteritis in father and son, *Gastroenterology* 10:6:939-51, June 1948.

3. Diane Drell, "Memories of a Health Care System That Worked," *Scottsdale Airpark News*, October 2006, 136. Her covering letter to JBK (mentioned below) is in his personal papers.

4. The author wishes to express his appreciation to Dr. David A. Morowitz, of Washington, D.C., for allowing him to record and interview him about his experiences at the University of Chicago and interactions with Dr. Kirsner, and for taking the time to prepare a number of written anecdotes and impressions of Dr. Kirsner.

5. Kirsner JB, The treatment of the "untreatable" patient, *Illinois Med J* 117:6, June 1960.

6. Kirsner JB, The treatment of the "untreatable" patient—revisited, *World J Gastroenterology* 9:885-87, May 2003.

7. Kirsner, JB, In defense of medicine and the physician, *Medical Forum on Medicine* 2:3:224-26, March 1979.

8. Kirsner JB, The changing medical scene (1929-1985): A personal perspective, *Perspect Biol Med* 29:2:227-42, Winter 1986.

9. Kirsner JB, Living with Hippocrates in a changing medical world, with particular reference to the patient-physician relationship, *Archives of Internal Medicine* 152:2184-88, November 1992.

10. Kirsner JB, The most powerful therapeutic force, *JAMA* 287:15:1909-10, April 17, 2002.

11. Norman Cousins, *The Biology of Hope* (New York: E. P. Dutton, 1989).

12. Kirsner, JB, We still are more than molecules, *Inflamm Bowel Dis* 8:1:56-57, 2002.

13. Francis W. Peabody, "The Care of the Patient," an address given to Harvard medical students on October 21, 1925, and printed in *JAMA* 88:877-82, 1927.

13 ✳ "A Great Capacity for Sustained Hard Work," 1976–2000

In June 1976 Dr. Kirsner completed his term as chief of staff and deputy dean of medical affairs. He would be 66 years of age in September of that year, past the age of 65, the age at which the University of Chicago usually mandated retirement. There was never a discussion with the dean's office or the chairman of the Department of Medicine, Alvin R. Tarlov, of Dr. Kirsner's retiring. His contract with the institution was renewed on a yearly basis. Dr. Kirsner began a process that he would continue over the next three decades of submitting an "Annual Activity Report," though no one had ever requested that he do so. It is instructive in understanding how he thought about himself and the critical assessment of his activities that he felt compelled to assemble this yearly critique. We will return to a sampling of these reports to gain a measure of how his energies were spent.

The groundwork for what would be Dr. Kirsner's future role at the university was laid in a letter he received in 1974 from University of Chicago's great president Edward H. Levi. Edward Levi was president of university from 1968 until 1975. A graduate of both the university's undergraduate college and the law school, he became the dean of the law school in 1950, a position he held until 1962, when he became the university's provost.

Dr. Kirsner received the following letter from the president's office on February 21, 1974:

Dear Dr. Kirsner:
    I have the honor and pleasure of inviting you to accept appoint-

ment as the Louis Block Distinguished Service Professor immediately.

The offer of this appointment, made on the recommendation of Provost [John] Wilson, is both an indication of the high esteem in which you are held by your colleagues and a recognition of your many contributions to scholarship and the University.

I am also delighted to inform you upon reaching the age of sixty-five you will be offered a three-year deferred retirement appointment as the Louis Block Distinguished Service Professor in the Department of Medicine, effective July 1, 1975. Such an appointment would be subject to the usual review for considerations of health.

We hope you will plan to accept such an appointment so that we may look forward your continued contribution to the excellence of the University.

Sincerely yours,

Edward Levi[1]

It is interesting to note that the somewhat "lawyerly" Levi had to add the sentence about considerations of health that could have been left to a signed contract. Dr. Kirsner held Edward Levi in great esteem and had great appreciation for his intellect and "forthright attitude." President Levi had supported the activities of GIRF on behalf of the university and was occasionally an honored guest at annual meetings.

A letter President Levi sent to Mrs. Kirsner on October 28, 1974, is a mark of his friendship with the Kirsners, and a fine example of his personal touch as chancellor of the university.

Dear Minnie:

This note is to you, and I have been meaning to write it for a long time. Without your insight and understanding, our University would be a much poorer place, and we are everlastingly grateful to you. It takes a lot of heroes and heroines to keep the University as strong as it is and with the superb quality it has, and you are at the top of the list of those who have made it possible.

As we think about the greatness of Joe, you should know we are also filled with the utmost admiration for you.

Sincerely,

Edward Levi

These letters were very important to Dr. Kirsner, and he had them both framed. They still hang in his study at home, over 30 years after they were written. Edward Levi would later serve as the nation's 71st attorney general, from 1975 to 1976. Appointed by President Gerald Ford, he helped restore the confidence of the American public in a justice system that had become politicized during the Nixon administration. President Levi passed away in 2000, having suffered from Alzheimer's disease. Dr. Kirsner would remark that this negated any theories he might have had about intellect and mental activity being a protection against the devastation of Alzheimer's.

Thus in June of 1976 Dr. Kirsner resumed his place in the Section of Gastroenterology as its most esteemed and recognized member. Over three decades later, the section has prospered and continues to command local, national, and international respect through the successive leadership of Dr. Irwin Rosenberg, Dr. Thomas Brasitus, and currently Dr. Stephen Hanauer and his associate chair, Dr. Eugene Chang. But for the generation of physicians and patients that experienced the Kirsner era, mention of gastroenterology and the University of Chicago immediately brings his name to mind.

Above all, Dr. Kirsner was a practicing gastroenterologist in an academic medical center. He maintained his clinical practice of seeing patients in the outpatient clinic two days a week and also his famous Saturday morning clinic. When there were unexpected calls, Dr. Kirsner was always ready to accommodate a patient needing to be seen on an urgent basis; he would not give a patient the usual alternatives of accepting the next available appointment, seeing another doctor, or going to the emergency room. The Saturday morning clinic remained a part of his life until the 1990s, when his wife's illness compelled him to discontinue it. He continued to be available to his patients both at work and at home. He continued to take his turn as the attending physician on the inpatient service for two months a year, often selecting those months, December and July or August, when he knew that many of the attending physicians might be out of town and their patients would be in greatest need. He also fulfilled his departmental duties in the Medical Center and the university, including interviewing prospective gastroenterology fellows and prospective medical students and residents. He actively participated in section meetings and conferences, as well as the many departmental committees and meetings required to keep the complex organism that constitutes the academic medical center running smoothly.

In 1976 the number of papers and books in Dr. Kirsner's bibliography stood at 578. Over the next three decades, the number would reach 771 in 2005 and still counting. Eleven of the textbooks that he authored, coauthored, or edited were written during these decades—most notably *Kirsner's Inflammatory Bowel Disease,* which was published in its 6th edition in 2004 under the editorship of Dr. R. Balfour Sartor, of the University of North Carolina, and Dr. William J. Sanborn, of the Mayo Clinic. This beautifully produced volume is a tribute to the growth of scientific research and clinical interest in inflammatory bowel disease, and Dr. Kirsner's eloquent foreword to the volume gives his perspective on the evolution of the textbook and the expanding scientific and clinical interest in the entire field of basic and clinical research in inflammatory bowel diseases.

During these years, Dr. Kirsner began taking care of the king of Morocco, as well as members of the royal family and other citizens of the country. This adventure, which included some 55 trips to Morocco, is recounted in full in chapter 10. He also continued his active role in guiding the activities of GIRF (see chap. 8). The years 1975 and 1976 saw the completion of his presidential report, prepared with Dr. Charles Winans, reviewing the status of the American Gastroenterological Association (AGA). This report, which played a vital role in shaping the future of the association, is discussed in chapter 7.

For the next three decades Dr. Kirsner was a faithful attendee at the Digestive Disease Week meeting, which has grown to 15,000 members attending these meetings from the United States and abroad. Dr. Kirsner's name is probably known by the vast majority of the members of the AGA for his contributions to the growth of this specialty. He would faithfully attend the plenary sessions and the papers devoted to inflammatory bowel disease. He was invariably seen in the front rows of these crowded meeting rooms and would often come to the microphone, easily gaining the attention of the moderator. He would begin his comments on the paper just presented with the simple words, "Kirsner, Chicago"—all that was needed to establish his credentials and engage the attention of the audience. He was never caustic, but neither was he shy about asking the speaker to explain how a piece of basic research might benefit their patients.

The Julius Friedenwald Medal

On July 1, 1974, Dr. Kurt J. Isselbacher, president of the AGA and a scientist and gastroenterologist on the faculty of Harvard Medical School and Massachusetts General Hospital, wrote Dr. Kirsner: "Dear Joe: I have the great pleasure of informing you that you have been nominated to receive the Friedenwald Medal of the American Gastroenterological Association in May 1975. It is a personal pleasure for me to transmit this good news to you, especially since the award can be made during my tenure as President of the AGA." The Friedenwald Medal was established in 1941 to honor Julius Friedenwald (1866-1941). Dr. Friedenwald practiced in Baltimore and had the distinction of inheriting Sir William Osler's desk in 1905 when Osler left Johns Hopkins to go to Oxford as the Regis Professor of Medicine. He wrote on many areas in gastroenterology, including the utility of roentgen rays in the diagnosis of gastrointestinal disease and aspects of gastric cancer. In his presentation of the 35th Friedenwald award to Dr. Kirsner at the AGA annual meeting in 1975, Dr. Walter Lincoln Palmer characterized Dr. Friedenwald as "small in stature, quiet, unassuming, possessed of dignity and charm and a true scholar and physician of the old school."[2]

In his address, Dr. Palmer began by highlighting some of the previous distinguished recipients of the award, including the first recipient, Walter B. Cannon, who had first utilized the newly discovered roentgen rays to document the motility of the digestive tract in cats; A. J. Carlson, the distinguished physiologist of the University of Chicago; and Max Einhorn, who had pioneered the early use of tubes in the study of the gastrointestinal tract. He then described the two great love affairs of Dr. Kirsner's life: the first was his wife, Minnie Schneider, whom he had married in 1934; the second was the University of Chicago. Dr. Palmer chronicled Dr. Kirsner's long career of faithful service to the institution, his rise up the academic ladder to the head of the Section of Gastroenterology, to deputy dean and chief of the medical staff, and to the Louis Block Distinguished Service

Professorship of Medicine. He reviewed his achievements in the field of gastroenterology and his dedication to the study of inflammatory bowel disease, and pointed out that Dr. Kirsner's professional career spanned the time from 1932, when Burrill B. Crohn and his associates first described regional enteritis, to the present. He also noted the leadership role that Dr. Kirsner had played in the major societies of gastroenterology, in many of which he had been a founding member, and his service to the NIH. Dr. Palmer made special mention of Dr. Kirsner's distinguished and voluntary service for three years of overseas duty during World War II.

He asked the audience, "But how has Joe been able to accomplish all of this?" He then answered his own question in a manner that few who heard or read Dr. Palmer's address have ever forgotten. He told the members of the AGA that Joe's achievements had come "only by exceeding diligence and continuous application for almost 20 hours per day, 7 days a week. I have never been associated with anyone with such a great capacity for sustained hard work." Dr. Palmer closed by noting that Dr. Kirsner had recently been relieved of the drudgery of administrative work (referring to Dr. Kirsner's completion of his service as deputy dean and chief of staff, and perhaps reflecting some of Dr. Palmer's own feelings on medical administration) and would be free to extend his research program, to teach, and to "bestow his skillful and tender care for which he is so famous." He then quoted Hippocrates, "Life is short and the art is long." Dr. Palmer, who remained active into his 90s, would not be surprised to learn that Dr. Kirsner at the age of 99 defies the first half of the aphorism but continues to exemplify the second.

Dr. Kirsner responded to the Dr. Palmer and to the AGA by saying,

This is the proudest moment of my life and one that I shall always cherish. I want to thank you, Walter, my dear friend of many years, for your generous remarks about me. You have been the most important influence in my professional life in the past and you continue so in the present. . . . Participation in the affairs of the American Gastroenterological Association is a most satisfying, educating experience rewarding not only for the opportunities to help advance our specialty of Gastroenterology but rewarding also for the warm and lasting friendships we made and for the opportunity to meet so many dedicated people.[3]

He publicly recognized his wife, Minnie, who, "as Walter has indicated and as many know, has been a key factor and an active partner in all of my activities. She indeed deserves a share of this Friedenwald Medal." He then reflected on the history of the AGA, recalling the first meeting he attended in the 1930s in the Claridge Hotel in Atlantic City when the audience counted less than 200 and the program encompassed one and a half days. Now, the AGA course on gastrointestinal cancer attracted 1,100 registrants and the Digestive Disease Week was attended by over 4,000 individuals. He closed by expressing his optimism for the future growth of the organization and the role it would play in the national health scene.

A Loyal Alumnus of Tufts

Over the years Dr. Kirsner has kept up strong ties with his alma mater, the Tufts University School of Medicine. On a number of occasions he responded to requests for alumni support for financial campaigns launched by the medical school. He has been a member of the Tufts School of Medicine Millennium Club since 1984, and in 1983, on the 50th anniversary of his graduation, he and his wife established a prize in their name to be given to the graduating medical student who epitomized humane care of patients.

In May 1978, at the ninth annual Tufts Medical Alumni Weekend in Newport, Rhode Island, Dean Lauro Carvazos announced the inception of the Dean's Society of Distinguished Graduates of Tufts University School of Medicine, established "to honor annually one member of its more than 4000 practicing alumni who have accomplished outstanding medical achievements during their career." As described in the *Tufts Medical Alumni Bulletin* that July, Dr. Kirsner was the first recipient of this honor. The *Bulletin* summarized the many honors and achievements that Dr. Kirsner had received and the many contributions he had made to the field of gastroenterology, which have "benefited mankind and our understanding of health and diseases." He was characterized as "a teacher, a scholar, a scientist, and a gentle and humane physician [who] has earned the love and admiration of his patients, his students, and his colleagues." The article contains several photographs of Dr. Kirsner, including one of him and Minnie standing with a very tall Dean Cavazos and Tufts University president Dr. Jean Mayer.[4]

In the spring of 1985, the *Tufts Medical Alumni Bulletin* ran another article on Dr. Kirsner, "Probing the Mysteries of the Gastrointestinal Tract," reviewing his accomplishments and career.[5] The article gives a colorful portrait of the then 75-year-old Dr. Kirsner. At an age when "most folks his age are still asleep in their retirement homes," at five in the morning he gets out of bed to begin his day. "Fittingly, for a man who is always advising his patients to eat properly, Dr. Kirsner now sits down to a healthful breakfast being set out by Minnie, his wife of 50 years. Besides orange juice and melon and cereal with banana, he has half a slice of bread and half a cup of coffee." The author notes that Dr. Kirsner drives to the hospital, but the doctor assures him that he walks "five miles a day through the hospital corridors making rounds, and that's enough." At six thirty he is sitting at his desk in the former Billings Hospital in an "unfashionable but comfortable office he carved out of a one-time men's washroom and a storeroom." After eleven hours of work—evidence the author notes of his taking things a bit easier—he returns home to watch the news and then eat a simple but wholesome dinner consisting of "tomato juice or soup, salad, baked chicken, half a potato, fruit yogurt and Sanka."

As part of the centennial celebrations of Tufts School of Medicine in 1993, the president of the university, Dr. John Di Baggio, the dean of the medical school, and the trustees of the university awarded Dr. Kirsner a degree of doctor of science, *honoris causa*. Dr. Kirsner was in good company that morning, April 15, 1993, since he shared the platform with Dr. C. Everett Koop, former U.S. surgeon general; Dr. Bernadine Healy, director of the NIH; and Dr. Robert G. Petersdorf, president of the Association of American Medical Colleges.

To honor Dr. Kirsner's 95th birthday, the winter 2005 issue of *Tufts Medicine* published an article about him titled "The Sage of Chicago."[6] The picture on the cover showed Dr. Kirsner standing on a grassy strip of the Midway with Billings Hospital in the background. The article reviewed some of the highlights of his 69-year career and offered observations by several current Tufts faculty members acknowledging Dr. Kirsner's role as a mentor during a their training.

As recently as March 2006, the dean of the Tufts School of Medicine, Dr. Michael Rosenblatt, again honored Dr. Kirsner with the Dean's Medal as a distinguished alumnus. The presentation was made at a meeting of the Chicago Tufts Alliance held at the Hyatt Regency on March 21. The theme of the meeting was "Hearts Matter," and Dr. Michael E. Mendelsohn, the executive director of the Molecular Cardiology Research Institute of Tufts–New England Medical Center, was the guest speaker.

The Horatio Alger Award

In 1978 Norman Stone, founder and chairman of the Stone Container Corporation, and Arthur Rubloff, founder of Arthur Rubloff Enterprises and a Chicago real estate magnate, both good friends of Dr. Kirsner's, nominated him for the nationally prestigious Horatio Alger Award. The awards committee consisted of honorary chairman Norman Vincent Peale, chairman Arthur Rubloff, and board of directors member Norman Stone. There was little doubt that Dr. Kirsner would receive the approval of the board.

The Horatio Alger Association of Distinguished Americans was founded in 1947. Its mission is to honor the achievements of outstanding individuals who have succeeded in spite of adversity and to encourage young people to pursue their dreams through higher education. Today the society awards more than $8.5 million annually in scholarships to young people. The association is named for Horatio Alger Jr. (1832-99), who wrote stories of courage and hard honest work that captured the imagination of generations of young Americans. His books were bestsellers, and 250 million were sold worldwide.

Again, Dr. Kirsner was in good company. Of the 18 Americans who received the Horatio Alger Award on May 18, 1979, in Columbus, Ohio, his friend and fellow Chicagoan Abraham Lincoln Marovitz, senior judge of the Northern District Court of Illinois, was also a recipient.

The Horatio Alger Association has a Web site that includes brief biographies and photographs of the award recipients. The page posting Dr. Kirsner's biography ends with a statement of his pride in receiving the Horatio Alger Award: "When I was a boy in Boston, I read all the Horatio Alger stories." He mentions that he and his wife had a principle by which they lived their lives: "We are here for the sake of others, known and unknown. We must constantly strive to give as much and more than we have received."

Memorial Service for Maurice Goldblatt

On July 23, 1984, Dr. Kirsner had the honor, but also the sad duty, of speaking at a memorial service at Swift Hall on the university campus in remembrance of his longtime friend and supporter Maurice Goldblatt. Like that of many other immigrants, the history of the Goldblatt family was in the Horatio Alger tradition. Beginning his brief but compelling remarks, Dr. Kirsner said, "On July 17, 1984, a remarkable man passed from our midst—merchant, philanthropist, humanitarian, family man and friend. He was a caring man and a great man for he himself did and he made possible wonderful things for people everywhere. We are not likely to see his kind again."[7]

Maurice Goldblatt was born in Poland in 1894. His parents, Simon and Hannah, moved with their children, Morris (later, his friends would always call him Maurice), Nathan, and Louis, to Chicago in 1905. A fourth brother, Joseph, was born in the United States. Their father entered the grocery business, and his sons sold newspapers and later worked as store clerks. By 1915 they had saved enough to set up their own store, and by 1936 the family had added the name Goldblatt to those already on State Street: Marshall Field and Carson Pirie Scott.

In 1944 his brother Nathan died of colon cancer, and Maurice withdrew from the family business and devoted the remainder of his life to raising funds for medical research on heart disease, cancer, and digestive diseases. Dr. Kirsner first met Maurice Goldblatt in 1947 when Dean Lowell Coggeshall asked him to check Mr. Goldblatt for abdominal symptoms. This initial contact led to a close friendship that lasted 40 years. Maurice Goldblatt was among the original backers who gathered in the early 1960s to support Dr. Kirsner and the Section of Gastroenterology. These efforts soon led to the formation of the Gastro-Intestinal Research Foundation (GIRF), as described in chapter 8.

One of Maurice Goldblatt's great moments came in Washington, DC, in 1948 when his eloquence persuaded a subcommittee of the U.S. Senate to establish the National Heart Institute. He was the first recipient of the Distinguished Service Medal presented by the Department of Health, Education, and Welfare.

As Dr. Kirsner described him in 1984, "His fund-raising activities were legendary. Under his inspirational leadership, with his family, the Nathan Goldblatt Society and the Cancer Research Foundation, millions of dollars came to the university, facilitating the recruitment of faculty and the establishment of new programs; the building of the Nathan Goldblatt Hospital and the Goldblatt Diagnostic Pavilion; and with his assistance, the Argonne Cancer Research Hospital (now the Franklin McLean Institute)."

Dr. Kirsner related that on the occasion of Maurice's 80th birthday, in 1971, the medical school had presented him with an honorary M.D., a doctor's bag, a stethoscope, and the traditional white coat. He loved this gift, and it was kept available for him when he visited Dr. Kirsner, saying, "Joe, let's make rounds." On occasion Dr. Kirsner brought Mr. Goldblatt to a special meeting with the fellows so that he might share his perspectives on the attributes of good patient care.

After Mr. Goldblatt's death, his wife, Bernice, continued to serve as president of the Cancer Research Foundation, and Dr. Kirsner has continued to serve as, first, an active consultant and, currently, as an honorary member of the foundation's board of medical consultants, regularly attending their meetings to review grant proposals.

Address to the Entering Medical School Class of 1986

On September 30, 1982, Dr. Kirsner was selected by his friend Joseph J. Ceithaml, who served as dean of students from 1951 to 1986, a period of 35 years, to address the entering medical school Class of 1986. The typewritten 10-page address reflects the characteristic seriousness with which Dr. Kirsner undertook this assignment, and it is an inspiring testament to his high regard for the calling the students were about to enter. The address, entitled "The University of Chicago Medical School and Hospitals: A Special Place," is well worth quoting in some detail. He begins his address as follows: "Ladies and Gentleman, Fellow Students: . . . congratulations on your successfully negotiating Dean Ceithaml's critical selective process. No greater opportunity or obligation can come to a human being than to be a physician. . . . [a] uniquely satisfying service to mankind." Note that he addresses the incoming class as "fellow students," affirming his own identity as a student and his belief that the profession of medicine requires the individual to devote his life to continual study. His opening words also affirm the personal rewards the students will garner from a career in medicine.

He points out that they are entering a changing world and that "medicine in the 1980s bears no resemblance to the medical world of 1929 when I entered medical school in Boston. . . . Medicine is no longer the universally respected and beloved profession of earlier years." But this is not entirely surprising, since the medical profession has come under criticism repeatedly in its long history. He reminds his audience of an epigram of John Owen's from 1620:

God and the Doctor we like adore.
But only when in danger—not before.
The danger over, both are alike requited.
God is forgotten and the Doctor is slighted.

He then takes up the complexities of the university and of the 126 medical schools in the United States, 108 of them (at that time) associated with universities. Answering the rhetorical question, "What then is so special about this place, the University of Chicago?" he says that "the University of Chicago and its medical school were conceived in greatness, have achieved greatness in its 55 years of existence, and the University of Chicago confers the opportunity for greatness upon its students and faculty." Of the 48 Nobel laureates associated with the university, 10 of them worked at one time or another in the medical and biological sciences.

He finds the reason for this position of leadership in the facts that, from the beginning, the university was dedicated to discovery and education; that the resources of the physical and biological sciences were in close proximity to the hospital and its patient-care areas;

and that the university took an entirely fresh approach to medical education, embracing a full-time system for its medical faculty and incorporating clinical activities within the Division of Biological Sciences. He gives the students a portrait of the Medical Center in 1935, when he joined the faculty, and the vibrant atmosphere he found there, mentioning the names of some of the faculty members from that era: A. J. Carlson and A. B. Luckhardt in physiology, E. M. Geiling in pharmacology, Robert R. Bensley in anatomy, E. C. Barron in biochemistry, Gail Dack in microbiology, Eleanor Humphreys in pathology, and Walter Lincoln Palmer in medicine.

He points out some of the highlights in medical progress made in the field of medicine since Billings Hospital opened its doors in 1927 and lists the achievements of some of the present faculty: the discovery of erythropoietin by Eugene Goldwasser, the use of nitrogen mustard in chemotherapy by Leon Jacobson, the work on the metabolism of insulin and the discovery of proinsulin by Donald Steiner, and discoveries in the transmission of genetic information and the nature of atherosclerosis and inflammatory bowel disease, naming each faculty member associated with these achievements. He also describes the growth of the individual components of the Medical Center and observes that while there are over 7,000 hospitals in the United States, fewer than 50 have university affiliations, and fewer than a dozen have appreciable full-time faculty. These advantages positioned the University of Chicago hospital to recognize and treat difficult and rare clinical challenges.

His address outlines the complexities of health care delivery in the modern era, the challenges that medical science faces in the quest to overcome disease, and the ethical and moral dilemmas that will face the students as physicians in the future. He urges them to retain their interest in the patient as a human being and to avoid the "creeping cynicism that seems to envelop some students between the first and second years." He points out that the master word in medicine in 1982 as in the Oslerian days of 1900 is *W-O-R-K.*" He closes with a message that meant a great deal to him over the years:

Medicine is a heritage, not to be abandoned lightly.
It is not a commodity to sell to consumers.

We are still human beings, not things.

It is the sanctity of life we seek to understand and defend.

It is still true, as when Hippocrates wrote long ago: "Where there is love of man—there also is love of the Art.

And finally, "Good luck and success in your medical school career and beyond."

A Critique of the University of Chicago Medical Center

That same year, 1982, as a part of his involvement with the Dean's Search Advisory Committee, Dr. Kirsner prepared a report on the current state of the university's medical school. This document reflects his ongoing participation in the affairs of the Medical Center at the highest levels, his keen insight into the problems and challenges faced by the academic medical center in the context of the university, and his long-term concern for patient care and other hospital issues he had encountered during his years as chief of staff and deputy dean.

He begins by pointing out the complex relationship between the Division of Biological Sciences and the Medical Center and the enormous and complex financial issues related to the administration of the center. He also calls attention to an ever-recurring area of concern, the problem of declining excellence in the care of patients. He observes that the dean's office under Robert Uretz has been compelled to expend a disproportionate amount of its resources on the affairs of the hospital to the exclusion of the needs of the basic science departments. He sees these issues as factors that will complicate the recruitment of the best-qualified candidates. He feels that the current administrative problems could best be approached through the creation of an associate dean for clinical affairs.

He is critical of the executive director of the Medical Center for failing to comprehend the need for "first-class patient care." Problems of illiteracy, indifference, and poor supervision of employees, and the lack of cleanliness, excessive noise, and insensitivity plague the Medical Center on many levels. On an administrative level, he is worried that hospital security is notoriously inadequate and that the financial affairs related to billing are poorly administered. For example, the hospital accounts for the prince of Morocco and for members of the Pritzker family had almost been turned over to collection agencies, but fortunately an alert secretary had stepped in. An attitude of indifference and mediocrity afflicts some members of the clinical faculty. The relationship of the University of Chicago School of Medicine and its hospital and clinics to Michael Reese Hospital, which he refers to as a "shotgun affiliation," continues to be a major area of concern. The connection has been of little benefit to the University of Chicago, and the entire matter needs thorough review. Only if the goals of the two institutions can be fully integrated can a brighter collaborative future be anticipated. He ends with the affirmation that these problems are correctable, but they require urgent leadership and the selection of a dean with experience in hospital affairs, awareness of the needs of a modern university hospital and medical center, and the willingness to delegate full authority to a qualified, experienced medical doctor to assist in the direction of the Medical Center.

The Bernard A. Mitchell Hospital

The construction of the Bernard A. Mitchell Hospital began with Dr. Kirsner. In 1978 at a monthly board meeting of GIRF, Bernard Mitchell approached Dr. Kirsner to ask him whether there were any special projects that Billings Hospital or the medical school needed funded. When Dr. Kirsner indicated that the nature of any project would be guided by the funds that would be available, Mr. Mitchell suggested that he name a figure. Dr. Kirsner proposed several possibilities that would require modest expenditures, but Mr. Mitchell suggested he "guess again." It soon became apparent that he was thinking of very significant sums of money, on the order of $15 million. In this one conversation was born the project that would culminate in the opening of the Bernard A. Mitchell Hospital.

Bernard A. Mitchell was born in Chicago in 1912. He graduated from Northwestern University with a bachelor's degree in business in 1936. His highly successful business career began that same year, when he founded the Mitchell Manufacturing Company. Some of the achievements of this enterprise included the invention and production of the first fluorescent desk lamp and the first hermetically sealed window air conditioner. Mitchell sold his company in 1954 and became involved in a number of other ventures, including "the first packaged high fidelity phonograph system, a vest-pocket transistor radio, a clock radio, a nationally promoted wig business and Chicago's first shopping center."[8] There were additional highly successful business enterprises with several New York investors and then a "retirement" in 1967, followed a year later by his founding the fragrance company Jovan, Inc., with "blockbuster" success. Jovan, Inc., was subsequently sold, and he founded a private investment firm, Mitchell and Company. Shortly before his death in 1983 at the age of 71, Mitchell expressed his love for the city of Chicago, saying, "I made my money here and I want to give back some of what I have earned." Through his conversations with Dr. Kirsner, he became convinced that "medicine is the purest form of philanthropy." It was in this spirit that he saw endowing a new hospital at the University of Chicago as the best investment in the community he could make. Mitchell declared, "My main interest is in excellent patient care, and the University of Chicago is the place where that can happen—and does." For the rest of his life, Bernard Mitchell, with characteristic modesty, referred to this contribution as "the little gift which I gave to the University of Chicago."

Dr. Kirsner's part in founding the new, much needed hospital was acknowledged by the university's president, Dr. Hanna Holborn Gray, in a letter sent to Dr. Kirsner's home on December 24, 1979:

Dear Dr. Kirsner,

It all began with you, the Bernard Mitchell gift, and it is because of you that we were able to proceed. I believe greatness is defined not only by the individual's accomplishments in his field, and you have so many, but also by his vision, and all it encompasses.

The University and its Medical Center are enormously indebted to you. I am personally most grateful for your many contributions over time, through your research and treatment of patients, but most of all through your vision of the University and its role.

Warm regards,

Hanna Holborn Gray

By 1980 construction of the new hospital was underway. "On a mild evening in October of that year; faculty, alumni and friends of the university and the Medical Center gathered under a yellow pavilion across from the construction site" to celebrate the unveiling of the cornerstone for the new hospital and intensive-care tower that would be the focus of the modernization program of the university's hospitals and clinics.⁹ While the hospital would be constructed of glass and steel, the cornerstone was a block of polished granite to be placed in the lobby of the new hospital. Like the original cornerstone of the Albert Merritt Billings Hospital, placed in October, 12, 1925, it would contain a time capsule with letters of pledges from donors, copies of the financial and feasibility studies, the roster of the faculty of the Division of Biological Sciences and the Pritzker School of Medicine, and copies of Thomas W. Goodspeed's history of the university and C. W. Vermeulen's history of the Medical Center.

Later in the evening, at a celebratory dinner at Hutchinson Commons attended by 300 guests, President Gray introduced the evening's keynote speaker, Dr. Joseph Kirsner. President Gray characterized Dr. Kirsner as epitomizing the "goals of the faculty in the Pritzker School of Medicine—those of research, of teaching, and of clinical care." She reviewed his hard work and dedication and characterized him as "the scholar and teacher, the scholar-physician, the teacher who inspires others to teach and to do research and to provide health care at the highest level."

The published version of Dr. Kirsner's address, "The University of Chicago Hospital—Yesterday, Today, Tomorrow, 1927-1980-2030," was captioned with one of his favorite epigrams, "Homines ad Deos nulla re proprius accedunt quam salutem hominibus dando (There is nothing by which man approaches nearer to the perfection of the Deity than by restoring the sick to the enjoyment of the blessings of health—Cicero)."¹⁰ He began by pointing out that the building of a new university hospital is a special event, undertaken no oftener than every 50 years or more. He harkened back 55 years to the groundbreaking ceremonies for the Albert Merritt Billings Hospital, when the speaker, Dr. Henry A. Christian of Peter Bent Brigham Hospital, predicted that the future hospital would be "devoted to medical education and investigation, with special types of diseases admitted for study." Dr. Kirsner reviewed the history and significance of the "Chicago experiment" and remarked on the changes in the medical world since then and the challenges and needs that the new hospital would face. Contrasting 1930 with 1979, he pointed out that in 1930 the number of hospitalizations at Billings was 100, a number that had risen to 23,000 in 1979, with approximately 300,000 outpatient visits; the professional staff had increased from perhaps 50 in 1930 to over 300 in 1979, plus 350 house staff and fellows; and hospital personnel had risen from approximately 500 in 1930 to 4,000 in 1979.

He also reviewed the important contributions of current living faculty members in the field of medicine and the increased recognition that the university enjoyed from national organizations. The Medical Center had been designated a National Cancer Research Center, a National Diabetes Research Center, a National Sickle Cell Center, a Special Research Center for Ischemic Heart Disease, a National Clinical Nutrition Center, and a Regional Burn, Peri-natal, and Emergency Medicine Center. With great optimism and enthusiasm he looked to the future. The new hospital would enable the Medical Center to adhere to a fundamental truth: "the essential unity of the science of medicine and the art of medicine in the best interest of the patient."

When the hospital opened in 1984, it was six stories high with 468 beds. There were three medical and surgical floors, each with an adjacent intensive care unit in the Arthur Rubloff Intensive Care Tower. The layout of the hospital included a 16-bed hematology/oncology unit for cancer patients, and 8 of the beds were equipped with reverse isolation. The emergency care center featured 20 adult beds equipped for intensive care, and the Radiology Center was located adjacent to it. The Arthur Rubloff Intensive Care Tower was an integral part of the Bernard A. Mitchell Hospital and provided 48 beds for intensive care. The Pediatric Emergency Room connected to Wyler Children's Hospital. Incorporated within the Bernard A. Mitchell Hospital were a 72-bed two-story area for the treatment of obstetric and gynecologic patients, a neonatal unit with the capacity for 36 seriously ill newborns, and a labor and delivery area with 26 suites.

In 2004, on the occasion of the Bernard A. Mitchell Hospital's 20th anniversary celebration, it could boast having provided 432,000 people with in-patient health care and 700,000 emergency room visits.

Research at the hospital has led to the first living-donor liver transplant, computerized mammography, and virtual colonoscopy. The hospital's obstetrics and gynecological facility includes a renowned program in fertility and reproductive endocrinology, and the neonatal intensive care unit cares for "one out of every 200 babies born below 750 grams in the United States.[11] The hospital serves patients in the Chicago and northwest Indiana area through a rooftop medical helicopter service flying more than 1,300 missions a year.

A Chicago Physician

Dr. Kirsner has always endeavored to maintain an active presence in the Chicago community of medicine. His name and the Section of Gastroenterology would automatically come to mind when physicians sought second opinions on patients suffering from complicated gastrointestinal problems. Evidence for his leadership role in the local medical community can be found throughout his career. As early as 1957, he served as president of the Chicago Society of Internal Medicine. The society held monthly meetings during the academic year at the Drake Hotel, and Dr. Kirsner regularly attended these meetings. He has retained his membership in the society into the current decade. In 1960 he served as the president of the Jackson Park branch of the Chicago Medical Society. He had been invited to be the president of the entire society that year but declined because his professional commitments precluded his taking on the additional responsibility. In 1968, along with Dr. Sumner Kraft, he founded the Chicago Society of Gastroenterology, which meets six times a year during the academic calendar. Dinner meetings are accompanied by an invited speaker, either local or from out of town, on a clinically important topic. In 1998, to celebrate the society's 30th anniversary, Dr. Kirsner was recognized as the founder of the society and was invited to speak on the topic "Gastroenterology, Then and Now."

The Institute of Medicine of Chicago (IOMC)—founded in 1915 by three preeminent figures in the history of medicine in Chicago, Frank Billings, Ludvig Hektoen, and William Allen Pusey—is another local community medical group in which Dr. Kirsner has maintained an active presence.[12] On the evening of May 2, 1984, at their annual meeting, the IOMC presented Dr. Kirsner with the institute's George Howell Coleman Medal for 1983. The Coleman Medal was presented to Dr. Kirsner by Dr. C. Anderson (Andy) Hedberg, president of the institute and a former fellow in the Section of Gastroenterology (see chap. 7). The Coleman Medal had been established in 1957 by friends of the late Dr. George Coleman, a famed Chicago clinician who served as secretary of the IOMC for 36 years. As Dr. Hedberg pointed out in his presentation, the award had last been given in 1980 to his own father. Dr. Hedberg reviewed for the audience the salient events in Dr. Kirsner's career, his many accomplishments, and his legendary capacity for hard work, and praised his "love for the art and science of medicine, and for his patients and students as limitless."

Dr. Kirsner began his talk by paying tribute to the IOMC as truly, in the words of the *Chicago Sun Times* columnist Arthur J. Snider, the "medical conscience of Chicago." He shared with the audience his perspectives on the changes that medicine had undergone during his career and then eloquently summed up his assessment of the current status of the field: "Medicine, in my view, has been excessively criticized for problems that originate outside the medical establishment, within our society. I believe with Dr. Paul Grider of Kentucky who writes:

The practice of medicine is not just another profession. Rather, the practice of medicine has the priest-like quality of a sacred trust. We are present at the beginning of life and the companion on the final path to death. We are privy to all the foibles of a flawed humanity, the revelation of innermost thoughts, hopes, dreams, sins, ambitions, and failures are ours to hear and to assuage, as best we can. We are expected to perform expertly without compromise by our own weaknesses. Fatigue must be overcome. Anger must be suppressed. Criticism must be shouldered. None of this is easy. At times it is impossible. Occasionally patients temporarily will become more than we can bear. Mistakes will be made either because we are tired, or too busy, or simply not thinking—seldom because we are ignorant or not trying. Let us not be discouraged. Our successes far out number our failures. Because ours is a sacred trust, the source of this trust gives us strength."[13]

He expressed optimism about the advancement in medical knowledge and faith in the continued idealistic goals of medicine, and urged that there be a determination not to allow the scientification of medicine to blunt the humanistic approach to the patient.

Dr. Kirsner continued his association with the IOMC, and more recently, on May 12, 2004, as part of the institute's 89th annual meeting and awards dinner, he was the recipient of the IOMC's first Lifetime Achievement Award. In a letter to Dr. Kirsner on April 24, the executive director, Dr. Arnold L. Widen, wrote: "The granting of the Lifetime Achievement Award to you is one more demonstration that your colleagues acknowledge, and thank you for, your outstanding career as a researcher, author and clinician, particularly in the field of Gastroenterology, and for your constant commitment to the welfare of patients, and to the health-care needs of all people in our society. You should feel particularly pleased since your name immediately came to mind when this new award was created."

In May 1984, during the spring meeting of Digestive Disease Week in New Orleans, Dr. Kirsner received the American Society of Gastrointestinal Endoscopy's highest award, the Rudolf Schindler Award. In presenting the award, Dr. Jerome D. Waye reviewed Dr. Kirsner's career in gastroenterology, highlighting his early days working with Dr. Schindler at the University of Chicago. Prominent in this account were his presence at the founding of the American Gastroscopic Club in Chicago both before and after World War II, and his being elected the 6th president of the American Gastroscopic Club in 1940. He credited Dr. Kirsner for championing the importance of endoscopy at a time when it was not fully recognized by the medical community.[14]

The Joseph B. Kirsner Center for the Study of Digestive Disease

The construction of the Bernard A. Mitchell Hospital freed up considerable space in Billings. At the time, the Section of Gastroenterology was scattered in multiple offices and laboratories on different floors throughout the building. The opening of available space in Billings Hospital Pavilion afforded an opportunity to create a geographically unified section. Through the help of the dean of the medical school,

Don West King, the members of GIRF agreed to raise $2 million, and the university contributed $3 million.

The high point of the dedication ceremonies, on May 8, 1986, was an all-day symposium devoted to advances in inflammatory bowel disease treatment. President Hanna Gray was on hand to welcome the audience, and Dr. Kirsner himself closed the symposium with remarks entitled "A Look Back."

The dedication took place in a large tent constructed for the occasion and was followed by a tour of the facilities and dinner, which was held in Hutchinson Commons at 57th and University Avenue. The lovely dining room, with its paneled walls and banners and high ceiling, is modeled on Oxford's Christ Church hall.

The program was presided over by B. Kenneth West, chairman of the Board of Trustees of the University of Chicago, who were the hosts of the dinner. Before dinner, Dr. Kirsner's son Robert, an associate professor in the Department of Germanic Languages at UCLA, gave the opening remarks. It is a rare opportunity to hear Dr. Kirsner's son speak about his father, and the comments are worth quoting at length.

Dear friends, as Dr. Kirsner's son, I have been asked to say a few words at this point, to represent the Kirsner family. It does not happen very often that a doctor has a building named for him, certainly not an academic physician, and certainly not often during his lifetime. This is a special event and I want to reflect for a moment on what this building and dedication means. Perhaps the best way is to tell you a story I read recently which reminded me of my father. It was in a book lent to me by a colleague at UCLA who teaches Japanese literature. The author is a man called Dogen and the book was written almost 750 years ago. Dogen is one of the people who brought Buddhism from China to Japan: the book in question is supposed to be a manual about life: how one should live.[15]

The beginning though is autobiographical. Dogen tells how he went to China to study and what happened to him there.

One day after the noon meal, Dogen saw an old man—the head cook—busy drying mushrooms in the sun. The cook carried a bamboo stick, but had no hat on. The sun's rays beat down fiercely. The cook was working hard; his body was bent over and drenched with sweat. Dogen sensed the work was too hard for the cook. He went up to him and asked how old he was. "Sixty-eight," the cook said. "This must be hard for you," Dogen said. "Why don't you let other people do it for you?" The cook answered, "Other people are not me." "I understand that you believe this is to be your work," said Dogen, "but why are you working so hard, in this scorching sun? Why don't you rest for a while?" But the cook replied, "If I don't do it now, when else can I do it?"

Now perhaps there is some justice in comparing a gastroenterologist and a cook, for I recognized "J.B.K." in this cook's answer to Dogen. We are here today to honor a physician who saw clearly what his lifework was, and who wanted and wants to do this work, now, between past and future (which is the only time any of us has), and to keep on doing it as long as he is able. We are also here today because of the very special relationship—the mutual recognition—which exists between this doctor, his students, and his patients. If my father is an unusual doctor, then you are unusual students and unusual patients in recognizing this and in making it possible—through this magnificent facility—for his work to be continued here—at this University— even in the future. This building honors not only the Joseph Kirsner it is named for but every individual who has helped make it possible.

Dr. Kirsner himself spoke after the dinner, and he began his remarks by telling the assembled guests, "This is a day to remember forever." The day was a historic occasion for the Section of Gastroenterology. "We have never before had completely adequate research facilities and, for too long, we have been widely dispersed throughout the medical center." He proceeded to succinctly review for the audience the history of gastroenterology as a specialty and the history of the Section of Gastroenterology, which began in 1927 when Dr. Walter Lincoln Palmer formed the first academic section of gastroenterology in the United States. He skillfully reviewed the subsequent history of the section, intertwining it with his personal perspective on these events. He is proud that the new center contains 10 research laboratories, offices, a library conference room, and a new state-of-the-art diagnostic unit. He pointed out that, since November 1985, when he became the fourth chief of section in its 60-year history, Dr.

Tom Brasitus had recruited Dr. Eugene Chang (from Columbia), Dr. Bernard Davis (from Yale), and Dr. Brett Lashner and Dr. Nick Davidson (from Columbia). Dr. Kirsner observed that these outstanding new faculty members had been recruited through the combined efforts of GIRF and the university. Finally, he praised the faculty for its dedication and expressed his and his wife's pride in the "doctors and scientists, who have also become our friends," and expressed his renewed confidence in the future of the Section of Gastroenterology.

Mentoring

From his earliest days as a physician, Dr. Kirsner has gladly provided advice and help to other physicians in promoting their careers in medicine. His affiliation with a teaching hospital put him in contact with younger physicians throughout his career. Up to the time when he was accepted as a member of the Department of Medicine at Chicago, he himself had had very little help in planning his career. His association with Dr. Walter L. Palmer marked his first real contact with a mentor who would help shape the direction of his career. It was perhaps this lack of guidance in his own early years, and the feeling that he would have been better served had he received such help, that made Dr. Kirsner so generous in his support of others.

It would be impossible to enumerate all the physicians whose careers have been touched by Dr. Kirsner. Every fellow who trained in gastroenterology at the University of Chicago received his full support—for their activities while they were fellows, for the opportunity to write articles that had a great likelihood of publication as a result of his name being added to the title page, for the uncountable letters of recommendations written on behalf of fellows, residents, and students. Even after fellows left the university, they would call upon him to support their applications for medical societies, universities, promotion committees, and research grants. Any physician who has trained with Dr. Kirsner knows full well that the mention of the University of Chicago and of Dr. Joseph Kirsner opened the door with referring physicians and helped to establish the confidence of patients. This kind of support is beyond calculation and is perhaps best reflected in the respect and admiration that all his former fellows have for him and the gratitude they feel for the opportunities he provided.

There are also numerous examples of the ways in which he intervened to help fellows in personal matters as well. New fellows who came from out of town were helped to find housing, and he used his influence to help families get their children into the Laboratory School. Dr. Prolla was helped with the medical expenses for the delivery of one of his children (see chap. 7), and Dr. Howard Schachter was helped when a fire destroyed his apartment on Hyde Park Boulevard one wintery evening.

In 1987 Terrance Barrett, who is now a leader in research in inflammatory bowel disease, was a fellow at the University of Chicago, committed to a career in research and academic medicine. He was interested in immunology and was working with Dr. Chang. When his wife gave birth to triplets, the young couple was faced with unexpected expenses that threatened his dream of a career in research. Dr. Barrett recalls that Dr. Kirsner, without any prompting from Dr. Barrett and because he recognized Dr. Barrett's promise in the laboratory, organized a dinner meeting at a suburban country club that was attended by many of Dr. Kirsner's supporters in GIRF, including Maurice Goldblatt, Joseph Valenti, and Martin Sandler. Dr. Barrett and his wife attended the meeting and were introduced to the attendees. At the end of the evening, enough money was raised to supplement Dr. Barrett's fellowship salary and allow him to do two more years of research at the university. He went to work in the laboratory of Jeffrey Bluestone in the Department of Immunology, where he devoted himself to studying new aspects of the immunology of inflammatory bowel disease. He published two significant articles in the *Journal of Experimental Medicine,* publications that enabled him to get the grants necessary to continue as an investigator. Dr. Barrett recognizes the help he received during the early stages of his career and currently serves as co-chairman of the CCFA Research Training Awards Committee. He also chairs the program for presenting new research into the etiology and pathogenesis of inflammatory bowel disease during the AGA's Digestive Disease Week Forum.

A Special Symposium in Greece

In April 1989 the Greek Gastroenterology Association hosted an international meeting in Athens. Dr. and Mrs. Kirsner both attended, and Dr. Kirsner presented an address entitled "What Is New and What Is Established in Inflammatory Bowel Disease." As a climax to the symposium, on the morning of April 22, several buses brought the attendees to the ancient temple of Asclepius in Epidauros, midway down the Peloponnesian peninsula some 60 miles from Athens, to hear Dr. Kirsner address the audience in the center of a stone amphitheater on the subject "Inflammatory Bowel Disease: Its Present and Its Future." At noon under a blazing Mediterranean sun and cloudless blue sky, he became the first physician in 2,500 years to deliver a speech at the temple site.[16] Without the benefit of a microphone, Dr. Kirsner rose to the occasion and spoke in a voice that could be heard by all present. Mercifully, someone in the audience came up with a brown felt hat to protect him from the sun.

He began, "As the first physician in centuries (2500 years) to speak in the Temple of Asklepios, I am deeply honored to represent my colleagues of the International Symposium on Inflammatory Bowel Disease and this assembly of outstanding physicians." He reminded the audience that the healing art as represented by Asclepius developed in the 6th and 5th century B.C. and continued into Christian times. It was in Epidauros that the guiding principle of ancient Greek medicine, "Nature is the physician of all diseases," began. In that era, religion, philosophy, and medicine were a single discipline. Dr. Kirsner conjured up the image of "Asklepios, the physician from Thessaly . . . and his followers minister[ing] to the sick and the troubled, utilizing the resources of fresh mountain air, sunshine, soothing baths, sleep in the temple, with dreams suggested to patients who were required to purify themselves by the rituals of abstinence, prayer, and sacrifice."

He observed that the Asclepian tradition eventually yielded to the medical lore acquired in the towns and on the battlefields of the ancient world and to the medical progress of Hippocrates and Galen. He told the audience, "Our mission as physicians of the twentieth century in principle does not differ radically from the time of Asklepios." Continuing with this historical perspective, he reminded them:

And so in this ancient place of healing and hope, more than 200 years after Morgagni's description of terminal ileitis in a young man, 130 years after Samuel Wilks of England described a case of ulcerative colitis in the celebrated case of Isabella Bankes, 75 years after Dalziel's classic description of regional enteritis in 1913, and nearly 60 years since the term Crohn's disease appeared in the medical literature, it is appropriate to reflect on the knowledge of inflammatory bowel disease we have acquired at this superb symposium; to assess the present and to anticipate the future.

Dr. Kirsner then reviewed the essence of the entire symposium, brilliantly highlighting the epidemiological and clinical observations that had been presented, and the complex basic science information on the genetics and pathogenesis of inflammatory bowel disease. His view of the future in the care of inflammatory bowel disease and research was full of optimism for the refinement of disease classification and characterization of disease activity, the refinement of biologic techniques for cancer screening, the development of newer drugs and fine-tuning in the use of existing medications, and greater understanding of the genetics, pathophysiology, and pathogenesis of these diseases.

Lincoln Laureate

In 1994 Dr. Kirsner was honored as a Lincoln Laureate by the state of Illinois in a ceremony held in Springfield. This honor represented the highest award bestowed by the state on one of its citizens. Among his "class" of laureates were Reagan's former press secretary James S. Brady, television anchor Bill Kurtis, businessman Robert H. Malott, and Arnold W. Weber, chancellor of Northwestern University. In receiving his medal, Dr. Kirsner said, "I am deeply honored to be chosen Laureate of the Lincoln Academy of the State of Illinois, an honor I will treasure, especially for its origin in the name of our great humanitarian president."[17]

Dr. Kirsner was very fond of the Lincoln Laureate medal, and in 2007 during the taping of an interview conducted by Dr. Russell Cohen of the Section of Gastroenterology, Dr. Cohen asked him to show this medal, which he proudly demonstrated. This interview was part of a video program prepared by the AGA to be played at all the convention hotels that were hosting that year's Digestive Disease Week.

Family Matters

There is a personal side of this story that must be told as well: Dr. Kirsner's deep devotion to his family, especially to Minnie and his son, Bob, and Bob's wife and children.

The bond between him and his younger brother, Morris, too, was always close. Six years separated their births, and Joe was the much admired older brother. Joe had left Boston at the age of 24 and had not had the opportunity to bond closely with his younger sisters. Morris Kirsner had remained in Boston, and his family maintained close contact both with his parents and with his younger sisters and their families. Morris successfully practiced law as a solo practitioner, maintaining his office on Congress Street into the 1990s. He had been charged by his mother as she lay dying to "keep the family together," and it was a responsibility he took seriously.

Looking at two typewritten letters that the brothers exchanged in 1984 on their respective office stationeries, one might overlook the strong bond they shared. However, in reading the letters, the affection between them is clear. The letter from Morris Kirsner, written in July, tells "Min and Joe" how impressed he was by the booklet *GIRF Celebrates.* Referring to his brother's important contributions in the field of medicine, he reflects on how proud "Ma and Pa are now," because he believes that, though deceased, they are still aware of the fate of their children. He mentions that he has spoken with both Gertie and Lee (their younger sisters), and they share his views and feelings. He remembers the time when the boys shared a room together, and that he was kept awake while his older brother studied into the "wee" hours of the morning. He regrets that he did not realize that there was an important birthday celebration (Dr. Kirsner's 75th) that year and that he did not attend.

On July 18, 1984, Dr. Kirsner responds "Dear Morrie," thanking him for the lovely letter. He explains that the GIRF ball, then in its 29th year, was a regular affair, and that in retrospect he wishes that they had let Morris know about the celebration. He promises that there will be another occasion that Morris and the rest of the family might attend. He writes, "Minnie and I are busy with our affairs centering on the University," and tells him that Bob and his family are in Holland. He muses that the years are going by more quickly than ever, "but despite some aches and pains increasing with age, I think we are doing pretty well." He relays his love to the entire family.

Morris wrote to Joe on June 29, 1990, to thank him for sending a copy of his recently published *The Development of American Gastro-enterology*. He expresses his pride and admiration on looking at the book and notes the dedication to Min. He says that he has shown the book to Lee, who feels as he does, and that he will soon "catch up with Gertie." He reports that he forwards on to the rest of the family all the news releases and other communications that Joe sends him, and further reflects on the fact that they "came from parents who were totally dedicated to their children." He is proud of all that his brother has accomplished. "I have often said in my conversations with other people who we both know, or over the years, when your name was brought up, that you were 'born to be a doctor.' The good Lord endowed you both with the mentality and the ability and patience to be a great one." He is looking forward to 1991, when he and Lee and hopefully Gertie and Eli (her husband) will be able to attend the GIRF ball. Finally, he suggests, "Perhaps I might be afforded the opportunity of speaking for a little while. I would have some most interesting remarks to make."

January 6, 1984, marked Minnie and Joe's 50th wedding anniversary. Married in the depths of the Depression on "a hope and a prayer," together they had traveled a long way and had much to be both proud of and grateful for. They had developed a large group of friends and admirers throughout the Chicago area. Their son Bob, who had early exhibited a flair for foreign languages, was a tenured professor in Germanic languages at UCLA and a well-known scholar of Dutch grammatical construction. He and his wife, Elaine, had two wonderful children, Danny and Rachel, now in their teens. Nancy Weiss, Minnie's niece and daughter of her sister Bea, and her husband, Paul, hosted the celebration for this special day at their home in Indiana. The Kirsners thought that they were going out for a quiet dinner, but when they arrived at the Weisses' house they found that a large party of celebrants had been assembled, including Bob and his family, and Joe's brother, Morris, and two sisters. The highlight of the event was a specially prepared pineapple upside-down cake to commemorate the cake Nancy's mother had baked for the newlyweds in 1934, the cake that notoriously went unnoticed and untouched the entire weekend in the refrigerator.

The year 1998 began with a joyous event, the wedding of the Kirsners' granddaughter, Rachel, in an Orthodox ceremony in New Jersey. For Dr. Kirsner, Rachel had become the "star" of the family. She had gone to undergraduate school at Harvard and then to the University of Chicago Law School. Dr. Kirsner and Minnie had played an important role in underwriting her education, as they had also done for her brother in his undergraduate studies at Yale.

The wedding was attended by Dr. Kirsner's Boston family, Morris and his sisters Gertie and Lee. Also attending were Erwin and Ruth Levin, who had played an important part in the story of this wedding. Dr. Erwin Levin had been a colleague of Dr. Kirsner's at the University of Chicago and coauthored many papers with him on peptic ulcer disease. Ruth had been the matchmaker that brought Bob Kirsner and his wife Elaine, the daughter of one of their neighbors in Cleveland, together and had attended their backyard outdoor wedding. Unfortunately, Minnie was not well enough to attend Rachel's wedding, but Nancy and Paul Weiss were there to represent her side of the family. Dr. Kirsner cherishes a beautiful photograph of the bride standing behind him at the wedding banquet.

In the early 1990s, while she was in law school in Chicago, Rachel had come to know her grandparents, and her grandmother in particular, very well. For most of her childhood, she had seen them only briefly. Her family had lived first in New York, while her father was at Columbia, and later in Los Angeles when he moved to UCLA. Her father's career as a linguist and a specialist in the Dutch language also necessitated their living for a number of years in the Netherlands. But now living in Chicago, she came to know and admire her grandmother a great deal. She often stayed in their apartment for several days to help her grandmother when Dr. Kirsner was out of town. During these visits she came to understand both the dedication and devotion with which Minnie had served her husband and supported his career and her own refined tastes and intelligence. She appreciated that Minnie had an inner strength and was entirely her own person. Minnie conveyed to Rachel her love of learning and her interest in and knowledge of the French language and the ballet.

It was during this time that Mrs. Kirsner first began to show signs of Parkinsonism. Rachel recalls that as her illness progressed, there were important social functions at the university or involving GIRF activities that her grandmother was unable to attend.

The gradual progress of Minnie's illness and her gradual loss of function were a source of sadness for Dr. Kirsner. Through the years of their marriage, she had been his constant companion, his confidant, his source of joy and purpose in striving to always do better. Many times he had replied to colleagues who sought his participation in a new venture, "Of course, I will have to talk it over with my wife." Her illness brought many changes for him. Dr. Kirsner originally tried to care for his wife at home. First, there was a companion during the day, but as her disabilities progressed, regular nursing assistance at home was needed. But difficulty in finding good and reliable help imposed hardships on him as he tried to continue his activities at the university. Ultimately Minnie suffered a stroke that took away her sight, and continued care at home became impossible.

With help from his friends, he was able to find the Lieberman Nursing Home in Skokie, Illinois, and it was there that Minnie spent the last three years of her life. Dr. Kirsner would visit her at the nursing home several times a week. His attentions to Minnie made it necessary for him to discontinue his beloved Saturday morning GI clinic. It was as if an era had come to an end.

Dr. Kirsner recalls visiting his wife and asking her what she thought about during the long days and nights that she remained sightless. She responded that she often would sing to herself to pass the time. His wife was very appreciative of the Sabbath service that the nursing home held every Friday evening, and Dr. Kirsner made a point of establishing a fund in her name at the Lieberman Nursing Home to support the continuation of this activity.

Mrs. Kirsner passed away peacefully in the nursing home on April 20, 1998. Within three days, a moving memorial service was held at the Sinai Temple on South Shore Drive, attended by a large group of friends and colleagues from the university. This was the same temple where they were married, in the rabbi's chambers, some 64 years earlier. Dr. Charles Winans, who had cared for Minnie as her personal physician, remembers the beautiful and moving eulogy for her grandmother that Rachel delivered to the congregation.

90th Birthday Celebration

Starting with Dr. Kirsner's 75th birthday, his birthday celebrations assumed greater significance, and the university community and his colleagues and GIRF strove to make each milestone celebration grander that the last. Dr. Kirsner's 90th birthday celebration in 1999 was no exception. The day further marked the completion of funding for the Joseph B. Kirsner Professorship at the University of Chicago Medical School. This professorship was the culmination of 20 years of planning beginning in 1997, when the idea was first conceived. Originally it was thought that the funding would require $500,000; the figure had now grown to three times that sum, $1.5 million. This birthday was a bittersweet occasion as well, however, since it was the first such event he faced alone, and he wished that his wife of over 60 years might have shared the joy with him.

Ceremonies that day included the renaming of a portion of Maryland Avenue in front of the University of Chicago Hospitals the Honorary Dr. Joseph B. Kirsner Drive, an honor initiated by Alderman Leslie Hairston. The description of the event in the Metro Chicago section of the *Chicago Tribune* on September 22, 1999, featured pictures of Dr. Kirsner and the street sign, and a long article about Dr. Kirsner reviewing the highlights of his 60-year career at the University of Chicago and the celebrations planned that day to honor his role as a leader in the field. The article began by characterizing Dr. Kirsner as the "Grandfather of Gastroenterology."[18]

Along with the celebrations marking his 90th birthday were a flood of letters from colleagues, former fellows, friends, and patients from all over the world wishing him the best and congratulating him on his lifetime of achievement. Kurt Isselbacher, the director of the Massachusetts General Hospital Cancer Center, wrote, "You have always been special to me Joe! Throughout my academic career you have served as an ideal role model." "The Gastroenterologist of the 20th Century," he called him, paraphrasing the title of his book. A letter from a Chicago physician, Angelo Creticos, observed, "I cherish the fond memories of my internship at the University of Chicago in 1947-1948 remembering your excellent teaching and your magnificent handling of patients when I rotated through the G.I. service.... For my part I want to thank you for exemplifying the best in medical teaching, medical care and humanism."[19]

As the year drew to an end, as a century came to an end and the world anticipated the beginning of a new millennium, Dr. Kirsner faced the future outwardly undaunted by the passage of time and determined to continue in his role as physician and educator and loyal member of the active faculty of the University of Chicago.

Notes

1. Unless otherwise stated, all quotations in this chapter from letters or unpublished papers are taken from Dr. Kirsner's collected papers, Special Collections, Regenstein Library.
2. Palmer WL, Presentation of Julius Friedenwald Award to Joseph B. Kirsner, *Gastroenterology* 69:3:575-77, 1975.
3. JBK's response to the Friedenwald Award is among his personal papers.
4. *Tufts Medical Alumni Bulletin* 37, no. 2 (July 1978).
5. The article had originally been written by Jack Star for the October 1984 issue of *Chicago Magazine,* published by the University of Chicago.
6. Bruce Morgan, "The Sage of Chicago," *Tufts Medicine* 66, no. 1 (Winter 2005): 13.
7. A typescript of this address and preparatory notes are in JBK's collected papers.
8. Quotations in this paragraph taken from materials prepared for the Bernard A. Mitchell Hospital 20th anniversary celebration, May 24, 2004.
9. "Cornerstone Ceremonies Mark Start of New Hospital Construction," *Medicine on the Midway* 35 (Fall 1980): 4-6.
10. JBK, "The University of Chicago Hospital—Yesterday, Today, Tomorrow, 1927-1980-2030," *Medicine on the Midway* 35 (Fall 1980): 7-10.

11. From materials prepared for the hospital's 20th anniversary celebration (see n. 8).

12. See the IOMC's Web site: http://www.iomc.org.

13. JBK, "Comments on Today's Medical Scene," *Proceedings of the Institute of Medicine of Chicago* 37 (1984): 74-76.

14. Waye JD, Presentation of the 1984 Rudolf Schindler Award to Joseph B. Kirsner, *Gastrointestinal Endoscopy* 30:6:329-30, 1984.

15. Taken from Zen Master Dogen and Kosho Uchiyama, *Refining Your Life*, trans. Thomas Wright (New York and Tokyo: Weatherhill, 1983), 9-10, Instructions for the Zen Cook (Tenzo Kyokun).

16. Kirsner JB, Inflammatory bowel disease: Its present and its future, *Amer J of Gastroenterology* 84:11:1358-61, November 1989.

17. For more on the Lincoln Academy, see their Web site: www.thelincolnacademyofillinois.org.

18. Margaret O'Brien, "Doctor Gets Street to Call His Own," *Chicago Tribune*, Metro Section, September 22, 1999.

19. Dr. Kirsner keeps in his office an album, put together after his 90th birthday celebration, that includes these letters.

14 ✳ A New Century, 2000 and Beyond

January 1, 2000, fell on a Saturday. As the world celebrated New Year's Eve that Friday night, Dr. Kirsner spent a quiet evening at home and later enjoyed watching some of the televised football games over the weekend. The beginning of a new year, let alone a new century, and a new millennium, however arbitrary, is a moment for reflection and introspection. Of the men and women born in the first decade of the 20th century, how few of them could have expected to see the birth of the 21st century, or even contemplated what that world would be like. Dr. Kirsner found himself in his tenth decade of life and, as others had quipped in 1995, at the beginning of his second 60 years at the University of Chicago.

The turn of the century brought with it a growing realization that while the benefits of science, medicine, and public health had dramatically raised the life expectancy of the population, a concern with the quality and conduct of life was for the so-called elderly an ever greater subject of public discussion. The progressive loss of cognitive and physical function, the diminishing capacity to control one's life, the threat of chronic illness or of confinement to a nursing home, and the demons of dementia and Alzheimer's disease loom ever more prominently in the public consciousness and debate. The public turns to individuals like Dr. Kirsner to reject the cold statistics and for guidance on ways to approach the challenge of advancing age. Dr. Kirsner, long a mentor and a role model for physicians, has now become a role model for how one might manage the advancing years. Dr. Kirsner's continued productivity into the second half of his tenth decade of life is a story that should be an inspiration to all.

For Dr. Kirsner, his very reason for existence was his long-held belief, which he shared with his late wife, Minnie, that "we are here to serve others." Medicine and his service to the University of Chicago were the means by which he sought to realize this ideal. He was not the kind of person to "rest on his laurels." At the university he continues to hold the active faculty rank of the Louis Block Distinguished Service Professor of Medicine and to occupy a modest three-room office on the second floor of the "M" corridor of the original Billings Hospital. He has the help of a secretary and continues to receive a yearly salary from the University of Chicago.

Although it was not required, he has continued his practice of assembling each year a carefully documented and bound "Annual Activity Report" that he sends to the dean of the medical school, the chairman of the Department of Medicine, and the chief of the Section of Gastroenterology. The reports, covering the period from July 1 of one year to June 30 of the next, give a clear overview of his professional activities at the university. The categories reflect an ambitious range of activities, including fund raising in support of the Section of Gastroenterology, GIRF-related activities, consultant work on behalf of university and various national health organizations, participation in significant university events, interviews, reviewing articles for scientific publications, serving on editorial boards, honors received, his regular clinical and patient care and attending responsibilities, teaching activity, regular conference and research meetings, publications, and his annual accounting of patient referrals made to physicians on the Section of Gastroenterology, to other university departments, and to non–University of Chicago physicians.

Dr. Kirsner as a Medical Historian

As can be seen in his publications and public addresses, Dr. Kirsner early on acquired a strong sense of the broader history of medicine. Having witnessed the remarkable progress in the field of medicine throughout the 20th century, and having personally followed the progress of his specialty for more than six decades, he wished to impart to his younger colleagues the perspective he had acquired. It was a view of medicine that few leaders in gastroenterology could claim.

His writings on medical history began to assume a prominent part of his bibliography in the mid-1980s. His historical perspective is evident in his address to the 1982 entering medical school class at the University of Chicago, discussed in chapter 13. In March 1985 he published an article in the *American Journal of Gastroenterology* titled "Inflammatory Bowel Disease at the University of Chicago: The First Fifty Years, Some Personal Reflections."[1] It could rightly be said that his personal involvement with inflammatory bowel disease paralleled the evolution of knowledge of Crohn's disease and ulcerative colitis, and that the University of Chicago, along with Mount Sinai Hospital and Medical School, had been the leading institution in the field. In 1986 he wrote another historical account, "The Changing Medical Scene (1929-1985)," published in *Perspectives in Biology and Medicine*.[2] He began to write and reflect on the path taken by the entire field of American gastroenterology, as reflected in the chapter, "One Hundred Years of American Gastroenterology," that he contributed to *Grand Rounds: One Hundred Years of Internal Medicine*, published in 1988.[3] He published similar accounts of the specialty of gastroenterology and its history in numerous journals, such as the *Journal of Clinical Gastroenterology*, *Postgraduate Medicine*, and *JAMA*. These efforts culminated in 1900 in a major historical survey, *The Development of American Gastroenterology*.[4] A second publication, which may be regarded as a companion work, *The Early Days of American Gastroenterology*, was published in 1996 and covered such topics as health care in colonial times, Benjamin Rush, William Beaumont, the development of American gastrointestinal physiology, and 19th- and early 20th-century specialization.[5]

An important contribution to the field of gastroenterology is a volume he edited in 1994, *The Growth of Gastroenterologic Knowledge during the Twentieth Century*.[6] This is a wonderful and still useful volume, and a testimony to Dr. Kirsner's stature in the field, since he was able to secure the participation of 40 leading contributors. The list of contributors is a virtual who's who in the field. To mention but a few: Horace Davenport, writing on gastric secretion; Basil I. Hirschowitz, on acid-peptic disease; Robert Donaldson, on the enteric flora of the gastrointestinal tract; Jules Dienstag, on viral hepatitis; and Donald O. Castell, on motility disorders of the esophagus.

His most complete historical survey of the history of inflammatory bowel disease is found in *Origins and Directions of Inflammatory Bowel Disease: Early Studies of the Nonspecific Inflammatory Bowel Diseases,* published in 2001.[7] The book traces the early history of ulcerative colitis and Crohn's disease, with a historical survey of the etiology and pathogenesis and an account of early therapeutic efforts.

The growth of the Crohn's and Colitis Foundation of America (CCFA), and the rapidly increasing interest in inflammatory bowel disease itself, were reflected in the establishment of the peer-reviewed journal *Inflammatory Bowel Diseases,* which began publication in January 1995. As in all areas of medicine, the underlying complexity of the basic science issues, the clinical issues related to the treatment of disease, and the need for specialized training and experience were making the treatment of inflammatory bowel disease a subspecialty of its own within the field of gastroenterology. The editorial board invited Dr. Kirsner to contribute major historical review articles, historical perspectives, and editorials for the new journal. His publications for this journal include "The Historical Basis of Idiopathic Inflammatory Bowel Diseases," which was the lead article in the first issue; "Historical Antecedents of Inflammatory Bowel Disease Therapy," which appeared one year later; and "We Still Are More Than Molecules," a 2002 editorial cautioning gastroenterologists, faced with an explosion of complex biologic therapies, not to neglect the psychological needs of their patients. In the same year, he published "Commentary on the 1958 National Institutes of Health Conference on 'New Frontiers in Ulcerative Colitis,'" documenting a historic meeting that marked the beginning of the NIH's involvement in the problem of inflammatory bowel disease. As recently as 2005, the journal published his "Inflammatory Bowel Disease at the University of Chicago: Early Experiences: A Personal Historical Account."[8]

There are other venues in which Dr. Kirsner has been able to pass on his knowledge of medical history. For example, on January 18, 2000, he presented medical grand rounds to the Department of Medicine, giving a talk entitled "20th-Century Events Transforming American Gastroenterology." This was the first in a series of presentations and publications describing the origin of critical discoveries and research accomplishments advancing gastroenterology. The Section of Gastroenterology was host at that time to a group of European physicians, including representatives of pharmaceutical companies, from France, Switzerland, Belgium, Holland, Norway, and Sweden. Dr. Kirsner was asked to speak every month to this group of visitors on the evolution of knowledge of inflammatory bowel disease. This program was a regular activity that he continued to participate in through 2006.

Dr. Kirsner has also had the opportunity to record his thoughts and experiences on tape. January 2001 saw the completion of a project that had occupied his attention for the previous six months: the review of the transcript of an interview that had been conducted on October 1, 1989, for the Alpha Omega Alpha Honor Medical Society's project titled "Leaders in American Medicine." This series of taped interviews had been initiated by Drs. Beatrice C. Seegal and David E. Seegal, of the Columbia University College of Physicians and Surgeons, in 1970. The interviews, now available through the History of Medicine Division of the National Medical Library in Washington, D.C., are with many of the widely recognized leaders of 20th-century American medicine.

The videotaping of Dr. Kirsner's interview took place against the familiar backdrop of his office, with its library of books, framed epigrams, photographs, and certificates. The interview was conducted by Dr. Arthur Rubenstein, then the chairman of the Department of Medicine at the University of Chicago, who with much affection and respect encouraged Dr. Kirsner to recount in his own words many of the events of his life and career that have been the subject of this biography.

A similar videotaped interview was made on March 9, 1995, by the then chief of the Section of Gastroenterology, Dr. Thomas Brasitus, to serve as an archival source for the history of the section and of the Medical Center. The events covered in that interview are very similar to those in the interview by Dr. Rubenstein, and the interview serves as another opportunity to observe Dr. Kirsner's clear and engaging style of relating his personal experiences and his perspectives on the field of gastroenterology, and his observations on the changes in medicine he has witnessed during his lifetime.

Mentor and Educator

Dr. Kirsner has always been interested in helping other authors prepare works for publication. He has lent his assistance by providing his perspective on textual issues and, by invitation, writing an appropriate preface or introduction to help place the new volume in proper perspective. An example is his work on a biography of James A. Campbell written by Malachi Flanagan.[9] Dr. Kirsner, a student of the history of the Medical Center and the University of Chicago, had a keen interest in the affiliation of Rush Medical School with the University of Chicago and its hospital and school of medicine when it was established in 1927, and he enjoyed working with Dr. Flanagan in reviewing this phase of the biography. Dr. Campbell, himself a graduate of the University of Chicago School of Medicine when the two institutions were still affiliated, was responsible for the reactivation of the new Rush Medical School in 1970.

As recently as June 2007, Dr. Kirsner was asked by Dr. Robert Kravetz, a gastroenterologist from Phoenix, Arizona, to write a preface for an edition of the writings of Howard Spiro, M.D., that he was preparing.[10] Dr. Kravetz had trained as a fellow in gastroenterology with Dr. Spiro. Dr. Kirsner's preface is an overview of the state of modern medicine, where the primary care physician has replaced the family doctor, and the hospitalized patient is cared for by a hospitalist and a team of specialists. Dr. Kirsner describes Howard Spiro, an emeritus professor of medicine and director of the Program for Humanities in Medicine at Yale University, as "a distinguished gastroenterologist, a master clinician, and widely recognized advocate of sick people. His writing style is challenging, respectful, and filled with pertinent reflections about patients interwoven with historical comments. . . . The quotations, which Dr. Kravetz has selected wisely, reflect the wide range of Spiro's observations, with emphasis on empathy, reassurance and hope. These are the magical words for a sick person and part of the tools of an expert physician." These observations reflect the basic values in the care of the patient that Dr. Kirsner wishes to see transmitted to a new generation of physicians.

Dr. Kirsner has also written the preface for a new book entitled *The Prescription and Over-the-Counter Drug Guide for Seniors,* by Drs.

Seymour Ehrenpreis and Eli Ehrenpreis, in which he is able to transmit some of the wisdom he has gained through years of experience in caring for elderly patients.[11] Dr. Kirsner points out that seniors are the fastest growing segment of the population, that they are taking on average more than five different medications, and that 90 percent of the prescriptions written in the United States are for seniors. He expresses concern about dispensing errors, inappropriate dosages, too-small print, and the dangers of certain medications, such as benzodiazepines, for the elderly. He stresses the need for the FDA to include individuals over 65 years of age in the clinical testing of new drugs, and for patients to become thoroughly familiar with the drugs they are taking and to be aware of possible adverse reactions and interactions with other medications.

Also around this time, Dr. Kirsner's collected papers were compiled and bound. His collected reprints in 10 volumes were sent to the University of Chicago Library. The volumes, spanning the years 1937-2002, were organized in large general categories and arranged chronologically. Volumes 1 to 3 contain his publications in clinical IBD; Volume 4 contains IBD history and experimental research. Another set was housed and cataloged in the John Crerar Library at the university, where they are available to the faculty and students at the Medical Center. The library also retains copies of all of Dr. Kirsner's published books on its shelves.

Retirement from Active Clinical Practice

In 2004 Dr. Kirsner recognized that ceasing to see patients in the clinic was a rational step for him to take. On the one hand, his ability to understand the needs of his patients and to help them negotiate the increasingly complex world of modern health care seemed undiminished. However, at age 95, he had lost the vision in one eye, and his loss of hearing (although partially improved with hearing aids) had become an impediment to consulting with patients in the clinic.

Retiring from active clinical practice was a difficult step for Dr. Kirsner. Throughout his professional career, he had been dedicated to service through the care of patients. He truly cared for his patients, and his role as a physician was a joy and source of personal satisfaction. For Dr. Kirsner, the medical literature had meaning as it related to rendering better care to patients. Ever the optimist and dedicated to serving the university and the medical profession, he was resolved to continue to make meaningful use of his position at the university. He still scanned a vast number of journals as they arrived each month, flagging what he saw as key articles in the field of inflammatory bowel disease and sending them to the editors of *Kirsner's Inflammatory Bowel Disease,* then in its sixth edition. He still diligently took calls from patients seeking advice and referrals on medical problems. He continued to attend and participate in clinical conferences and research conferences both in the section and in the Department of Medicine. He also actively continued to work with the GIRF board, and to assist the Medical Center in encouraging philanthropic donors. By 2004 the citations in his bibliography stood at 769. He was still writing book reviews for *Perspectives in Biology and Medicine,* articles on the history of inflammatory bowel disease for *Inflammatory Bowel Diseases,* and a foreword for the sixth edition of *Kirsner's Inflammatory Bowel Disease.* National and international visitors to the section were given the opportunity to meet with Dr. Kirsner and to share with him his perspective on clinical and research activities in the field of gastroenterology.

The Third Annual Conference on Inflammatory Bowel Disease was held in October 2004 at the Fairmont Hotel in Chicago. On October 9, marking his retirement from active clinical practice, Dr. Kirsner was the guest of honor at a dinner closing the conference. The topic of his talk that evening was "Highlights of a 69-Year Career." Ambassador Abdeslam Jaidi of Morocco, together with a delegation of doctors who had joined with Dr. Kirsner in treating the late king Hassan II, was present at the dinner. Dr. Kirsner attended the entire conference and after his talk greeted and was photographed with many former trainees and colleagues who came to his table to converse with him.

A Memorable Trip to New York

On February 28, 2005, Dr. Kirsner's third great-grandchild was born. This was his granddaughter Rachel's third child, a daughter named

Amira Hadas. Rachel and her husband, Steve, had two other children, both boys, Yaron Gamliel, who was then six years old, and Gilad Asher, who was four. Dr. Kirsner made up his mind that he would travel to New York to visit his granddaughter and see his new great-granddaughter and great-grandsons. With the help of his attorney and longtime friend Harry Rosenberg, the trip was arranged, including a flight to New York and accommodations at the Mark Hotel. Bob joined his father in Chicago to assist him in making the trip.

Harry Rosenberg, a distinguished Chicago attorney and close friend of the Kirsners, had first met Joe and Minnie when his father, the Kirsners' attorney at the time, suffered a stroke, and he took over his father's law practice. His father and mother, who had come from Louisville, Kentucky, were members of the distinguished Jewish community that flourished in Chicago. As a young lawyer, Harry made "house calls" on Sundays to the Kirsners' apartment to review financial and tax matters with Minnie, who managed their affairs. Sundays were chosen so as not to take Dr. Kirsner away from his hospital concerns. Harry felt that although Dr. Kirsner was happy to let his wife handle such things, Minnie wanted Joe to be informed about them. In later years, Harry helped Joe during the difficult period of his wife's illness, accompanying him on his trips to the nursing home in Skokie. The two old friends would take the opportunity to enjoy lunch together at one of the local delicatessens.

Harry was an avid sports fan and was impressed with Dr. Kirsner's knowledge of professional sports. He remembers how his children had been thrilled when Joe took them to Wrigley Field to see a Cubs game and they had met the Cubs' manager, Leo Durocher, a friend of Dr. Kirsner's. Harry and Joe had also frequently gone together to see the Chicago Bears play. Harry and his wife frequently invited Dr. Kirsner to their home to celebrate Passover seders and Thanksgiving dinners. Dr. Kirsner had also served as Harry's personal health care advocate whenever the need arose. He diagnosed Harry's hyperparathyroidism, which was successfully treated in 1981 at the University of Chicago by Dr. Edward Kaplan, Dr. Kirsner's choice of surgeon.

In the last 10 or 15 years, Harry Rosenberg has continued to play an important role in helping Dr. Kirsner navigate both his financial and his personal affairs. For example, he persuaded Dr. Kirsner to agree to a live-in housekeeper, a woman named Livia. A fairly recent immigrant from Romania, she has proven to be a wonderful match for Dr. Kirsner's needs. She provides companionship, frequently pointing out articles in the newspaper that she thinks will be of interest to him, and she assists him in attending the many important functions to which he is invited.

The trip to New York was a great success. Dr. Kirsner was thrilled to see his granddaughter and her children, in particular the new baby. He had nothing but admiration for the calm and assured manner with which Rachel handled both the infant and her two very active boys. For her part, Rachel was equally delighted by her grandfather's visit. She was pleased at how comfortable he was in her home and how delighted he was with his great-grandchildren.

One of the highpoints of the trip was a dinner that was arranged with his old World War II buddy and great admirer Dr. Murray Dworetzky. Bob really enjoyed watching the two of them interact. He particularly enjoyed Murray's story that while they were in Nagoya, whenever members of the hospital staff went out to dinner, Murray and Dr. Kirsner, who were both married and faithful to their wives, were referred to by the nurses as the "vestal virgins."

Bob was a great help to his father in making the trip, and he knew that his dad realized how difficult travel and accommodation had become for him with advancing age. For Bob, this was a trip not without accompanying stresses. He held his breath as his father insisted on very slowly navigating his way across crowded airline terminal corridors to the men's room, negotiating the steady stream of passengers hurrying to and from their flights. In the post-9/11 world, the security personnel made sure that Dr. Kirsner did not enter the boarding area until he was completely checked and "wanded." Even the luxury hotel was not without its challenges for a 95-year-old man: getting the bed to the right height and navigating the environment of a strange bathroom, where things were not in their usual place. Reflecting back on the trip, Bob feels that it was very good for his father, and he gives his dad lots of credit for making the trip. In his words, "It was pushing the envelope, even for him."

Dr. Kirsner was forced to decide that future travel out of the city would be too difficult. With this came the sad acceptance of the fact that he would no longer travel to American Gastroenterological Association (AGA) meetings for Digestive Disease Week and that he would have to decline invitations to attend meetings in other cities or events to which he was invited as a speaker or to receive an honor.

The Promise of Medical Research

One of the pillars of Dr. Kirsner's career was motivating medical students and young physicians to pursue biomedical research in the advancement of medical care. On August 24, 2006, the Division of Biological Sciences held its 12th Annual Summer Research Forum. Over the years Dr. Kirsner made it a point to regularly attend these meetings. The meeting that year consisted of an entire day of papers presented by students, 28 papers ranging from studies analyzing cost of care to basic laboratory research. Dr. Kirsner spoke at the conclusion of the program. He described Pavlov's mistake in concluding that pancreatic secretion was under the control of the vagus nerve, thereby losing the opportunity to be the first to identify a hormone, secretin. Subsequent studies by W. M. Bayliss and E. H. Starling in 1902 revealed the error in his conclusions, when it was demonstrated that pancreatic secretion was under hormonal control. These remarks reflect his interest in the nature of scientific discovery, a theme that can be traced through a number of his writings during this period.

He was fond of citing the critical events leading up to important scientific discoveries, and liked to pose these examples to fellows and younger colleagues in the form of a question: What was Fleming looking for when he noted the lytic areas that surrounded the grayish green mold *Penicillium notatum* in a discarded petri dish on a culture of *Staphylococcus aureus*? How did Joseph Goldberger conquer the epidemic of pellagra without the help of a laboratory? He saw the pathways to discovery as often springing from serendipity: the unplanned observation or chance discovery presented to a prepared mind (e.g., x-rays, penicillin), the flash of insight (secretin, gastrin), the exploitation of an unexpected observation (hepatitis viruses), the clinical application of an unrelated laboratory finding (allowing the attachment of iodine to the phenothalein molecule and the discovery of oral cholecystography), the result of sophisticated technology (the development of gastrointestinal flexible fiberoptic endoscopy, advanced radiologic imaging like CAT scans and MRIs), and the inquiring mind of a clinician not encumbered by dogma (the discovery of *H. pylori* and its link to the etiology of peptic ulcer disease).[12]

In the 21st century, medical research has become an enormously complicated, expensive, and collaborative venture—a drastic change from 1935, when Dr. Kirsner cleared out a vacant storeroom in Billings Hospital and recruited and trained a homeless patient to serve as his laboratory technician. Over the years, Dr. Kirsner has played a key role in securing major contributions for both the university and the university hospital. It is his strong belief in the essential role of medical research in conquering disease and promoting progress in medicine that allows him to present the issues to groups of informed lay persons in such a way that they are convinced of the importance of contributing funds to this work. In the words of Michael Levine, the chief development officer in charge of philanthropy on behalf of the Division of Biological Sciences, "No one that I have ever met in the department was better at being able to present these issues to a potential donor possibly interested in contributing to the university."

A Tribute to Lowell T. Coggeshall

During the summer of 2006, Dr. Kirsner was busy with preparations for the Lowell T. Coggeshall Honorary Lecture, to take place that fall. The lecture was established to honor Dr. Coggeshall (1901-87), who had served as chairman of the Department of Medicine starting in 1946, and then as dean of the Division of Biological Sciences from 1950 to 1966.

Known by his colleagues as Cogg, he had played an important part in Dr. Kirsner's career, and the two men had many interests in common. Dr. Coggeshall had received his medical degree from Indiana University and then done his internship and residency at the University of Chicago from 1928 to 1932. From 1932 to 1935 he was an assistant professor in the Department of Medicine and the Section of Infectious Disease. In 1936 he went to the Rockefeller Institute to study the biology of malarial species, and in 1941 to the University of Michigan as chairman of the Department of Epidemiology and Tropical Diseases, returning to the University of Chicago in 1946. Like Dr. Kirsner, Dr. Coggeshall had made an important contribution during World War II, tracking the distribution of malaria throughout the Middle East and China.[13] The lectureship was established through a grant from the R. R. Donnelley family to create a lectureship that would stress important ethical aspects of medicine. Dr. Kirsner was the ideal candidate to give this lecture.

His lecture was titled "The University of Chicago Medical Center: Its Beginnings, Challenges, and Fulfillments—Seven Decades of Personal Observations." In preparation, he reviewed in detail the historical events and the vision of the individuals who had played a role in the formation of the university and the Medical Center. He readily admitted with a smile that the prospect of an enthusiastic turnout for the presentation energized his enthusiasm as he prepared for the event. He also gathered photographs that he would use to accompany the lecture. Although the ability to develop a slick PowerPoint presentation was beyond his expertise, he was not going to neglect this important tool. He called on the help of Dr. David Rubin, a member of the gastroenterology section and Dr. Kirsner's personal physician, to prepare a PowerPoint that brought images onto the screen as he made individual points in his presentation.

The lecture was scheduled for noon in the larger lecture hall, Billings Auditorium, P-117, the site of the weekly medical grand rounds and other major conferences and thus a familiar location for Dr. Kirsner. Through long-established practice, he was able to approach the room unassisted, entering the hall from the stage door and thus avoiding the long flight of stairs that runs down the length of the lecture hall. By noon, the entire auditorium was filled with invited guests and members of the medical staff, house staff, and students (the latter enticed in part by the box lunches distributed at the entrance to the lecture hall, a part of the tradition for grand rounds). Dr. Mark Siegler, the Lindy Bergman Distinguished Service Professor and director of the MacLean Center for Clinical Medical Ethics, introduced the Coggeshall lecture, and Dr. Stephen Hanauer introduced Dr. Kirsner. Dr. Hanauer briefly summarized Dr. Kirsner's special role as his own mentor and mentor to the Medical Center and read part of an article recently published by one of his grateful patients, "Memories of a Health Care System that Worked" (see chap. 12). Both Dr. Siegler and Dr. Hanauer urged the audience to contemplate the significance of his seven decades of service to the university.

Dr. Kirsner delivered his talk standing over the computer. He spoke at length about the early history of the institution without reading or referring to notes. He momentarily forgot the name of one of the early presidents of the university, but he did not let this fluster him and assured the audience he would shortly recall it. True to his word, he soon remembered the name of President Ernest Burton and wove it seamlessly into his presentation. He then recalled highlights of the Medical Center and his career. Concluding his lecture, he summarized his thoughts on the state of the Medical Center, both its continuing challenges and its bright future. He expressed confidence in the abilities of the current leaders of the hospital and medical school to rise to the challenges in delivering quality medical care. There were touches of humor as he exhorted his audience to strive to be number one in the country in all departments, almost winking that "number seven" (the center's ranking at the time) was not bad either. In the end he received a well-deserved standing ovation. In the minds of all present was admiration not only for his dedication to the university but also for his ability to deliver such a polished and meaningful talk six weeks into his 98th year. Dr. Kirsner was delighted with the audience's response to his talk and with the numerous notes and telephone calls he received from members of the faculty and friends.

Enthusiasm for the lecture prompted the University of Chicago Alumni Association of the Medical and Biological Sciences to ask Dr. Kirsner to give a similar talk during the alumni weekend festivities the next year. Dr. Kirsner presented his talk, "Early Experiences in the Development of the University of Chicago Medical Center 1935-2007," that June to an enthusiastic group of alumni, speaking again with the assistance of a PowerPoint presentation (again courtesy of Dr. Rubin). He captivated his audience with a mixture of little known or forgotten historical details on the history of the Medical Center, intermingling his personal experiences with the institution and some of its great names. Dr. Rubin reports that as late as seven thirty that morning Dr. Kirsner was enlisting his help in correcting or editing certain points on the PowerPoint.

Relaxing over a cup of coffee and a doughnut after his lecture to the medical alumni, Dr. Kirsner had wryly commented, referring to the briefcase of materials he had assembled for this talk, that he was "going to put it up on a shelf and forget about it." Instead, he continued his study of the medical school's early beginnings and its relationship to the larger university. He read with great interest a biography of William Rainey Harper, the first president of the University of Chicago, and gave considerable thought to the troubled relationship between Rush Medical College and the university's founders and with Robert M. Hutchins. His conclusions were that neither party, the university or Rush Medical College, fully understood the aims of the other. He acknowledged that perhaps the treatment of Rush Medical College by Hutchins in the late 1930s left something to be desired.

Ongoing Relationship with Gastroenterological Organizations

Dr. Kirsner's role as a leader in the major societies representing American gastroenterology has been significant in furthering the growth of gastroenterology as a specialty. Periodically, the senior members of the AGA and the American Society for Gastrointestinal Endoscopy (ASGE) have found it important to acquaint their membership with a historical perspective on their specialty. In 2006 the *ASGE News* published, in three successive issues, an interview with Dr. Kirsner conducted by Dr. Joseph Geenan, a past president of the ASGE and a pioneer in the development of endoscopic retrograde cholangiopancreatography. Dr. Kirsner is the only surviving cofounder of the society, which began its existence in 1941 as the American Gastroscopic Club (see chap. 6). The interview covered many of the important events in both gastroenterology and gastrointestinal endoscopy. In response to a question about where he thought the future of gastrointestinal endoscopy was headed, Dr. Kirsner responded that it was a wide-open field, and the application of physics and optics to new and interventional techniques lay ahead. He cited as an example the recently presented studies on confocal endoscopic visualization of cellular details of living tissues (*in vivo*), which had made a tremendous impression on him at the 2005 Digestive Disease meeting in Chicago.[14]

In April 2007 Russell Cohen of the Section of Gastroenterology videotaped an interview of Dr. Kirsner in his office to be shown on a closed-circuit interhotel television channel at Digestive Disease Week that May in Washington, D.C. The subjects covered in the interview included his recollections of early meetings of the AGA and of gastroenterology in 1936 when he entered the field. For Dr. Kirsner, attending Digestive Disease Week on an annual basis was the most exciting event of the academic year, and something that he gave up with sadness and a sense of loss. These meetings were a time to gauge the scientific progress being made in his specialty and to appreciate its continued growth in terms of both advances in science and the scope and size of the meetings. This growth had been phenomenal. Digestive Disease Week regularly attracts over 14,000 attendees from all over the world and requires gigantic convention centers, in contrast to the early days, when audiences numbered less than 200. It perhaps gave Dr. Kirsner pleasure to know that the videotaping gave him a presence at the 2007 meeting. Dr. Cohen reported that many members, both recent and senior, commented on how interesting they found the interview and how they mere amazed at the decades of progress Dr. Kirsner had witnessed.

Another organization dear to his heart is GIRF. June 1, 2007, was the date of the 46th Annual GIRF Ball, "Together for Tomorrow." As was his custom, Dr. Kirsner reserved a table for himself and selected guests. They included Nancy and Paul Weiss; Dr. B. H. Gerald Rodgers and his wife, Mae; and Mrs. Hortense Singer, a former patient and friend of Dr. Kirsner's and a loyal supporter of GIRF. As he had done for many years, Paul Weiss provided the transportation and assisted Dr. Kirsner in maneuvering the lobby and ballroom of the Sheraton Hotel in Chicago. It was a bittersweet occasion for Dr. Kirsner. A few days before the ball, his longtime friend, confidant, and founding member of GIRF Joseph Valenti had passed away from injuries suffered in a fall at home. Also within a few weeks of the GIRF Ball that year, Martin Boyer, for whom the Martin Boyer Professor of Medicine was named, passed way. In addition, Earl Brown and Sid Port, both long-standing strong supporters of GIRF, had died that year. Dr. Kirsner had the sad task of recognizing the contributions of these men and their leadership on behalf of GIRF over the years, and he asked the audience to observe a moment of silence in their memory.

The annual GIRF ball is truly a remarkable and festive event. Jayne Hanauer, Dr. Hanauer's wife, and Barry Katz have been the organizers of the ball in recent years. It is now attended by over 800 people celebrating the Section of Gastroenterology and seeking to contribute to the research of the section. The evening always includes a major entertainment event, and there is a "reversed auction," conducted by the ball's talented and perennial auctioneer, Barry Kaufman, in which money earmarked for a specific research project at a specified amount is raised by securing pledges until the amount is raised. At the 2007 ball $50,000 was raised for a microscope to study DNA for Dr. Eugene Chang's laboratory. Remembering that in the early 1960s GIRF was a small organization meeting in the living room of Joseph Valenti or Martin Sandler, and seeing how it had grown to an organization of its current size and stature, must have given Dr. Kirsner a tremendous sense of pride and satisfaction.

98th Birthday Celebration

On September 21, 2007, Dr. Kirsner celebrated his 98th birthday. He received numerous calls and birthday greetings from friends and colleagues. Sundown on September 21 was the beginning of the Jewish High Holy Day of Atonement, Yom Kippur. To help celebrate his birthday and observe the holiday, his son Robert came to Chicago, and they were able to attend the evening services at Sinai Temple in Hyde Park. During the service the rabbi told the congregation that Dr. Kirsner was attending the service and also observing his 98th birthday, and afterward he was able to greet many friends and acquaintances in the lobby. His good friend and former patient Hortense Singer gave "Dr. Joe" an elegant birthday dinner in her home, inviting many of his close friends and colleagues as well as Nancy and Paul Weiss.

Mount Sinai Inflammatory Bowel Disease Consultants Course

In the summer of 2007, Dr. Kirsner was invited by Dr. Lloyd F. Mayer, professor of medicine at Mount Sinai Hospital and School of Medicine and director of the school's Center for Immunology, to speak at the Fourth Annual Mount Sinai Consultants Course on inflammatory bowel disease that was to take place on November 2, 2007, in New York City. This meeting marked the 75th anniversary of the publication of Dr. Burrill B. Crohn's landmark paper "Regional Enteritis: A Pathologic and Clinical Entity," which had appeared in *JAMA* in 1932. The course organizers sought to recognize Dr. Crohn's contribution to the field of inflammatory bowel diseases by asking Dr. Kirsner to present a historical perspective. Although Dr. Mayer hoped that Dr. Kirsner would attend the meeting, his advanced age made travel to New York impossible, so the idea of a closed-circuit live video presentation was agreed upon.

During that summer and fall, Dr. Kirsner put much thought and energy into rereading the original papers on Crohn's disease. He also wanted to include in his presentation his thoughts about future research into the causes of these diseases.

On the day of the lecture, Dr. Mayer, standing before the audience of specialists assembled in the Atrium Plaque Room at the Mount Sinai Medical Center in New York City, introduced Dr. Kirsner. He recollected that at most of the Digestive Disease Week meetings that he could remember, Dr. Kirsner was present in the front row during the IBD sessions, and while he might have appeared to be asleep, he was one of the first members in the audience to go to the microphone and frame an insightful question for the speaker or a comment on the implications of the work that had been presented.

Dr. Kirsner spoke for about 45 minutes from the conference room on the fourth floor of the Billings Pavilion. He began by mentioning earlier contributions in the literature dating back to those of Morgagni in the 18th century, Wilks and Moxon in the 19th, and Sir Kennedy Dalziel, an Edinburgh surgeon, who in 1913 described nine patients with chronic intestinal enteritis. He then reviewed papers of Abraham O. Wilensky and Eli Moscowitz in the *American Journal of Medical Sciences* in 1923 and 1927 describing nonspecific granulomas of the intestine, and papers of Burrill B. Crohn, Leon Ginzburg, and Gordon D. Oppenheimer in *Transactions of the American Gastro-enterological Association* and *JAMA* in 1932. Dr. Kirsner noted that Dr. Crohn paid particular attention to a history of a prior appendectomy, a frequent feature of these cases, and pointed out that more recent observations have noted the impact of appendectomy on the flora of the intestine.

He then summarized subsequent events in the history of inflammatory bowel disease research, including the first allocation of funds for research by the NIH in 1955; President Eisenhower's small-intestinal obstruction in 1962, a result of his Crohn's disease, which brought the disease into public awareness; the formation of the CCFA by Irwin and Susan Rosenthal in 1967; the discovery of the *NOD2* and *CARD15* genes by Drs. Judy Cho and J. P. Hugot, which furthered our understanding of the genetics of the disease; and the development of infliximab and the recognition that anti-tumor necrosis factor alpha represented a major therapeutic advance in the treatment of Crohn's disease.

Dr. Kirsner then reviewed both the epidemiologic and the pathologic evidence pointing to an infectious cause of Crohn's disease and summarized the directions he felt would be most productive in future research. He stressed that investigations should include intestinal M cell ("K Factor"), the significance of mesenteric fat inflammation, intestinal cell/bacterial interactions, genetic mutations, microbial agents, and the role of tobacco as an aggravating factor in Crohn's disease and its "protective role" in ulcerative colitis.

Concluding his presentation, Dr. Kirsner stressed his willingness to meet with representatives of the NIH to propose a research program that they might fund for $5 million. In closing the morning session, Dr. Mayer concurred with his remarks and indicated that he would be glad to accompany him to that meeting.

99th Birthday Celebration

As Sunday, September 21, 2008, dawned in Chicago, a fog hung over the city. By noon, as thousands of football fans were pouring into Soldier Field to watch the Chicago Bears play the Tampa Bay Buccaneers, the temperature had risen into the upper seventies and the fog had vanished, revealing Chicago's glorious lakefront sparkling in the bright sunlight of a beautiful cloudless day. In Hyde Park, the Midway and the campus of the University of Chicago mirrored the beauty of the day, the trees and vegetation a rich green, nourished by the heavy rains of the previous weekend. In the heart of the campus, friends, relatives, and colleagues of Dr. Kirsner assembled at the Quadrangle Club on the corner of University Avenue and 57th Street to celebrate his 99th birthday. The Quadrangle Club, with its stone floors, paneled walls, stained glass windows, and adjoining tennis courts, was an excellent site to celebrate Dr. Kirsner's birthday, since over the years Dr. Kirsner had frequently enjoyed dining there with Minnie.

After a buffet brunch, the director of the gastroenterology section, Dr. Stephen Hanauer, who along with his administrative assistant, Betsy Hunt, had planned the event, began the speeches honoring Dr. Kirsner. Tributes were paid by his son Bob and by David Hefner, president of the University of Chicago Hospital and Clinics. Dr. David Rubin, on behalf of the Section of Gastroenterology, presented Dr. Kirsner with a DVD player and assorted documentary films (installation guaranteed by Dr. Rubin, since, as Dr. Kirsner frequently observed, he didn't do well with gadgets).

Seymour (Sy) Taxman, patient, friend, and loyal supporter of GIRF, stole the show when he rose and recalled how Dr. Kirsner had helped his family when his son was thought to have developed Crohn's disease, a fear that Dr. Kirsner was able to dispel. Mr. Taxman, carrying an armful of leather-bound binders, then presented Dr. Kirsner with a series of tributes. The office of the mayor of the city of Chicago had issued a proclamation that, in honor of Dr. Kirsner's birthday and his contributions to the community, September 21, 2008, would be Dr. Joseph B. Kirsner Day in Chicago. Not to be outdone by the mayor, Alderman Edward M. Burke, chairman of the Committee on Finance for the city, had announced that the Chicago City Council had adopted a resolution declaring September 21, 2008, as Dr. Joseph B. Kirsner Day. Michael J. Madigan, Illinois Speaker of the House, had offered House Resolution No. 1468 proclaiming the legislature's wishes for a special birthday. And finally, Republican congressman Mark Steven Kirk of the 10th District of Illinois had introduced House Resolution No. 6865 to award a congressional gold medal to Joseph Barnett Kirsner, M.D., Ph.D. The resolution included the provision that "the Secretary of the Treasury strike a gold medal with suitable emblems, devices and inscriptions to be determined by the secretary."

The festivities concluded with the serving of strawberry cake and the assembled guests enthusiastically singing "Happy Birthday" to, variously, Dr. Kirsner, Dr. Joe, and just Joe. The rendition as it gained momentum was quite enthusiastic, although, as noted by his good friend and colleague Dr. John Fennessy, apparently accustomed to more mellifluous renditions, it was quite out of tune. During the day, phone calls came in from friends and former colleagues around the country. Most appreciated was a call from his old friend from his days in Morocco, Ambassador Abdeslam Jaidi, who had a floral tribute sent to Dr. Kirsner's apartment that "filled the entire living room." If the Chicago football fans were despondent that afternoon when the Bears lost to Tampa Bay 27-24 in overtime, they might have taken heart from the knowledge that September 21, 2008, in the fair city of Chicago was Dr. Joseph B. Kirsner Day.

A Story without an End

The man and the legend are intertwined. The legend is that of Dr. Kirsner rising every morning at five thirty to arrive at his office by an early hour when the hospital is just beginning to stir and the elevators come at the press of a button. The phone is silent, and perhaps an hour is available to read an article or review a manuscript in preparation, to meet with a colleague to plan a new project or address a problem before the secretaries arrive. All this and also get ready to face the rush of the day: calls to return, patients to be seen in the hospital and clinic, meetings to attend, a schedule that will last late into the afternoon when again the office is quiet and the secretaries and most of his colleagues have gone home. The legend was not a myth; it was an enduring reality and characterized his daily schedule at least well into his 80s.

At 99 years of age, however, Dr. Kirsner is a realist, and he has bowed, however reluctantly, to the march of time. He no longer comes into his office five days a week, and in the last year he has reduced his schedule from four office days a week to three. He arrives punctually between eight and eight thirty and works into the early afternoon on Monday, Tuesday, and Thursday—although an important meeting or event he wishes to attend on a non-office day will find him back in the hospital. With a little twinkle in his eye or wry smile, he tells anyone who inquires about his activities that on the other mornings he is at home working, and that is indeed the case. He still takes telephone calls while at home from friends and former patients seeking advice about whom to consult for medical problems or acting as a sounding board for their thoughts on their medical care and reassuring them that they are on the correct path to solving their medical problems. The voice message on his office telephone informs the caller of his schedule and provides his home telephone number. These calls are in a certain sense like the oxygen he breathes. They reaffirm his worth and purpose in life. The calls are treated with the utmost seriousness and the same diligence he applied to the care of his patients during his entire career. He is never reluctant to call a physician to alert them to a referral or to inquire about the outcome. And he always ends these calls with a cheery and sincere message, "Keep me informed."

The disciplined habits of a lifetime serve Dr. Kirsner well. He remains focused on the several projects he is working on at the current time, especially gathering materials for or proofreading drafts of a new chapter of a work on medical history that he hopes to publish. In his briefcase—usually the typical briefcase given by drug companies to attendees of Digestive Disease Week—he carries a folder with him to and from work that includes lists of the phone numbers and addresses of people he might wish to call, notes made to himself at home on things he wishes to attend to in the office, and articles or letters he wishes to complete reading.

Procrastination is not a word in his personal lexicon. Any task at hand is immediately taken care of, and any call that must be returned is completed expeditiously. He expects this of colleagues as well, and if he leaves a message he anticipates a prompt call-back and will not hesitate to call and leave the message a second time. He says he does not do well with "gadgets," and this means those devices that make our offices and living rooms "electronic playgrounds." While his secretary handles e-mails and faxes, he prefers to speak directly over the telephone and to send materials and letters by standard U.S. mail.

When he attends a meeting or event at the Medical Center, the university, or off campus, he gives the impression of a commander planning a military campaign. The logistics of the event—including transportation to and from, assurance that washroom facilities are conveniently located, and securing a front-row seat so as to readily hear the speakers—are mapped out in his mind in advance. He allows adequate time to "get himself situated" and remain in control of the situation.

Optimism is a personal characteristic that is at the heart of his approach to life. This is repeatedly seen in his comments on problems within the Medical Center. However critical he might be in demanding that the needs of the patient be met, he always in the end would emphasize that the issues he had identified could be solved. The same optimism permeates his writing on the future of gastroenterology and the field of medicine. He seeks to transmit this feeling to medical students and younger physicians whenever he is in contact with them.

Optimism has also guided his vision of the university. He feels deeply that the University of Chicago is an institution that is growing in its renown and importance as a center of excellence in the academic world. His career and loyalties are intertwined with the University of Chicago School of Medicine and its hospitals and clinics. Loyalty is another virtue in life that he cherishes. At times in his career he was approached by other institutions seeking to lure him away from the university with the offer of an elevated academic position and salary. While flattered, he never seriously entertained or pursued such a change. Loyalty to the University of Chicago and optimism about its future were his guiding principles. He was always grateful to the university for the opportunity he was given in 1935 when he joined the Department of Medicine. The famous violin virtuoso Isaac Stern published his memoirs reflecting his joy of life under the title *My First Seventy Years*. In 1995, at the time of his 85th birthday, it was frequently noted at various festive occasions that Dr. Kirsner was celebrating his first 60 years at the University of Chicago. Now a decade into the second half of that promise, he strives to continue on a parallel course with the institution he loves. He remains informed of and a participant in the changing affairs and personnel at the Medical Center and the university.

Another personal characteristic that has always been an asset to him in his career and his interactions with patients and colleagues is his personal warmth. Even at this time in his life, when he must cope with the difficulties of age, he maintains a warm and friendly demeanor. He stands to greet all visitors, invariably with a smile and a handshake. The warmth and openness is evident in his voice when he answers the telephone and carries on a conversation. He loves to relate stories about the university and the many adventures he has had in his career, and he delights in informing listeners about past events. When he attends conferences given by the Section of Gastroenterology or lectures by faculty members or invited speakers, he is often asked for his thoughts on the presentation. As Geoffrey Chaucer wrote of the Clerk from Oxenferd (Oxford) in the *Canterbury Tales,* "and gladly would he lerne, and gladly would he teche."[16]

Dr. Kirsner has wanted the experiences recounted in this biography to serve as an inspiration to young men and women, in medicine or any other endeavor, as to what can be achieved through diligence and hard work, by seizing the opportunities that present themselves, and through an abiding interest in doing good and being of service to mankind. Thus there can be no more fitting ending than to give him the last word. What follows, "Envoi: A Brief Look Back and Thoughts on the Future," is his special message to the reader to bring his biography to a close.

Notes

1. Kirsner JB, Inflammatory bowel disease at the University of Chicago: The first fifty years, some personal reflections, *Amer J Gastroenterology* 80:3:219-26, March 1985.

2. Kirsner, JB, The changing medical scene (1929-1985): A personal perspective, *Perspect Biol Med* 29:2:227-42, Winter 1986.

3. JBK, "One Hundred Years of American Gastroenterology," in *Grand Rounds: One Hundred Years of Internal Medicine,* ed. Russell C. Maulitz and Diana E. Long (Philadelphia: University of Pennsylvania Press, 1988), 117-57.

4. JBK, *The Development of American Gastroenterology* (New York: Raven Press, 1990).

5. JBK, *The Early Days of American Gastroenterology* (Cedar Knolls, NJ: Lippin-cott-Raven-Healthcare, 1996).

6. JBK, *The Growth of Gastroenterologic Knowledge during the Twentieth Century* (Philadelphia: Lea and Febiger, 1994).

7. JBK, *Origins and Directions of Inflammatory Bowel Disease: Early Studies of Non-specific Inflammatory Bowel Diseases* (Dordrecht: Kluwer Academic, 2001).

8. The articles by JBK in the journal *Inflammatory Bowel Diseases* listed in the text: The historical basis of the idiopathic inflammatory bowel diseases,

1:1:2-26, January 1995; Historical antecedents of inflammatory bowel disease therapy, 2:73-81, May 1996; We still are more than molecules, 8:1:56-57, 2002; Commentary on the 1958 National Institutes of Health conference on "New Frontiers in Ulcerative Colitis," 9:1:61-69, 2003; Inflammatory bowel disease at the University of Chicago: Early experiences: A personal historical account, 11:4:407-16, April 2005.

9. Malachi J. Flanagan, *To the Glory of God and the Service of Man: The Life of James A. Campbell, M.D.* (Winnetka: FHC Press, 2005).

10. *Medical Humanism: Aphorisms from the Bedside Teachings and Writings of Dr. Howard M. Spiro, M.D.*, collected by Robert Kravetz, under the auspices of the Program for Humanities in Medicine, Yale University School of Medicine (forthcoming).

11. JBK, preface to Seymour Ehrenpreis and Eli Ehrenpreis, *The Prescription and Over-the-Counter Drug Guide for Seniors* (New York: McGraw Hill, 2003).

12. JBK, "Review Article, 100 Years of American Gastroenterology: 1900-2000," *Medscape General Medicine* 2, no. 1 (2000) (posted January 1, 2000).

13. Leon Jacobson, "Lowell T. Coggeshall: 1901-1987," in *Remembering the University of Chicago: Teachers, Scientists, and Scholars*, ed. Edward Shils (Chicago: University of Chicago Press, 1991).

14. "ASGE Founding Member, Interview with Joseph B. Kirsner," conducted by Joseph Geenan, *ASGE News*, March/April, May/June, and July/August 2006.

15. Copies of these documents can be found in Dr. Kirsner's personal papers, in the Special Collections department of Regenstein Library.

16. Geoffrey Chaucer, *The Canterbury Tales*, Norton Critical Edition (New York: W. W. Norton, 1989), 10 (line 308).

Envoi: A Brief Look Back and Thoughts on the Future

Joseph B. Kirsner, M.D., M.A.C.P., Ph.D., D.Sc. (hon.)

During my youth, I developed an interest in preparing myself for a life of service to humanity, an interest generated by numerous childhood illnesses and hospitalizations. Although we were poor, my parents made every effort to create this opportunity. After two years at Tufts University, I began the study of medicine in 1929, at Tufts University School of Medicine in Boston, at the onset of the Great Depression. My father sold his life insurance for $200 to pay for my tuition for the first half of year one; subsequent major costs were to be earned by me. I completed the four years of medical school in 1933, with excellent grades, oriented to the general practice of medicine. The prime mission of the Tufts University School of Medicine then, with the help of the Bigelow Fund, was the development of general physicians for the New England community area. However, forgoing an early opportunity for private practice and financial gain, I joined Chicago's Woodlawn Hospital for two years of additional training in general internal medicine. My interest in a more comprehensive medical education and in an academic career began in 1934 after I married the talented Minnie Schneider of Des Moines, Iowa. I decided then to remain in the Midwest and sought an academic position. My career at the University of Chicago began in the fall of 1935, as an assistant in medicine, and, in time, advanced to the Louis Block Distinguished Service Professor of Medicine. My academic progress was interrupted during World War II when I served as a medical officer in the U.S. Army, in both the European and the Pacific theaters of war (1943-46), including the Normandy campaign, the Ardennes campaign in Belgium, the battle of Germany (three battle stars); and in the Pacific, the Philippines and a year-long period of duty with the initial Occupation Army of Japan, beginning in September 1945.

Medicine has been the ideal career for me. I have experienced enormous satisfaction helping sick people, developing a major medical discipline (gastroenterology), and guiding many young physicians in their professional development. Overall, my life has been noteworthy for its extraordinary opportunities, each leading to new challenges in medicine and gastroenterology; fulfilling personal experiences; the opportunity to study medicine; an appointment at the University of Chicago; marriage to Minnie Schneider; active physician participation in World War II; association with the skilled Dr. Walter L. Palmer; the creation of major gastroenterologic societies; the development of the Gastro-Intestinal Research Foundation, and its support of our research activities; and the development of the nationally ranked Section of Gastroenterology at the University of Chicago. Today, at the age of 99, I have the same enthusiasm for academic medicine at the University of Chicago and for the continuing opportunity to advance gastroenterology and medicine as I enjoyed 70 years earlier. I am especially pleased with the many accomplishments of my colleagues (some of them former students) and with the national and international recognition of our gastroenterology section in the Department of Medicine at the University of Chicago, under the leadership of Dr. Stephen Hanauer and Dr. Eugene Chang.

Two major precepts influenced my medical career: the compassionate approach in the care of patients, and the great importance of biomedical research to the increased understanding and the successful treatment of human illness. Both principles were acquired early during my medical training and were enhanced in my academic experience. At the height of the Great Depression (1929-33), accelerated preparation for general medical practice was our urgent goal. My early hospital experience (Chicago, 1933-35), while strengthening my care of patients, actually reinforced my interest in academic medicine. The decisive change began in January 1936, when I came under the influence of the master clinician-scientist Dr. Walter L. Palmer, at the University of Chicago. I began to witness the positive interaction between the compassionate, skilled physician and the patient. For the first time also I was introduced to the exciting world of biomedical research and its opportunities, an experience that kindled an enduring curiosity about the gastrointestinal tract. Clinical and laboratory research became an integral part of my university career. In 1937, recognizing the need for rigorous research training and encouraged by Dr. Palmer and by my wife, I embarked upon a Ph.D. program, while maintaining my clinical and teaching responsibilities. This demanding effort culminated in 1942 in the award of a Ph.D. degree in the biological sciences at the University of Chicago. My research subject was alkalosis, a significant biochemical complication of the Sippy (antacid) treatment of peptic ulcer, popular during the first half of the 20th century. During this five-year period, I benefited scientifically and personally from frequent contacts with distinguished members of the University of Chicago faculty, including Dr. George F. Dick, chairman of the Department of Medicine; A. J. Carlson, noted professor of physiology; E. S. Guzman Barron, professor of biochemistry; Lillian Eichelberger, professor of biochemistry; and Eleanor Humphreys, professor of pathology—in addition to Dr. Palmer, who in the 1920s had reported one of the first controlled clinical investigations in gastroenterology (mechanism of pain in peptic ulcer).

When I returned to the University of Chicago after World War II, the patient-physician relationship became an indispensable ally in my care of patients, many of whom became my friends. My research interests changed and in the 1950s led me into the emerging sciences of gastrointestinal microbiology, immunology, and the genetics of gastrointestinal disease. This parallel interest--in the patient as a sick human being and in basic research on the nature of the inflammatory bowel diseases (ulcerative colitis, Crohn's disease)—became an exciting and demanding challenge. Extraordinary opportunities allowed me to join with colleagues in the development of gastroenterology societies and in the support of basic GI research through my 20-year-long (1955-74) association with the National Institutes of Health. This exceptional experience established for me the unity of the humanity of medicine and the science of medicine in the care of sick people.

Now, some thoughts on the future of medicine and gastroenterology: The remarkable progress of science and technology during the 20th century, of course, will continue during the 21st century. Significant research advances in health and in lengthening our life span will continue, as described in the fascinating book *Fantastic Voyage: Live Long Enough to Live Forever,* by Ray Kurzweil and Terry Grossman (Penguin, 2005). Continuing attention to the health-care system, as it is affected by the extraordinary advances in basic sciences and renewed awareness of the role of life's stresses in the course of human illness, will strengthen the relationship between the science and the humanity of medicine.

New sciences (e.g., molecular genetics, stem-cell biology, nanobiology, pharmacogenomics, and bioinformatics) will facilitate the development of safer therapeutic agents. Since clinical advances often follow initially unrelated scientific investigation, basic research will continue to play a major role in health care. The new knowledge will reshape medicine and further clarify disease mechanisms, including individual determinants of illness. National health problems (e.g., substance addiction, obesity) will receive continued attention. Enlightened health-care partnership relationships will allow the treatment of routine clinical problems at local hospitals, ease the pressure on burgeoning emergency rooms, and facilitate the expert management of complex diseases at the University of Chicago Medical Center, a program now succeeding on the South Side of Chicago.

Academic medical departments will reorganize administratively to incorporate the new scientific disciplines and accommodate the changing interdisciplinary research directions. Enlightened cooperation between academic and clinical medicine and industry will encourage basic science discoveries and facilitate their clinical applicability.

The challenges in health-care economics will continue, fueled by escalating demands for health care, chronic illness (cardiovascular disease, cancer, diabetes, rheumatologic and gastrointestinal disorders), innovative costly technology, the "medicalization" of natural biological events, and the needs of a growing aging population; and some form of governmentally financed program, hopefully universal health care, will emerge.

Finally, medicine will continue to attract "the best and the brightest" men and women dedicated to excellence in the care of the sick, oriented to the control of health-care excesses, and focused upon the significant health-care advances of the future.

Index of Names

Ogden, W.M., 37
Oglesby, Paul, 126n35
Olin, Harry, 25
Omar, Ben, 203
Oppenheimer, Gordon, 215, 292
Ortmayer, Marie, 43, 62-63, 65, 77n13
Osler, William, 38, 59, 73, 77n11, 183, 244
Overholt, Bergen, 197
Owen, John, 251
Owens, F.M., 225, 238n2

Packard, Rollo, 24-25, 30
Palmer, Donald, 44
Palmer, Elizabeth, 47, 129
Palmer, Henry, 44
Palmer, Robert, 44
Palmer, Walter Aaron, 44
Palmer, Walter, x, 40, 43-47, 53n8, 53n11,
    55, 61-63, 66-70, 72-73, 77n20, 77n22,
    77n24, 81, 84, 86-87, 90, 94, 98n9,
    101-102, 104, 107-108, 111, 124n2, 124n4,
    124n6, 124n10, 125n14, 125n16, 125n18,
    125n22, 125n24, 127, 129-30, 132, 136,
    140, 151-52, 158n23, 205, 209, 215n1,
    216n4, 216n5, 216n7, 225, 244-46, 252,
    262-63, 272n2, 303-304
Papanicolaou, George N., 134
Paracelsus, 237
Pavlov, Ivan P., 285
Pavlova, Anna, 27
Peabody, Francis, 151, 158n24, 237, 238n13
Peale, Norman, 248
Pearlstein, Joe, 8
Peltz, Mrs. Howard, 165
Petersdorf, Robert, 247
Phaneuf, Lois, 19
Phemister, Dallas, 40, 49
Pogofsky, Tony, 162
Pollack, M.C., 89
Pollard, H. Marvin, 103
Polley, Howard, 107, 124n13
Poncher, Jerry, 162, 165
Popper, Hans, 104-106, 124n7, 124n9, 192
Port, Sidney, 162, 290
Pratt, John, 19
Present, Daniel, 213, 215
Prolla, Gabriel, 135

Prolla, João, xiv, 133-37, 148-49, 157n4,
    157n6, 229, 264
Prossman, Martin, 142
Pusey, William, 258

Raffensperger, John, 33n8
Rafferty, Michael, 90
Rappaport, Henry, 145
Raskin, Howard, 134
Raue, Leona, 166
Reagan, Ronald, 190, 266
Redfield, Robert, 75
Reed, Peter, 164
Reed, Walter, 295
Reichstein, Tadeus, 107
Reiff, Janice, 33n1
Reilly, Richard, 130, 134, 137, 210-11
Renshaw, John, 65
Resnic, Burton, xiv, 7, 21n3
Reuterskiold, Knute, 41-42
Rice, Edwin, 49-50
Ricketts, Elizabeth, 44
Ricketts, Howard, 38, 44, 50
Ricketts, William, 104-105, 124n4, 124n6,
    125n24
Ridgeway, Matthew, 10
Rimpila, Julian, 211
Rockefeller, Elizabeth, 37
Rockefeller, John, 36, 38, 205
Rodaniche, E.C., 73-74, 216n4, 216n5
Rodgers, B.H. Gerald, xiv, 196-99, 204n6,
    290
Rodgers, Mae, 198-99, 290
Roentgen, Wilhelm, 56, 76n3, 102
Roosevelt, Franklin, 6, 79, 116-17
Roothaan, Clemens, 153
Rosen, Peter, 174
Rosenberg, Anna, 28
Rosenberg, Harry, xv, 283
Rosenberg, Irwin, 130, 155-56, 159n29,
    159n30, 171, 242
Rosenow, Edward, 73-74
Rosenthal, Irwin, 213-14, 293
Rosenthal, Susan, 293
Rosenthal, Suzanne, 213, 216n12
Rosenwald, Julius, 40
Roskamp, Paul, 91